Like the bloody scythe of Death, the red giant rises above the planet, Gideon E.

The silver domes and spires of the colonies lay mangled and lifeless. Crushed under the merciless heels of the new masters!

Masters as cold and unfeeling as the machines that maintain them. A malevolent force wrought in the pits of Hell!

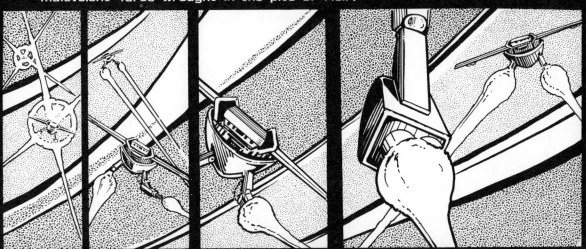

This is our story. A grim opus of life and death.

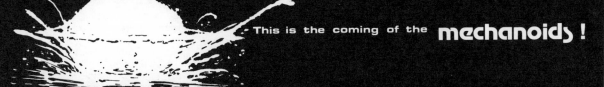

This is the coming of the **mechanoids**!

Dedicated to Tony (the Tōn) Falzon who helped me through the early days.

The Mechanoids is published by Palladium Books,
5926 Lonyo, Detroit, Michigan 48210.

Palladium Books Presents . . .

Written By: Kevin Siembieda

Edited By: Alex Marciniszyn

Adventure Scenarios By: Erick Wujcik
Illustrated By: Kevin Siembieda
Additional Art By: Michael Gustovich
Keylining By: Matthew Balent
Typed By: Maryann Siembieda
Logo Design By: Michael Gustovich
Cover Painting By: Kevin Siembieda

Special Thanks to Randy McCall and
Matthew Balent for their input; and to Maryann
and Alex for being there when needed most.

TABLE OF CONTENTS

SUPPLEMENTAL INDEX

ABOUT THIS GAME

It happened in 1981. **Palladium Books'** very first game product, a 7X10, 48 page, science fiction game printed on newsprint and selling for the ridiculously low price of $3.75. That game was the **Mechanoid Invasion**, the first and most popular of a trilogy of game books. Despite the low quality of the paper and zillions of typos, people were attracted to the **Mechanoid Invasion** because of its fun ideas, fast-paced action and graphics. Over the years the **Mechanoid Invasion** has grown into a sort of "cult favorite".

In that first book I proclaimed that there would not be a fourth book or supplement, unless there was an out-pouring of requests for one. The book in your hands is the result of such an outcry. **The Mechanoids** is NOT the collection of all three original books nor is it a simple re-print of the original **Mechanoid Invasion** with a handful of extra gimmicks. The events depicted in **The Mechanoids** take place approximately one month after the chronology established in the **Mechanoid Invasion**. The conflict is escalated, there are new weapons and new discoveries that should satisfy those gamers familiar with the **Mechanoid Invasion**. At the same time NEW players will be able to play this **complete** game without fear of having missed something in the first book.

The **Mechanoid Invasion** is out of print and will not be reprinted in its original form. **The Mechanoids** will act as a replacement for the old Invasion book. Although the game system has been up-dated to keep in step with our newer game products, I hope to have recaptured the clean, fast-paced excitement, play and fun of its predecessor.

How To Play

The Mechanoids game is intricately linked to the establishing environment of fierce battle, revenge and survival. It is a savage environment filled with desperation, daring and death. This generally leads to exciting, action packed games with a high mortality rate for playing characters. Consequently, I've tried to keep character generation as quick and simple as possible without forsaking too much depth of character.

This type of environment can quickly degenerate into a hack and slash game with a host of new characters every time. However, if the game master and players take some effort they'll find that a long and satisfying campaign with the same characters CAN be maintained. I know of several Mechanoid games that have played for over a year with their original cast of characters.

When a character does die the game master should try to incorporate a new "replacement" character for that player as soon as possible. This can be easily done by having the new character assigned to the team or some chance encounter, and so on. G.M.'s remember, it is no fun to lose a character and have to sit out a game for hours. I realize the conditions of a particular scenario may make bringing in a new character difficult or even impossible, but try to do so when possible.

Glossary

Attributes: These are numbers used to evaluate the strengths and weaknesses of your character. For example, P.P. means Physical Prowess, how smooth, agile and quick a character is in combat. A P.P. of 4 would indicate that the character is pretty clumsy. A P.P. of 10 would be an average, fairly coordinated human being. While a P.P. of 16 or more would belong only to characters with exceptional speed and reflexes. Attributes are also called Statistics or Stats.

Campaign: A word used to describe an on-going game. If you play the same characters with the same game master on a regular basis then you are in a Campaign.

Character: Every player (except the G.M.) has a character that serves as an imaginary playing piece, also called Playing Character.

Death: Just as in real life, characters can die. The death of heroes in comic books, or in games, is a fairly rare event. The amount of death in a campaign usually depends on the individual game master. Players should take a character's death calmly. Remember, this is ONLY a game and superheroics is a dangerous line of work. G.M.'s should allow players to roll up a "NEW" character and include it in the game as soon as is appropriate for the on-going game. However, characters should not be a dime a dozen.

Dice: There are a variety of different dice used in role-playing games. First of all, there are the standard six-sided dice, the kind you use for most board games. We call them "D6". Often we let you know how many dice to roll with an expression like "roll 3D6". This means "roll three six-sided dice and add all the results together". Dice are also available with four-sides (D4), eight-sides (D8), ten-sides (D10), and even twenty-sides (D20). They are available at most hobby stores.

Game Master: (G.M.) This is the person who controls the game "world". All the non-player characters, innocent by-standers, police and politicians, even the weather is controlled by the G.M.

Player: A player is a person who plays a character in a role-playing game.

Role-Playing Game: Sometimes called a role-playing game (RPG), or fantasy role-playing (FRP), these are games with game masters and imaginary characters.

Roll A Twenty Sided: Simply roll a twenty-sided die for a number.

Roll Percentile: Take two ten-sided dice of different colors. Let's say we have one green and one red. First you declare which die will be high ("I call red high"). Next you roll the dice. First you read the High die and then the Low die, just put the numbers together and you have a percentile. For example, "Red is 4 and green is 8, so I have a 48%"

Run: This is just a term gamers use to describe playing a game. Example, "He runs an excellent campaign," "I ran in Kevin's game last week".

Saving Throw: This is a roll (usually on a twenty-sided die) to avoid some unpleasant event. For example, a character might have to roll a saving throw to avoid being overcome by tear gas.

Scenario: This is a specific adventure that confronts the characters in a role-playing game. A scenario is usually a story with a beginning (hearing about the criminal), a middle (tracking down the criminal's hide-out), and an end (defeating the criminal). Most campaigns are developed around a number of scenarios.

Creating A Playing Character

The creation of a character is relatively simple, requiring four main steps.

Step 1: The Eight Attributes (and bonuses)
Step 2: Hit Points and S.D.C.
Step 3: Determining Psionics
Step 4: Selecting an Occupational Character Class
Step 5: Equipment and Money

Step 1: The Eight Attributes and Attribute Bonuses

The first step in creating a character is to roll-up the eight attributes, I.Q., M.E., P.S., P.P., P.E., P.B., and Spd.

Three six-sided dice are rolled to determine each attribute. The higher the number, the greater the ability. If an attribute is "exceptional", 16, 17, or 18, then an additional six-sided die is rolled and added to the total for that attribute.

Intelligence Quotient (I.Q.): Indicates the intelligence of the character. The exact I.Q. is equal to the I.Q. attribute multiplied times ten. Characters with an I.Q. of 16 or better will receive a one-time bonus added to all the character's skill percentiles.

Mental Endurance (M.E.): Measures the amount of mental and emotional stress the character can withstand.

Mental Affinity (M.A.): Shows the character's personal charm and charisma. Natural leaders with an M.A. of 16 or higher have a bonus to invoke trust or intimidation in others.

Physical Strength (P.S.): This is the raw physical power of a character. The P.S. times 10 indicates how heavy an object (in pounds) the character can carry. A character can lift 30 times the P.S. Exceptionally strong characters having a P.S. of 15-19 can carry 20 times their P.S. and lift 40 times their P.S. Someone with a P.S. of 20-23 can carry 30 times their P.S. and lift 60 times their P.S. Anyone with a P.S. of 24 or higher can carry 50 times their P.S. and lift 100 times their P.S. Any character with a P.S. of 16 or better receives a bonus to damage in hand to hand combat.

Physical Prowess (P.P.): Shows the degree of dexterity and agility of the character. A P.P. of 16 or higher is rewarded with bonuses to dodge, parry and strike.

Physical Endurance (P.E.): Demonstrates the character's stamina and durability. The amount of physical punishment and resistance to fatigue and disease are determined by P.E. A character can carry the maximum weight load (see P.S.) for the P.E. times 4 minutes. Carrying the maximum weight while running or fighting can only be done for the P.E. times 2 minutes. If a character lifts the maximum weight (see P.S.), then it can only be held for as many melee rounds (15 seconds each) as the character has points of P.E. A character can run at maximum speed for one minute for each point of P.E. Character's with a P.E. of 16 or better receive bonuses to save vs. coma, death and toxins.

Physical Beauty (P.B.): Is an indication of the physical attractiveness of the character. A P.B. of 16 or better will be rewarded with a bonus to charm or impress.

Speed (Spd.): Specifically, this is the character's maximum running speed. The Spd. times 20 is the number of yards that the character can run in one minute. If the Spd. is 16 or higher, the character has a bonus to all dodge rolls.

ATTRIBUTE BONUS CHART

	I.Q.	M.E.	M.A.	P.S.	P.P.	P.E.%	P.E.+	P.B.	Spd
16	+3%	+1	45%	+1	+1	+5%	+1	40%	+1
17	+4%	+1	50%	+2	+1	+6%	+1	45%	+1
18	+5%	+2	50%	+3	+2	+7%	+2	50%	+1
19	+6%	+2	60%	+4	+2	+8%	+2	55%	+2
20	+7%	+3	65%	+5	+3	+9%	+3	60%	+2
21	+8%	+3	70%	+6	+3	+10%	+3	65%	+2
22	+9%	+4	75%	+7	+4	+11%	+4	70%	+3
23	+10%	+4	80%	+8	+4	+12%	+4	74%	+3
24	+11%	+4	84%	+9	+5	+13%	+5	78%	+3
25	+12%	+5	88%	+10	+5	+14%	+5	82%	+4
26	+13%	+5	90%	+11	+6	+15%	+6	86%	+4
27	+14%	+6	92%	+12	+6	+16%	+6	90%	+4
28	+15%	+6	94%	+13	+7	+17%	+7	92%	+4
29	+16%	+7	96%	+14	+7	+18%	+7	94%	+4
30	+17%	+7	98%	+15	+8	+19%	+8	96%	+4

The Attribute Bonus Chart Represents The Following:

I.Q.	Skill bonus (add to all skills)
M.E.	Save vs. Psionics
M.A.	Degree of Charm and Influence; Trust/Charisma
P.S.	Hand to Hand Combat damage
P.P.	Bonus to Strike, Parry and Dodge
P.E.	Save vs. Coma/Death
P.B.	Degree of Physical Beauty; Charm/Impress
Spd.	Bonus to Dodge

Step 2: Hit Points and S.D.C

HIT POINTS

Hit points might best be thought of as life points because they indicate how much physical damage (cuts, bruises, etc.) a character can withstand before he/she dies. These are the points that are observed during a battle (or melee) to determine how much damage is inflicted on friend or foe. Each time a character is struck by a weapon he takes physical damage. The individual players keep score of how many hit points their character has by subtracting the damage from his/her character's hit points each time that character is hit by a weapon. Likewise, the game master keeps score of how much damage the player inflicts upon his opponent. When a character has zero hit points he is in a coma and will soon die unless extensive medical aid is applied. When a character's hit points have been knocked far below zero, he is dead and beyond saving.

DETERMINING HIT POINTS

Now that you have some idea of what hit points are about, let us get into the technical aspects of their determination and use.

1) Base Hit Points: Having rolled up your 8 attributes you will recall that one is physical endurance (P.E.). The physical endurance score indicates your character's base/starting amount of hit points. This number means that he/she can lose that many hit points before dying.

Some of you will have a character with many hit points, . . . don't get too cocky, a sword in the right hands can whittle you down to size in one melee round. Others will find themselves with a character who has only a handful of hit points (as little as 3), . . . don't despair or feel cheated, you'll just have to use cleverness and cunning in avoiding direct confrontations until you've built up your hit points.

2) Building Hit Points: After determining your base hit points, pick up on six-sided die, roll it and add the number rolled to your hit point base. Only roll one six-sided die one time.

As your character grows in knowledge and experience

he will gain more skill and expertise in his chosen profession (see: Occupational Character Classes). At the same time he will also mature physically, increasing his hit points. Thus, each time a character attains a new experience level, roll one six-sided die and add it to the existing hit points.

RECOVERY OF HIT POINTS

After a battle, characters who have sustained physical damage must tend to their wounds. The attending of wounds can be administered by fellow characters, trained medical personnel or by oneself if the character has first aid skills and is not physically impaired.

First aid type skills include basic and immediate medical treatment such as bandaging and cleaning of wounds, stopping of bleeding and so on until the character can receive better medical care.

Recovery: non-professional treatment. This is basic first aid type treatment by oneself or non-medically trained and professionally experienced people. This type of treatment may be used if the character is not able to seek professional treatment immediately. It is not necessarily inferior treatment, especially for not too serious of an ailment, but just lacks the full facilities and experience of a major medical institution. **Rate of Recovery: Two hit points per day (24 hours).**

Recovery: professional treatment. This is medical treatment from a doctor, clinic or hospital. **Rate of Recovery:** Two hit points per day for the first two days, and four hit points per day for each following day until the character has regained all his/her original hit points.

DAMAGE

Serious Physical Damage

A character receives serious physical damage when he loses a great amount of hit points. The following is a list of side effects from physical damage. The effects of the damage are generally temporary and cumulative. Thus, if a character suffers the loss of a great deal of hit points within a short time he will suffer the multiple affects of physical damage. **Roll each time severe damage is endured.**

Roll Percentile	Damage	Minuses
1-14	Minor bruises and lacerations	Spd -2 -1 to dodge
15-29	Severely bruised and battered muscles	P.P. -1 Spd -3
30-44	Damaged (sprain, pulled, cut, etc.) arm or shoulder	P.P. -3
45-59	Damaged leg or hip	Spd is ½ -2 to dodge
60-74	Damaged hand and/or wrist	P.P. -1 P.S. -2
75-89	Head Injury	-5% on all skills, Spd -2
90-00	Damaged back or pelvis	P.E. -1 P.P. -2 Spd -3

NOTE: None of these effects are permanent nor life threatening. Minuses apply to that one limb. Speed minuses affect the whole body. Remember effects are cumulative; roll each time the character is badly hurt.

Side-Effects from Physical Damage (Hit Points)

Roll on this table when 75% to 99% (almost all) hit points are depleted. **Impairment** is temporary, lasting 1-4 weeks (roll 1 four-sided die).

Roll Percentile	Damage	Minuses
1-10	Severely battered and bruised	Spd -2 -3 to dodge
11-20	Torn arm muscle	P.P. -3 P.S. -2
21-29	Torn leg muscle	Spd is ½ -2 to dodge
30-39	Fractured bone: arm	P.P. -2 P.S. -3
40-49	Fractured bone: leg	Spd is ½ -4 to dodge
50-59	Fractured bone: ribs or pelvis	P.E. -2 Spd is ½
60-69	Broken bone: arm	P.P. is ½ P.S. is ½
70-79	Broken bone: leg	Spd is 1/3 -6 to dodge
80-89	Broken bone: ribs	P.E. -3 P.P. -1 Spd -3
90-00	Severe Concussion	-8 on all skills, Spd -3

NOTE: None of these effects are permanent nor life threatening, although painful and debilitating. Minuses apply to that one particular limb. Speed minuses affect the whole body. Remember, effects are cumulative.

About blood loss. When a character is severely hurt, has only 15% of his hit points and is bleeding; he will soon die of blood loss unless he or she receives immediate medical attention. Even a basic first aid and no or little movement can bind wounds and prevent further blood loss/damage. Without medical aid the person will continue to lose blood and take **one point (hit point) of damage every minute/4 melee rounds.**

Surviving Coma and Death

When a character's hit points are reduced to zero (or less) he/she collapses; lapsing into a coma. This character is near death and will die in a matter of hours unless he/she receives immediate medical treatment.

How much damage below zero a character can undergo is indicated by the physical endurance (P.E.) attribute. A character can take one point of damage below zero (negative 1, -2, -3, etc.) for each P.E. point.
Example: A character with a P.E. of 9 will lapse into a coma at zero hit points, but still lives up to negative 9. However, if the character receives more damage (which is very possible) than the P.E., he is dead with no hope of recovery. Thus, if a character with a P.E. of 9 takes 10 points or more, below zero, exceeding his P.E., he is beyond medical help and dies.

Coma Length

The length of time a character will survive without treatment in a coma is again indicated by the P.E. Add one hour for each P.E. point. Example: P.E. 9=9 hours; P.E. 10=10 hours, and so on.

Recovery from a Coma

Whether a character survives the coma and is stabilized (brought back to at least one hit point above zero) is determined by the roll of percentile dice. If the player rolls two successful recovery rolls out of three tries the character breaks out of the coma and is no longer in danger of dying. This also means that he is brought up to one hit point above zero. Recovery of hit points from that time on are standard; see Recovery of Hit Points. **NOTE:** This can be attempted every hour.

Recovery Ratio (roll 2 out of 3)

- Treatment from non-professional medical individual, but with medical skills, 1-18%
- Treatment from an intern or nurse (R.N.) 1-32%
- Treatment from a doctor without proper facilities 1-46%
- Treatment from a doctor at a clinic (fair facilities) 1-56%
- Treatment from a hospital 1-66%
- Treatment from a major, large hospital 1-70%

Optional Recovery Side-Effects from Severe Damage/Near Death (hit points)

Roll on this table when a character has lost all of his/her hit points and has been near death (coma). Impairment is permanent as a result of the grave physical damage. NOTE: This is not a mandatory table, but is left up to the game master's discretion.

1-10	No permanent damage.
11-20	Major stiffness in joints; reduce P.P. by 2.
21-39	Minor stiffness in joints; reduce P.P. by 1.
40-55	Legs impaired; walk with a limp; reduce Spd by 2
56-70	Major scarring; reduce P.B. by 2.
71-82	Chronic pain; reduce P.E. by 1.
83-92	Minor brain damage; reduce I.Q. by 1.
93-00	Major brain damage; reduce I.Q. by 2 and M.E. by 1.

STRUCTURAL DAMAGE CAPACITY (S.D.C.)

Most things living and non-living have a Structural Damage Capacity.

The S.D.C. of objects and structures such as doors, walls, safes, tables, hand-cuffs, cars, etc. is the amount of damage that the object can withstand. These S.D.C. points function exactly like hit points. Any damage sustained is subtracted from the S.D.C. When the S.D.C. is reduced to zero it is broken or smashed beyond repair.

Natural Body Armor has a similar S.D.C., but is tougher and is in addition to regular S.D.C. If an attack does not penetrate the A.R. of a natural body armour no damage is taken, not even off the S.D.C. It is only if the attack penetrates the A.R. that damage is subtracted. Damage is first subtracted from the body armour's S.D.C.; once depleted, the body armor is ineffective and damage is subtracted from the S.D.C. of the physical body. After the S.D.C. of the physical body is depleted, damage is subtracted from the hit points.

Artificial armor such as bullet proof vests and bionic or robotic armor also has an armor rating (A.R.) and S.D.C. The armor rating indicates exactly how much protection is afforded by the armor and how easily it is penetrated.

The higher the A.R. the better. If an attack roll to strike is less than the A.R. of the armor NO damage is inflicted. It may hit, but the armor has provided total protection. If the attack roll is higher than the A.R., the armor takes FULL damage from the attack. ONLY AFTER all of the armor's S.D.C. is depleted do attacks affect a character's hit points. Psionics and drugs may by-pass armor.

Step 3: Determining Psionics

Psionics or extra sensory perception abilities are powers of the mind such as telepathy, empathy, telekinesis and so on. While more common among alien races (see Rovers), humans have exhibited varying degrees of psionic powers.

Each player rolls percentile dice to determine if their character is psionic with the following results:

1-59	No psionics (typical human being)
60-79	Minor psionic
80-89	Major psionic
90-00	Master psionic

If MAJOR or MASTER psionics were rolled the player can capitalize on his/her mind powers by selecting the ESPER O.C.C. as his/her occupation. All players with any level of psionics should read the Psionics Section and ESPER O.C.C. before selecting an Occupational Character Class (O.C.C.).

Step 4: Selecting An Occupation and Skills

For the sake of simplicity each player choses ONE Occupational Character Class (O.C.C.) with its small selection of skills in a major area of expertise and elective skills. Each O.C.C. indicates a major area of study and knowledge as is pertinent to the character's occupation. Unlike Heroes Unlimited or the Palladium Role-Playing Game the skill selection is very limited and does not include secondary skills. However, players will find their characters to be capable as well as different from every other O.C.C. This quick character generation system will enable players to build characters quickly and completely. The scope of the establishing scenario setting is, in itself, limiting so playing characters have been designed to fit snugly into that environment with maximum playability. It is for playability that characters such as doctors, electricians, merchants, teachers, etc. and related skills have been intentionally deleted.

Each O.C.C. has skills or skill bonuses in areas not available to the other O.C.C.'s. Consequently, players may want to consider what O.C.C. their fellow player is selecting in order to build a well rounded team or group of characters. For example, a group of five L.B.A.'s could find themselves severely limited in what they can do when not locked into a combat melee. Of course this does NOT mean that every player should select a different O.C.C.; it simply means to consider the desired scope and versatility of your team when selecting an O.C.C. The same is true when selecting individual skills. The team with the most versatility and combined strengths is most likely to persevere (and this is a team oriented game). A good, basic rule of thumb is that every team should have one communications engineer, at least one pilot (a back-up pilot or person with piloting skill is a good idea too), one L.B.A. or commando and/or one E.B.A. The addition of an ESPer, field scientist or more men of arms is okay too. The cast of characters and their respective O.C.C.'s will depend on the number of players and personal preferences. I would recommend that players go with what they feel most comfortable playing and their instincts above all else.

O.C.C. REQUIREMENTS

The selection of an O.C.C. is limited only by the minimum attribute(s) requirement needed to play. The eight attributes should have been determined already by the roll of three, six-sided dice (see Creating a Character: Step 1). Generally, a player will be able to choose from two or three possibilities. NOTE: Only the ESPer O.C.C. requires psionic abilities.

O.C.C. SKILLS

With the exception of ESPer, each O.C.C. has two skill categories: Major area of expertise and elective. Skills under the heading of Major Area of Expertise are skills that everyone in that chosen O.C.C. have trained in. Areas of Expertise are basic and crucial skills to that occupation. Elective skills are other areas of skill and training known by the character. They may augment the occupational skills or simply reflect other interests.

SKILL BONUSES

The base proficiency or skill level is denoted in each skill description. However, you'll notice that many of the skills under every O.C.C. will have a skill bonus indicated. The skill bonus will be shown as a plus (+) symbol followed by a number. For example: the communication engineer has the skill "sensory equipment +30%". The +30% is added to the normal skill base of 25% for a total of 55% (30% bonus +25% base = 55%). ALL skill bonuses are a one time bonus applicable immediately. As the character grows in experience (via experience levels) the skill proficiency also grows. For example: the sensory equipment skill of 55% becomes 60% at second level, 65% at third level, 70% at fourth level and so on. NOTE: Maximum skill ability is 98% because there is always some margin for error.

If NO skill bonus is indicated then this means there is no bonus available from that O.C.C. ONLY the unmodified base skill proficiency is used. Example: Sensory equipment without an O.C.C. bonus is 25%+5% per each level of experience.

See skill descriptions for specific explanations and proficiencies.

MULTIPLE O.C.C.'s

Considering the war torn combat conditions, it's unlikely that a character would really get an opportunity to study more than one area of expertise. Consequently, a multiple O.C.C. could be more of a hindrance than a help. However, for those of you who still desire a split character class, here are the rules and conditions.

1) The character must meet the physical and/or mental attribute requirements.
2) Must first reach third level or higher in his or her original O.C.C.
3) Begins the New O.C.C. at zero experience and at "field training level", which means the usual O.C.C. skills are selected but NO BONUSES APPLY.
4) Players must score 2000 experience points before attaining first level. At fist level all the usual bonus points are added to each skill and regular experience point accumulation begins at zero.
5) The previous/original O.C.C. skill knowledge and proficiency and experience points are permanently frozen at the point when the new O.C.C. was selected. This means that, while the character retains his previous O.C.C.'s skill knowledge and abilities, those skills are NOT increasing because he/she spends the bulk of the time in perfecting the new O.C.C. skills.

However, if the same skill is chosen in both O.C.C.'s that skill will continue to improve, but ONLY beginning after it has reached the previous skill level. Example: if the skill is frozen at level three, it remains so until the skill level of the new O.C.C. reaches level three. At that point, the experience points/level can again apply to that skill and the character's skill proficiency in that particular area will continue to increase at the same level as his/her current O.C.C.

Step 5: Equipment and Money

All characters are issued a set of standard equipment as well as equipment available in the field or under special conditions. Also assume each character has a number of "common" personal items such as a modest wardrobe, stereo, video/T.V., artwork, knickknacks, booze, and so on. Each character also has his own small, one bedroom, studio-type apartment. Characters can spend their income on a larger apartment, wardrobe, weapons, special items and so on.

Money is referred to as "credits". Each specific Occupational Character Class (O.C.C.) indicates the monthly salary in credits and the formula for determining the character's available savings in credits. Players may use their character's savings/credits as deemed appropriate. Since this is a life and death combat situation it's not likely that characters will be too concerned with creature comforts. NOTE: Not all weapons and equipment are available for purchase such as E.B.A., particle beam rifles, plasma ejectors and so on. Of course characters may be able to bribe an unscrupulous official or purchase stolen goods. Availability of illegal contraband is left solely up to the game master's discretion.

Rounding Out Ones Character Alignments

THE ALIGNMENTS

> **Good:** Principled and Scrupulous
> **Selfish:** Unprincipled and Anarchist
> **Evil:** Miscreant, Aberrant and Diabolic

Alignments are an important factor in developing a character, his/her attitudes and moral principles. ALL players must choose an alignment for their character.

NEUTRAL

First of all, there is no such thing as an absolute or true neutral. All people tend toward good or evil or self-gratification. An absolute true neutral could not make a decision, go on an adventure, kill or take any action of any kind without leaning toward good, evil or self-gratification. It is humanly impossible and is therefore eliminated in the context of this game. (I realize that some of the philosophers out there may disagree with this, but that's a topic for philosophical debate and not a factor of this game. Sorry, no neutrals).

GOOD ALIGNMENTS
Principled
Scrupulous

Because a character is of a good alignment it does not make him/her a saint. Good characters can be just as irritating, obnoxious, arrogant, even prejudiced and full of quirks. However, life and freedom are of the highest priority. Such a person can always be trusted in a life and death situation.

Principled (good)

Principled characters are generally the strong moral character. Superman is of a principled alignment with the highest regard for others lives, well being, truth and honor. **Principled characters will . . .**
1. Always keep his word.
2. Avoids lies.
3. Never kill or attack an unarmed foe.
4. Never harms an innocent.
5. Never tortures for any reason.
6. Never kills for pleasure.
7. Always helps others.
8. Works well in a group.
9. Respects authority, law, self-discipline and honor.
10. Never betrays a friend.

Scrupulous (good)

Scrupulous characters have a high regard for life and

freedom. This type of character is typically portrayed in many Clint Eastwood and Charles Bronson films; the vigilante that works beyond the law, yet for the law, and the "greater good" of the people.

Scrupulous character will . . .
1. Keep his word to any other good person.
2. Lies only to people of selfish and evil alignments.
3. Never kill or attack an unarmed foe.
4. Never harm an innocent.
5. Never torture for pleasure.
6. Never kills for pleasure.
7. Helps others.
8. Works with groups, but dislikes confining laws and restrictions.
9. Distrusts authority.
10. Never betrays a friend.

SELFISH ALIGNMENTS (BUT NOT NECESSARILY EVIL)
Unprincipled
Anarchist

Unprincipled (selfish)

This basically good person tends to be selfish, greedy and holds his/her personal freedom and welfare above almost everything else. He/she dislikes confining laws, self-discipline and distrusts authority. This is the Han Solo, Star Wars, character. The guy who is always looking for the best deal, associates with good and evil characters, is continually tempted to lie and cheat, and hates himself for being loyal and helping others.

Unprincipled characters will . . .
1. Have a high regard for life and freedom.
2. Keep his word of honor.
3. Lie and cheat if necessary (especially to those of anarchist and evil alignments).
4. Will not kill an unarmed foe (but will take advantage of one).
5. Helps those in need.
6. Does not use torture unless absolutely necessary.
7. Works with a group, especially if profitable.
8. Never harms an innocent.
9. Never kills for pleasure.
10. Dislikes authority.
11. Never betrays a friend.

Anarchist (selfish)

This type of character likes to indulge himself in everything. He is the insurgent, con-man, gambler and high roller; the uncommitted freebooter seeking nothing more than self-gratification. This character will at least consider doing anything if the price is right. These people are intrigued by power, glory and wealth. Life has meaning, but his has the greatest meaning. Laws and rules infringe on personal freedom and were meant to be broken. An anarchist aligned person is always looking for the best deal and will work with good, selfish or evil to get it, as long as he comes out of the situation on top. The anarchist is continually teetering between good and evil, rebelling, bending the laws to fit his needs.

Anarchist characters will . . .
1. May keep his word.
2. Lies and cheats if he feels it necessary.
3. Are not likely to kill an unarmed foe, but certainly knock out, attack or beat-up an unarmed foe.
4. Never kill an innocent (but may harm or kidnap).
5. Is not likely to help someone without some ulterior motive (even if its only to show off).
6. Seldom kills for pleasure.
7. Will use torture to extract information (not **likely** to torture for pleasure).
8. Does not work well in a group (this is the cocky loud-mouth who is likely to do as he damn well pleases).
9. Has little respect for self-discipline or authority.
10. May betray a friend.

EVIL ALIGNMENTS
Miscreant
Aberrant
Diabolic

All evil characters are not bent on universal genocide or domination over all living creatures. They are not maniacal people actively seeking to harm innocent people. Nor are all evil characters sadistic and untrustworthy. Many evil characters may actually seem kind or likable.

There is nothing wrong with playing an evil character although he may not survive too long if he betrays or harms too many people. This is fantasy role-playing, not reality. You can play any type of character you desire, just continue to play in character.

Evil alignments are a step beyond the self-gratification of the selfish alignments. Evil characters are ruthless individuals who are willing to say or do anything to achieve their goal. Human life has little meaning to them and friends tend to be (but not always) people to use and discard when they are no longer of value. Evil aligned people do not automatically slay any good aligned person because of different ethics and philosophy. All the better to use good to achieve their own goals for the end always justifies the means.

Miscreant (evil)

This self-serving, unscrupulous character is out only for himself. Power, glory, wealth, position and anything that will make his life more comfortable is his goal. It matters not who gets caught in the middle, as long as he comes out smelling like a rose. This person will lie, cheat and kill anyone to attain his personal goals.

Miscreant characters will . . .
1. Will not necessarily keep his word to anyone.
2. Lie and cheat anyone, good or evil.
3. Most definitely attack an unarmed foe (those are the best kind).
4. Use or harm an innocent.
5. Use torture for extracting information and pleasure.
6. May kill for sheer pleasure.
7. Feels no compulsion to help without some sort of tangible reward.
8. Work with others if it will help him attain his personal goal.
9. Kill an unarmed foe as readily as he would a potential threat or competitor.
10. Has no deference to laws or authority, but will work within the law if he must.
11. Will betray a friend if it serves his needs.

Aberrant (evil)

The cliche that there is "No honor among thieves" is false when dealing with the aberrant character. This is a person who is driven to attain his goals through force, power, and intimidation. Yet the aberrant person stands apart from the norm with his own personal code of ethics (although twisted ethics by the standards of good). He expects loyalty from his minions, punishing disloyalty and treachery with a swift, merciful death. An aberrant person will always keep his word of honor and up-hold any bargains. He will define his terms and live by them whether anyone else likes it or not.

Aberrant characters will . . .
1. Always keep his word of honor (he is honorable).
2. Lie and cheat those not worthy of his respect.
3. May or may not kill an unarmed foe.
4. Not kill (may harm, kidnap) an innocent, particularly a child.
5. Never kills for pleasure.
6. Does not resort to inhumane treatment of prisoners, but torture, although distasteful, is a necessary means of extracting information.
7. Never tortures for pleasure.

8. May or may not help someone in need.
9. Works with others to attain his goals.
10. Respects honor and self-discipline.
11. Never betrays a friend.

Diabolic (evil)

This is the category where the megalomaniacs, violent, and most despicable characters fall. This is the cruel brutal killer who trusts no one and has no value for any life other than his own. A diabolic person will anyone or anything that gets in his way. Aberrant aligned characters find these unhonorable people just as revolting as a good aligned character.

Diabolic characters will . . .
1. Rarely keep his word (and have no honor).
2. Lie and cheat anyone.
3. Most certainly attack and kill an unarmed foe.
4. Use, hurt and kill an innocent without a second thought or for pleasure.
5. Use torture for pleasure and information.
6. Kills for sheer pleasure.
7. Is likely to help someone only to kill or rob him.
8. Does not work well within a group (consistently disregarding orders to do as he pleases).
9. Despises honor, authority, and self-discipline.
10. Associates mostly with other evil alignments.
11. Betrays friends (after all, you can always find friends).

Experience

An Experience Level System is used for two reasons: 1) to fit in with the other Palladium Books games; 2) because I've found it to be a fun and realistic system. After all, nothing can substitute for real experience especially in a combat situation.

Readers will also notice that each Occupational Character Class (O.C.C.) has its own experience level tables. The varying levels of experience needed for each O.C.C. reflects the difficulty of certain skills or areas of study, as well as game balance. Players will also notice that characters are extremely capable and well trained to begin with. These people are space explorers/colonization experts selected for their skill, knowledge or natural aptitude. All are trained professionals.

EXPERIENCE POINTS

Except in specially devised scenarios and tournaments, there is no winner in a role-playing game. The accumulation of heroic deeds, friends, prestige, weapons, equipment, knowledge and skills can be construed to be the results of winning. If a character survives and meets with success in his endeavors, that is winning. However, there are rewards besides the acquisition of material goods and reputations and that's developing your character's skills, knowledge and abilities. This is accomplished through the gathering of experience points.

Why an experience point system?

The reason I use an experience point system is because I find them extremely realistic and practical. Training is useful, but there is no substitute for experience. I don't know how many times I've read a comic book with the main character thinking to himself something like "Only my years of experience enabled me to beat him" or "He's good but lacked the years of experience and training to handle the situation". Practical experience in the field is an important and real factor in the development of a character.

The experience system is specifically designed so that characters will mature fairly rapidly, tapering off as they reach higher levels of experience (around fifth or sixth level).

Why do the experience levels only go to level 15? Because characters are not likely to ever reach that level even after years of regular play. In my original **Palladium Role-Playing Game** play-test campaign, after two years of weekly, long (average 9 hours), playing sessions; the characters averaged 7th to 9th level and progressing ever so slowly toward tenth level. Realistically, a high level character is not necessarily all that fun to play unless the campaign maintains a high level of challenge and adventure.

Experience Points and Their Application

It's difficult to devise a point system by which a game master can judge and reward his players fairly. The ultimate purpose of experience points and experience levels is to provide a means in which the player's character can grow and develop. Many fantasy role-playing games have their own unique system, charts, equations and computations for distributing experience points. You may want to adopt one of these systems to this game if that's what you're comfortable with.

On the other hand, I use a very subjective method of observation and logic. I feel that any twit can chop or blast a creature that has just pounced out from around the corner. Most experience points concentrate on the "kill factor", but what about the thought process? What about the decisions, plans, or motives for a particular action? Doesn't cleverness and a cool head count? Aren't these the true ingredients of good role-playing? It seems unfair to me that the person who devises a clever plan should get much less experience points than the players who carry out the plan because they are better skilled to do so. And what about role-playing? Shouldn't the brilliant medical student playing a character with an I.Q. of 3 (and staying firmly in character, saying and doing things as the character even though he realizes the stupidity as a player) get experience for playing in character? Hell yes! Considering how flexible and subjective most of the other role playing conditions and rules are, I don't see the logic in having a strict, limited experience point system. So, here is my chaotic, subjective experience system.

Each player's character involved in a given situation/confrontation should receive the appropriate experience points. The game master (G.M) should make a list of his players at the beginning of the game and jot down each player's experience points as they gather them throughout the course of the game. At the end of the game, the G.M totals each player's points and gives them each totals so that they can keep track of their growing experience and skills.

The difficulty with this system of determining experience points is the subjectivity. The G.M. must utilize the preceding experience outline with some thought. **Example:** Eight third-level characters armed to the teeth and in heavy armor kill an average opponent. The eight players should receive experience points for killing a minor menace. After all, the creature didn't have a chance and presented no real threat to the characters. However, if one or two first or second level characters killed or subdued the same opponent, they should receive experience points for killing a major or even a great menace, because the threat and the ingenuity involved is much greater.

I've found this method stimulates imaginative playing instead of promoting slash and kill. G.M.'s don't be Santa Claus, heaping wonderful amounts of experience points; be fair and tolerant. Let your players truly earn their experience points, growing in skill and knowledge. If you have a group of players rising rapidly in experience levels, you will know it's because they are clever and imaginative players. And that's what this game is all about.

Character (O.C.C.) Experience Levels

Each Occupational Character Class (O.C.C.) has a listing for Levels of Experience. A character involved in an adventure gains experience points for his thoughts, actions and deeds. As these experience points accumulate, the character will reach new plateaus indicating his continual growth, development and mastery of his chosen O.C.C. and the skills, knowledge and abilities involved. Each time a player's character accumulates enough experience in a particular O.C.C.), his skills increase accordingly. This is why the skills are listed by levels.

A clever plan, a quick attack all earn experience points. The more experience a character receives, the higher the level he attains in that occupation; the greater the skills. **Players:** be certain to keep a careful record of the experience given to you at the end or each game. When a character attains a new level be certain to tell the G.M. so that the skills and hit points can be increased accordingly.

Experience and Hit Points

Each time a character reaches a new level of experience the player gets to roll **one** six-sided die and add the number rolled to the character's hit points. This indicates the physical development and maturity of the character as he develops.

Per Level of Experience

Per level of experience, or per each level of experience or per level of the (and O.C.C.), indicates that the person can perform a skill, spell or ability at his highest level of experience. This often indicates the amount of damage that can be inflicted or a duration.

Awarding Experience Points

Points	The Action
25	Performing a skill (successful or not)
25	Clever, but futile idea.
100	Clever, useful idea or action
100	Quick thinking idea or action.
200	A critical plan or action that saves the character's life and/or a few comrades.
400-1000	A critical plan or action that saves the entire group or many people.
100-300	Endangering the character's own life to help others.
500-700	Self-sacrifice (or potential self-sacrifice) in a life and death situation (like leaping in front of a blast meant for someone else to save that person, even though likely to die, or offering own life to save the group or another).
100	Avoiding unnecessary violence.
100-200	Deductive reasoning and/or insight.
50	Good judgment
50	Playing in character bonus.
50-100	Daring (clever or not)
25-50	Killing or subduing a minor menace.
75-100	Killing or subduing a major menace.
150-300	Killing or subduing a great menace.

A.V.P.M.

Level	
1	0000-1850
2	1851-3700
3	3701-7200
4	7201-14,000
5	14,001-20,000
6	20,001-29,000
7	29,001-39,000
8	39,001-50,500
9	50,501-71,000
10	71,001-101,000
11	101,001-136,000
12	136,001-186,000
13	186,001-236,000
14	236,001-286,000
15	286,001-326,000

G.V.P.M.

Level	
1	0000-1800
2	1801-3600
3	3601-7000
4	7001-12,000
5	12,001-18,000
6	18,001-28,000
7	28,001-38,000
8	38,001-50,000
9	50,001-70,000
10	70,001-100,000
11	100,001-135,000
12	135,001-185,000
13	185,001-235,000
14	235,001-285,000
15	285,001-325,000

Communication Engineer

Level	
1	0000-1750
2	1751-3500
3	3501-7000
4	7001-14,000
5	14,001-20,000
6	20,001-29,500
7	29,501-40,000
8	40,001-52,000
9	52,001-72,000
10	72,001-102,000
11	102,001-137,000
12	137,001-187,000
13	187,001-237,000
14	237,001-287,000
15	287,001-327,000

Field Scientist

Level	
1	0000-1900
2	1901-3800
3	3801-7300
4	7301-14,300
5	14,301-21,000
6	21,001-30,000
7	30,001-40,000
8	40,001-53,000
9	53,001-73,000
10	73,001-103,000
11	103,001-138,000
12	138,001-188,000
13	188,001-238,000
14	238,001-288,000
15	288,001-328,000

GUSTOVICH

Warrior (Rover)

Level	
1	0000-1900
2	1901-3800
3	3801-7600
4	7601-12,000
5	12,001-20,000
6	20,001-30,000
7	30,001-40,000
8	40,001-50,000
9	50,001-70,000
10	70,001-100,000
11	100,001-133,000
12	133,001-183,000
13	183,001-233,000
14	233,001-283,000
15	283,001-323,000

L.B.A.

Level	
1	0000-1875
2	1876-3750
3	3751-7250
4	7251-14,100
5	14,101-21,200
6	21,201-31,200
7	31,201-41,200
8	41,201-51,200
9	51,201-71,200
10	71,201-101,500
11	101,501-136,500
12	136,501-186,500
13	186,501-236,500
14	236,501-286,500
15	286,501-326,500

Commando

Level	
1	0000-2000
2	2001-4000
3	4001-7600
4	7601-15,000
5	15,001-22,000
6	22,001-32,000
7	32,001-43,000
8	43,001-54,000
9	54,001-74,000
10	74,001-104,000
11	104,001-140,000
12	140,001-190,000
13	190,001-240,000
14	240,001-290,000
15	290,001-340,000

Esper (Rover)

Level	
1	0000-1750
2	1751-3500
3	3501-7100
4	7101-14,200
5	14,201-22,000
6	22,001-32,000
7	32,001-42,000
8	42,001-53,500
9	53,501-74,000
10	74,001-104,000
11	104,001-141,000
12	141,001-191,000
13	191,001-241,000
14	241,001-291,000
15	291,001-341,000

E.B.A.

Level	
1	0000-1860
2	1861-3700
3	3701-7300
4	7301-14,200
5	14,201-21,400
6	21,401-31,600
7	31,601-41,800
8	41,801-52,000
9	52,001-72,000
10	72,001-102,000
11	102,001-136,500
12	136,501-187,000
13	187,001-238,000
14	238,001-288,000
15	288,001-328,000

Esper

Level	
1	0000-1925
2	1926-3850
3	3851-7450
4	7451-14,900
5	14,901-21,000
6	21,001-31,000
7	31,001-41,000
8	41,601-53,000
9	53,001-73,000
10	73,001-103,500
11	103,501-139,000
12	139,001-189,000
13	189,001-239,000
14	239,001-289,000
15	289,001-339,000

Thief (Human or Rover)

Level	
1	0000-1850
2	1851-3700
3	3701-7400
4	7401-13,000
5	13,001-21,000
6	21,001-31,000
7	31,001-41,000
8	41,001-51,000
9	51,001-71,000
10	71,001-101,000
11	101,001-131,500
12	131,501-181,500
13	181,501-231,500
14	231,501-281,500
15	281,501-331,000

Note: The Optional Underwater O.C.C.'s experience levels are identical to their land based counterparts.

Occupational Character Classes (O.C.C)

OCCUPATIONAL CHARACTER CLASSES (O.C.C.)

Human O.C.C.	Requirements
Esper	Major or Master Psionic
Communication Engineer	I.Q. 10
P.A.V.M./Pilot Air Vehicle Mechanic	I.Q. 9, P.P. 9
P.G.V.M./Pilot Ground Vehicle Mechanic	I.Q. 5, P.P. 5
Field Scientist	I.Q. 12

Men at Arms	
L.B.A. Division	I.Q. 7, P.P. 7
E.B.A. Division	I.Q. 6, P.S. 10
Commando	I.Q. 10, P.S. 12, P.P. 12

Rover O.C.C.'s	
Thief	P.P. 11
Warrior	P.S. 9
Esper	Major or Minor Psionics

Esper

Esper

An ESPer is a human being who exhibits Extra Sensory Perceptions (E.S.P. or Esper, a common slang term of this future time). These exceptional people, once feared by normal humans, are now accepted as valuable members of society, actively sought and trained to develop their powers. Espers are especially coveted for space and planet exploration (as well as covert military operations), where their psychic abilities can often bridge gaps between alien cultures much more quickly than conventional methods. Empathy, telepathy, see aura, sense good or evil, and other psionic mind probes are crucial in alien communication. While object reading and biological manipulations such as bio-regeneration, resist fatigue or thirst, and other abilities make them equally valuable for the rigors of exploration and investigation.

Since Gideon-E has a wealth of ancient alien ruins with still active devices and is inhabited by the heavily psionic "Rovers", Espers were a vital part of the research colonization program.

Although Espers are generally accepted in society they are still often the victims of prejudice; feared and resented for their "unnatural" powers and high social, economic and political positions. Because their powers are so valuable, Espers are usually paid superior wages and treated with the prestige of a celebrity. Relations on Gideon-E are much better than in most communities, but prejudice still exists.

The category of Esper is an occupation (O.C.C.) with the development of psionic abilities taking the place of actual skills. So much time and effort is devoted to development of psionic abilities which takes the place of skills. So much time and effort is devoted to developing his or her psionic strengths and disciplines that there is very little time for more conventional areas of study. Consequently, only a handful of elective skills are available. The Esper O.C.C. has no skills in the category of **Major Areas of Expertise**.

Elective Skills: Choose three at level one, two at level three, one at level six and one at level nine.

A.V. Mechanics
Climbing
Computer Operation +10%
Computer Programming +10%
Electronics +10%
Hand to Hand: Basic

Medical: First Aid
G.V. Mechanic
P.A.V. (Pilot Air Vehicle)
P.G.V. (Pilot Ground Vehicle)
Pick Pockets
Swimming: Basic
W.P. Handgun
W.P. Laser Rifle

Combat and Weapons

Generally, an Esper is <u>not</u> a combat occupation. However, because of their unique abilities and the prevalence of resentment by society, basic hand to hand combat training is made available. Likewise the use of a handgun or laser rifle can also be learned (See W.P.). Remember, **any** character may use **any** weapon, but no bonuses to strike apply unless trained in the use of that weapon (Weapon Proficiency/W.P.).

Attacks Per Melee: Two plus any possible additions from hand to hand combat skill.

Use of Battle Armor: Uncommon, although a web vest or studded leather can be attained for personal use. Light Battle Armor (L.B.A.) may be issued for dangerous assignments. E.B.A. is NEVER worn.

Standard Equipment:
Mini tool pack
Flashlight
Utility belt
Mini flashlight
Rocket flare
Binoculars
Hand held directional communicator
Gas mask or air filter
Gloves
Food rations and water (one week)
First aid kit

Authorized Clearance Upon Assignment: Handgun and/or laser rifle, web vest or L.B.A., land buggy or hovercraft-scout (but only if the person has a piloting skill).

Monthly Wages: Approximately 3800 credits at levels 1-4; 5th level or higher, or master psionics proven in the field may get 5800 credits or more. Roll 1D8 X 1000 to determine savings.

Attribute Requirements: Major or Master Psionics

PSIONICS

ALL players should roll percentile dice to determine if their character has any psionic abilities (as explained in the character creation section).

1-59	No psionic abilities
60-79	Minor Psionic (not considered an Esper)
80-89	Major Psionic (Esper material)
90-00	Master Psionic (Esper material)

Save vs Psionic Attacks

Non-Psionic	15 or higher
Minor	12 or higher
Major	12 or higher
Master	10 or higher

Communication Engineer

COMMUNICATIONS ENGINEER O.C.C.

This character can be as crucial as any of the men at arms O.C.C.'s, for he or she represents the vital link of communication. ALL communications engineers have a thorough background in the use and understanding of audio/visual and sensory equipment. This means that they can operate any known state of the art technology involving radio, video, radar, sensors, surveillance, photography, computer and related.

Attribute Requirements: I.Q. 10

Major Areas of Expertise:

Audio/Visual Communications	+30%
Computer Operation	+25%
Sensory Equipment	+30%
Surveillance Systems	+15%

Elective Skills: Choose four at level one, two at level three, one at level six and one at level nine.

A.V. Mechanics (Air Vehicle Mechanics)	+5%
Climbing	
Computer Programming	+10%
Electronics	+15%
G.V. Mechanics (Ground Vehicle Mechanics)	+10%
Linguistics	+20%
Medical: First Aid	+10%
Medical: Paramedic	+10%
P.A.V. (Pilot Air Vehicles)	
P.G.V. (Pilot Ground Vehicles)	
Swimming: Basic	
Swimming: S.C.U.B.A	
W.P. Handgun	
W.P. Laser Rifle	
W.P. Knife	

Combat and Weapons

The Communications Engineer O.C.C. is a non-combat occupation hired for a non-combat situation. Consequently, they are NOT trained in hand to hand combat.

However, the use of common weapons in the field such as knives, handguns and laser rifles are necessary (See W.P.). Remember, **any** character may use **any** weapon, but no bonuses to strike apply unless the character has a weapon proficiency (W.P.).

Attacks Per Melee: Two

Use of Battle Armor: Limited to web vest or L.B.A., E.B.A. is NEVER used.

Standard Equipment:
Mini tool pack
Laser Lance
Flashlight
Utility belt
Work overalls and uniform
Insulated gloves and hiking boots
Protective goggles
Leather jacket (many pockets)
Gas mask or air filter
Hand held, short range directional communicator;
    Range: 4.8km/3 miles
Video camera
Portable Scan Dilator: weight: 9.1kg (20lbs); has full scanning capabilities including: Long range, wide band radio (range: 80km/50 miles), Short range directional radio (range: 4.8km/3 miles); Frequency scrambler, Radar (range: 8km/5 miles); Motion detector (range: 60m/200ft); Heat sensor (range: 30m/100ft); Dosimeter (range: 30m/100ft).

Authorized Clearance Upon Assignment: Additional sensory scanning equipment, surveillance equipment, optical enhancements, video and photography equipment, any type of handgun, LR-20 Laser rifle and even a PBR-10 particle beam rifle but only for extremely dangerous assignments. Armor is limited to web vest or L.B.A. Any conventional ground vehicle and/or hover scout (if a skilled pilot).

Monthly Wages: 3000 credits at levels 1-4, 3800 credits at 5th level or higher. Roll 1D6X1000 to determine savings.

Pilot Air Vehicle Mechanic (P.A.V.M.)

PILOT AIR VEHICLE MECHANIC (P.A.V.M.) O.C.C.

Characters with this occupation are skilled pilots of air vehicles including the hover jet fighter, orbital shuttle, and dreadnought. Like the P.G.V.M., they are also skilled mechanics practiced in the repair of the air vehicles listed in this book.

Attribute Requirements: I.Q. 9, P.P. 9

Major Areas of Expertise:

P.A.V. (Pilot Air Vehicle)	+35%
A.V. Mechanics	+30%
Sensory Equipment	+15%
P.F.G. (Pilot Flying Gun)	+30%

Elective Skills: Choose three at level one, two at level three, one at level six and one at level nine.

Audio/Visual Communications	+10%
Climbing	
Computer Operation	+10%
Computer Programming	
Electronics	+15%
G.V. Mechanics	+15%
Medical/First Aid	+10%
P.G.V. (Pilot Ground Vehicle)	+15%
Swimming: Basic	
Swimming: S.C.U.B.A.	
W.P. Knife	
W.P. Handgun	
W.P. Laser Rifle	

Combat and Weapons

The air pilot/mechanic O.C.C. is a non-combat occupation hired for a non-combat situation. Consequently, they are NOT trained in hand to hand combat. However, their piloting skills enable a P.A.V.M. to pilot such vehicles of war as the flying gun, and hover fighter. The use of common handguns and laser rifle may also be learned for protection in the field (See W.P.). Remember, any character may use any weapon, but no bonuses to strike apply unless the character has a weapon proficiency (W.P.) in that weapon.

Attacks Per Melee: Two

Use of Battle Armor: Very uncommon, except in a potential combat situation in which a web vest or L.B.A. will be issued.

Standard Equipment:
Mini tool pack
Laser Lance
Fusion Torch
Flashlight
Utility belt
Work overalls
Insulated gloves and boots
Protective goggles
Gas mask or air filter

For Flight:
Flight suit, gloves, boots
Helmet with radio communication-link
Independent oxygen supply
Bio-scan
Dosimeter

Authorized Clearance Upon Assignment: Gas mask, binoculars, hand held communicator, additional tools, handgun and/or laser rifle, L.B.A. and hover scout or other air vehicle (subject to the requirements of the assignment) or a ground vehicle if trained in P.G.V.

Monthly Wages: 2800 credits at levels 1-4, 3800 credits for 5th level or higher. Roll 1D6X1000 to determine savings.

Major Areas of Experience:

P.G.V. (Pilot Ground Vehicle)	+30%
G.V. Mechanics	+30%
Sensory Equipment	+5% to operate, +10% to repair
E-Clip Recharge	+10%

Elective Skills: Choose three at level one, two at level three, one at level six, and one at level nine.

Audio/Visual Communication	+5%
A.V. Mechanics	+10%
Climbing	
Computer Operation	(10% to repair ONLY)
Electronics	+10%
Locksmith	+10%

Pilot Ground Vehicle Mechanic (P.G.V.M.)

PILOT GROUND VEHICLE MECHANIC (P.G.V.M.) O.C.C.

Characters under this O.C.C. are skilled ground vehicle pilots and auto-type mechanics. The Pilot Ground Vehicle (P.G.V.) skill includes all conventional ground vehicles excluding only the operation of the hover plasma tank which is a separate elective skill.

Attribute Requirements: I.Q. 5, P.P. 5, NOTE: Add 5% bonus to each skill if I.Q. is 13 or higher.

Hand to Hand Combat (Basic)
Medical: First Aid
P.A.V. (Pilot Air Vehicle)   +5%
P.P. Tank   +20%
Swimming: Basic
W.P. Knife
W.P. Handgun
W.P. Laser Rifle
<u>Combat and Weapons</u>

The pilot/mechanic O.C.C. is a non-combat occupation although basic hand to hand combat skill and a handful of W.P. skills are available elective skills. Remember, **any** character may use **any** weapon, but no bonuses to strike apply unless the character has a weapon proficiency (W.P.) in that weapon.

<u>Attacks Per Melee:</u> Two, plus possible hand to hand bonus attacks.

<u>Use of Battle Armor:</u> Web vest or L.B.A. are commonly used especially in a combat or potentially dangerous situation. E.B.A. is NEVER worn.

<u>Standard Equipment:</u>
Mini tool pack
Fusion Torch
Laser Lance
Flashlight
Utility belt
Work overalls/jumpsuit
Insulated gloves and boots
Protective goggles
Gas mask or air filter

<u>Authorized Clearance Upon Assignment:</u> Handgun and/or laser rifle, web vest or L.B.A., hand held communicator, radiation scanner, additional tools, lock picking equipment, land vehicle of any type (subject to the requirements of the assignment), or possibly a hover scout if trained in P.A.V.

<u>Monthly Wages:</u> 2500 credits at level 1-4, 3400 credits for 5th level or higher. Roll 1D4 X 1000 to determine savings.

Field Scientist

<u>FIELD SCIENTIST O.C.C.</u>

The field scientist is an O.C.C. that I've included due to continual requests for a more cerebral and science oriented character. Like the other O.C.C.'s, I've limited the character's abilities rather sharply as to not conflict with the other characters and to fit into the overall mechanoid scenario.

The field scientist is a sort of "jack-of-all-trades" using his or her varied knowledge to form rudimentary hypotheses, inspection, analysis, interpretation, cataloging and indexing of alien specimens. In depth research or experimentation would require that a special team of scientific experts be brought in or the specimens sent out.

ALL field scientists are familiar with many elements and areas of science as they generally apply to the exploration of alien worlds. These include mathematics, physics, biology, pathology, basic botany, anthropology, analytical chemistry and computer sciences.

<u>Attribute Requirements:</u> I.Q. 12 (High M.E. is helpful too, but not a prerequisite).

<u>Special Skills:</u> The ability to deduce an unknown device's purpose 25%; deduce specific use and operation 10%. Add

5% for every EIGHT hours of intense study with a maximum cut off point of 80% (after all, there's always an elusive element when dealing with the unknown). If the roll is unsuccessful the process must be repeated. Roll only **once** per each category. Players may wait to roll once to determine their success after several 8 hour periods (always increasing the odds of success) OR roll once every eight hours **without** the collective bonuses of hours and hours of study. This means rather than spending additional time in intense study (which adds to the rate of success), the player may opt for his character to simply do a brief analysis to determine its use and operation and roll at the base 25% (purpose) and 10% operation once every eight hours. **Important NOTE:** The player MUST <u>first</u> successfully determine the device's intended **purpose** <u>before</u> he or she can roll to determine its actual **use** and **operation.** Consequently, the player **first** rolls to ascertain its purpose and **secondly** rolls to determine its operation, but ONLY IF he/she has successfully rolled to determine its purpose. If the device's purpose has not been ascertained the field scientist cannot figure-out how the device actually functions or how to use it himself. Likewise, the character may correctly deduce the device's purpose but be unable to deduce its operation without several hours, days or even weeks of intense and constant study. NOTE: Once the purpose is learned the player no longer needs to roll in that category and can concentrate entirely on its use and operation. Furthermore, while the character may have deduced both its purpose and use/operation, he/she **CANNOT** use the device unless that character has the necessary skills. For example, the field scientist can deduce the purpose, use and operation of an air vehicle, but CANNOT pilot it unless he/she is trained in piloting air vehicles (P.A.V.). Of course the scientist **can** instruct others with the proper skill background to operate the device.

<u>Alien Technology Penalty:</u> Totally alien science and technology reduces the base rate of success to 10% to deduce its purpose and 4% to deduce its use and operation. Only a meager 2% is added for every eight hours of study.

<u>Mechanoid NOTE:</u> As a result of in depth study on the Mechanoids, the alien technology penalty DOES NOT Apply. Instead; use the normal formula.

<u>Major Areas of Expertise:</u>

Computer Operation	+30%
Computer Programming	+20%
Sensory Equipment	+20%
Medical: Paramedic	+20%

<u>Elective Skills:</u> Choose five at level one, two at level three, two at level six and two at level nine.

Audio/Visual Communications	
A.V. Mechanics	+15%
Climbing	
E-Clip Recharging	+20%
Electronics	+20%
G.V. Mechanics	+15%
Locksmith	
Mechanical Engineer	+20%
P.A.V. (Pilot Air Vehicle)	
P.G.V. (Pilot Ground Vehicle)	
Prowl	+10%
Surveillance Systems	+5%
Swimming: Basic	
Swimming: S.C.U.B.A.	
Swimming: Deep Sea	
Tracking (outdoors)	+10%
W.P. Knife	
W.P. Handgun	
W.P. Laser Rifle	

<u>Combat and Weapons</u>

The Field Scientist is a non-combat occupation hired for a non-combat situation. Consequently, they are NOT trained in hand to hand combat. However, the use of handguns or laser rifles are often necessary in the field and are available skills (See W.P.).

Attacks Per Melee: Two

Use of Battle Armor: Restricted to web vest, L.B.A. or experimental. E.B.A. is NEVER worn.

Standard Equipment:
Mini tool pack
Laser Lance
Flashlight
Knife
Utility belt
Uniform and work overalls
Insulated gloves and boots
Protective goggles
Gas mask or air filter
Hand held, short range directional communicator; Range: 4.8km/3 miles.
Portable laboratory
Portable personal computer

Authorized Clearance Upon Assignment: Any handgun and/or Laser Rifle, web vest or L.B.A., sensory scanning equipment, surveillance equipment, video or photography equipment, fusion torch, binoculars and other optics, lock picking equipment, additional tools, conventional land vehicles or hover scout (ONLY if a trained pilot); and access to laboratories and research facilities.

Monthly Wages: 3800 credits at levels 1-3; 4200 credits for 5th level or higher. Roll 1D8 X 1000 to determine savings.

Light Battle Armor Division (L.B.A.)

LIGHT BATTLE ARMOR DIVISION (L.B.A.) O.C.C.

The L.B.A. division are men and women trained in combat for the expressed purpose of law enforcement and protection against hostile elements. The L.B.A. division is more of an elite police force than combat trained soldiers. They are generally experts in hand to hand combat, handguns, laser rifles and surveillance.

In addition to law enforcement, members of the L.B.A. division often accompany scouting parties and scientific expeditions for protection. Under the current circumstances the L.B.A. division has become an important factor in the colonists' struggle against the Mechanoids.

NOTE: New trainees into the L.B.A., as well as E.B.A. divisions, are continually being recruited to combat the invading aliens.

Attribute Requirements: I.Q. 7, P.P. 7

Major Areas of Experience:

Hand to Hand: Expert	
W.P. Handgun	
Surveillance Systems	+20%
Investigation	+15%

Elective Skills: Choose four at level one, two at level three, one at level six and one at level nine.

Audio/Visual Communication	
Climbing	10%
Computer Operation	
Medical: First Aid	
P.A.V. (Pilot Air Vehicle)	
P.G.V. (Pilot Ground Vehicle)	+6%
P.F.G. (Pilot Flying Gun)	+16%
P.P. Tank (Pilot Plasma Tank)	+14%
Sensory Equipment	+5%
Swimming: Basic	
Tracking (outdoors)	+20%
W.P. Knife	
W.P. Laser Rifle	
W.P. Explosives	+6%

Combat and Weapons

ALL characters with an L.B.A. Division O.C.C. are trained for combat and police work. Standard issue of a LP-10 (Laser Pistol) and L.B.A. (Light Battle Armor) are mandatory. Remember, any character can use any weapon, but no bonuses to strike apply unless the character has a weapon proficiency (W.P.) in that weapon.

Attacks Per Melee: Two (See Hand to Hand Expert skill)

Use of Battle Armor: Light Battle Armor (L.B.A.) is mandatory. Web vest may be used in undercover operations.

L.B.A./Light Battle Armor NOTES:
1) A.R. 12
2) S.D.C. 72
3) High temperature resistant weave of nylon and synthetic fibers.
4) Reinforced polycarbonate body plates and helmet.
5) Fire resistant up to 245°C.
6) Insulated
7) Short range directional communicator built into helmet; Range 16km/10 miles.
8) Gas mask and face protector attaches to helmet.
9) Emergency oxygen supply (lasts two hours)

Standard Equipment:
L.B.A.
L.P. 10
Flashlight reinforced to be used as a bludgeon if necessary, does 1-6 damage.
Uniform
Utility belt
Dosimeter

Equipment for Condition Red (extremely dangerous or special operations)
L.R.-20 Laser Rifle
Flying Gun (P.F.G. skill needed to operate)
Surveillance devices and portable monitor
Vehicle: any conventional ground vehicle, hover scout, modified or unmodified hover transport.

Authorized Clearance Upon Assignment: Gas and special equipment/weapons, any vehicle (as long as trained in its operation), field equipment, surveillance equipment, and limited access to other skilled personnel such as communication engineers and pilots. NOTE: in the case of the latter, this individual(s) may be requested and, if approved, temporarily assigned to the L.B.A. Division or team. Likewise a member(s) of the L.B.A. Division may be assigned to assist a non-combat team such as a scientific research team or outpost, reconnaissance or exploration.

Monthly Wages: 2600 credits at levels 1-4; 3500 credits for 5th level or higher. Roll 1D6 X 1000 to determine savings.

Light Battle Armor Division(L.B.A.)

LASER LANCE

Environmental Battle Armor Division (E.B.A.)

ENVIRONMENTAL BATTLE ARMOR DIVISION (E.B.A.) O.C.C.

The E.B.A. division are men and women trained for heavy combat. Although not soldiers in the sense of a government operation, they are generally skilled in combat weapons and military operations.

During peace time the E.B.A. division acts as a back up for the L.B.A. division in law enforcement and as a ready deterrent to potential hostile elements such as alien assaults, pirates, terrorists and so on. The E.B.A. division has become the front line defense against the Mechanoid invaders.

NOTE: New trainees into the E.B.A. and L.B.A. divisions are constantly being recruited to combat the Mechanoids.

<u>Attribute Requirements:</u> I.Q. 6, P.S. 10
<u>Major Areas of Experience:</u>
Hand to Hand: Expert
W.P. Handgun
W.P. Laser Rifle
P.G.V. (Pilot Ground Vehicle)   +10%
<u>Elective Skills:</u> Choose four at level one, one at level three, one at level six and one at level nine.

Audio/Visual Communication	+10%
Climbing	+10%
Computer Operation	
Medical: First Aid	+10%
P.A.V. (Pilot Air Vehicle)	
P.F.G. (Pilot Flying Gun)	+12%
P.P. Tank (Pilot Plasma Tank)	+14%
Prowl (minus 25% in E.B.A.)	
Sensory Equipment	+5%
Swimming: Basic	
Swimming: S.C.U.B.A.	
W.P. Knife	
W.P. Heavy	
W.P. Explosives	+12%

Combat and Weapons

ALL characters with an E.B.A. Division O.C.C. are combat trained and skilled in the use of most weapons. Weapons skills (See W.P. skills) often include W.P. heavy, the use of heavy weapons such as the P.B.R.-10 particle beam rifle and plasma ejectors, and W.P. explosives. The IB-10 ion blaster and LR-20 laser rifle are standard issue as is the use of E.B.A. or L.B.A. body armors. Remember, any character can use any weapon, but no bonuses to strike apply unless the character has a weapon proficiency (W.P.) in that weapon.

<u>Attacks Per Melee:</u> Two (See Hand to Hand: Expert skill)
<u>Use of Battle Armor:</u> Members of the E.B.A. can use either E.B.A. or L.B.A. Although E.B.A. is standard issue, the use of L.B.A. may be desired especially for covert operations. NOTE: E.B.A. is a heavy, somewhat cumbersome body armor reducing one's prowl percentage by 25%. E.B.A. use is limited exclusively to the E.B.A. division and commando.

<u>E.B.A./ Environmental Body Armor NOTES:</u>
1) A.R. 15
2) S.D.C. 150
3) Complete "Environmental" Battle Armor suitable for use in space and other hostile environments.
4) Computer controlled life support system.
5) Internal cooling and temperature control.
6) Humidifier
7) Gas filtering and artificial circulation.
8) Independent oxygen supply and purge system; automatically engages in low oxygen or polluted environment.

(six hour oxygen supply maximum).
9) Insulated, high temperature resistant weave of nylon, synthetic fibers and metal mesh.
10) Fire resistance up to 344°C. Note: normal fires do no damage, but plasma weapons have full effect.
11) Radiation shielded.
12) Mounted with protective metal alloy body plates.
13) Helmet with computer enhanced optics: infra-red and ultra-violet (41m/120ft range), telescopic (400m/1300 feet range).
14) Tinted, light sensitive visor.
15) Built in dosimeter.
16) Short range directional communicator built into the helmet, range 16km/10 miles.

<u>Standard Equipment:</u>
E.B.A.
IB-10 Ion blaster handgun
LR-20 Laser rifle
Flashlight reinforced (does 1-6 damage as a blunt weapon)
Knife
Uniform
Utility belt
<u>Equipment for Condition Red</u> (extremely dangerous or special operations)
PBR-10 Particle beam rifle
Plasma Ejectors
Flying Gun
Explosives
Vehicle: any conventional ground vehicle, hover scout, modified or unmodified hover transport.
Plasma Tank requires special authorization.
<u>Authorized Clearance Upon Assignment:</u> Gas and special equipment, vehicles and weapons, PBR-10, L.B.A., field equipment, Hover Plasma Tank, Flying Gun, Juggernaut

E.B.A. II. Limited access to other skilled personnel is also possible. See L.B.A. Division for specific conditions.

<u>Monthly Wages:</u> 2800 credits at levels 1-4; 3800 credits for 5th level or higher. Roll 1D6 X 1000 to determine savings.

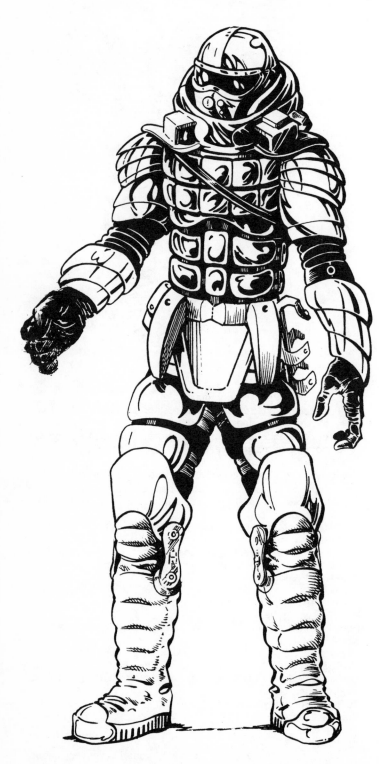

Commando

COMMANDO O.C.C.

The commando O.C.C. is a special operations division which often operates along side the E.B.A. and, to a lesser degree, the L.B.A. division. During peace time their purpose is identical to the E.B.A. division with an emphasis on covert operations, counter espionage and anti-terrorism. Now, with the assault by the Mechanoids, the commandos are involved in reconnaissance, special operations of seek and destroy, and so on.

Attribute Requirements: I.Q. 10, P.S. 12, P.P. 12
Major Areas of Experience:

Hand to Hand: Martial Arts or Expert	
W.P. Handgun	
W.P. Laser Rifle	
Prowl	+20%
Climbing	+20%
Sensory Equipment	+10%

<u>Elective Skills:</u> Choose five at level one, two at level three, two at level six and one at level nine.

Audio/Visual Communications	+10%
Computer Operations	+5%
Electronics	+5%
Locksmith	+20%
Investigation	+20%
P.A.V. (Pilot Air Vehicle)	+10%
P.G.V. (Pilot Ground Vehicle)	+10%
P.F.G. (Pilot Flying Gun)	+10%
Pick Pockets	+15%
Surveillance Systems	+15%
Swimming: Basic	
Swimming: S.C.U.B.A.	
Tracking (outdoors)	+12%
W.P. Heavy	
W.P. Explosives	+20%
W.P. Knife	

Combat and Weapons

Commandos are combat trained and skilled in the use of most weapons. Like the E.B.A. Division O.C.C., the commando can elect weapon skills (See W.P. skills) in explosives, heavy weapons, and is often the first to gain access to experimental weapons. The commando's specialty is death and destruction and his skills should reflect that area of expertise. Remember, any character can use any weapon, but no bonuses to strike apply unless the character has a W.P. in that weapon type.

<u>Attacks Per Melee:</u> Two (See Hand to Hand: Martial Arts)
<u>Use of Battle Armor:</u> Commandos can select any type of body armor including web vest, L.B.A. and E.B.A. The latter is rarely used because of its bulk which impairs mobility. E.B.A. penalty: reduce prowl -25%, climb and speed by 25% (NOTE: the climb and speed penalty does NOT apply to the E.B.A. Division O.C.C.).
<u>Standard Equipment:</u>
Choice of body armor.
LP-10 Laser pistol
LR-20 Laser rifle
Survival knife
Nylon cord for climbing and grappling hook
Gun and utility belt
Flashlight
Short range directional communicator (hand held - range: 4.8km/3 miles)
Uniform
Gas mask or air filter
Protective tinted goggles
<u>Equipment for Condition Red</u> (extremely dangerous or special operations)
PBR-10 Particle Beam rifle

Plasma Ejectors
Spike Launch Rod
Explosives
Vehicle: any conventional ground vehicle, hover jet or flying gun.

Authorized Clearance Upon Assignment: Gas and experimental/special equipment, vehicles and weapons, PBR-10, flying gun, multi-arm antagonizor, and limited access to special personnel (same as L.B.A. and E.B.A. divisions).

Monthly Wages: 3000 credits at levels 1-4, 4400 credits for 5th level or higher. Roll 1D6 X 1000 to determine savings.

Commando

THE HUMAN THIEF (optional)

There is no O.C.C. for human characters as thieves. Unlike a fantasy adventure game, thieving skills are not as applicable or useful. Strict laws and the life and death combat situation makes it futile to steal from one's companions or peers. Rover characters are from an entirely different society, upbringing and primitive environment. For them, thieving is as natural as breathing, but hardly a useful skill to combat the Mechanoids.

Ah, but for those die-hard players who love to play larcenous characters the following OPTIONAL rules for the human thief are provided. The human thief O.C.C. is up to each individual game master's approval

Creating the Human Thief O.C.C.

1) **Select an ordinary O.C.C.** The character has knowledge in all the "major areas of expertise", but ALL skill bonuses are <u>half</u> of what is listed.

2) Instead of selecting the usual amount of **elective skills** the player chooses FOUR from the following list:

Climbing	+15%
Computer Operation	+10%
Computer Programming	+10%
Electronics	+10%
Hand to Hand: Basic	
Investigation	+10%
Locksmith	+15%
P.A.V.	
P.G.V.	
Pick Pockets	+12%
Prowl	+12%
W.P. Explosives	
W.P. Handguns	
W.P. Knife	
Sensory Equipment	+5%
Surveillance Systems	+12%

Note: This character is clearly not as competent in his alleged ordinary O.C.C., but does have other expertise. His or her lack of competency in the ordinary O.C.C. will prevent the character from ever rising above the basic starting pay or position regardless of the level of experience.

3) **Alignment** must be anarchist or evil to be a practicing thief.

Skill Descriptions

ALPHABETICAL SKILLS LIST

Audio/Visual Communication
A.V. Mechanics
Climbing
Computer Operation
Computer Programming
Electronics
E-Clip Recharging
G.V. Mechanic
Hand to Hand: Basic
Hand to Hand: Expert
Hand to Hand: Martial Arts
Investigation
Locksmith
Mechanical Engineering
Medical: First Aid
Medical: Paramedic
P.A.V. (Pilot Air Vehicle)
P.F.G. (Pilot Flying Gun)
P.G.V. (Pilot Ground Vehicle)
P.P. Tank (Pilot Plasma Tank)
Pick Pockets
Prowl
Sensory Equipment
Surveillance Systems
Swimming: Basic
Swimming: S.C.U.B.A.
Swimming: Deep Sea
Tracking (outdoors)
W.P. Explosives
W.P. Handguns
W.P. Heavy Weapons
W.P. Knife
W.P. Laser Rifle

SKILL DESCRIPTIONS

Audio/Visual Communication: Knowledge in the use of radio communications, broadcasting, recording, video, film and subsequent equipment and techniques. This includes the establishing of intercommunication networks. **Base Skill is 30%+5% per level.**

A.V. Mechanics: Air Vehicle Mechanics is the in depth understanding of the workings of all colony air vehicles. Includes the ability to repair, rebuild, modify and redesign conventional air vehicles (including hover jet and shuttle). There are _two_ base skill percentages, the first is the ability to diagnose the mechanical problem while the second is the ability to repair it. 20%diagnose/15% repair +5% (for both) per level.

Climbing: Knowledge of the tools and techniques in climbing up sheer surfaces. Players should roll once for every 6 meters (20ft) of a vertical climb. Every "skilled" climber gets a second roll to recover his/her hold. Base Skill is 50%+8% per level of experience.

Computer Operation: A knowledge of how computers work along with the skills to operate peripherals like keyboards, printers and modems. Characters can follow computer directions, enter and retrieve information and similar basic computer operations. However, this does NOT include programming. **Base Skill is 50%+5% to operate; 20%+5% to repair per level of experience.**

Computer Programming: Designing, programming, debugging and testing computer programs/software. NOTE: Computer Operation is required before taking computer programming. **Base Skill is 40%+5% per level.**

Electronics: An understanding of electronic principles, circuits, wiring and repair. Characters can diagnose and locate electrical problems (the first percentage number) and effect repairs (the second percentile number) as well as by-pass circuit/surveillance systems, etc. Base Skill is 40% +5% (for both) per level of experience.

E-Clip Recharging: This is the specialized skill of recharging depleted Energy Clips for the various energy weapons. A failed roll means an unsuccessful attempt and may result in an explosion (22% chance) within 10 to 60 seconds. Explosion of an ion or laser E-clip does 5 to 50 points damage (5D10) while plasma or particle beam E-clips do 100 to 600 points of damage (1D6 X 100). **Base Skill is 42% +8% per level of experience.** NOTE: this skill is limited to P.G.V.M. O.C.C. and Field Scientist O.C.C.

G.V. Mechanics: The comprehensive knowledge and ability to repair, build, modify and redesign all colony ground vehicles. As with A.V. Mechanics, the first percentile number is the ability to diagnose and pinpoint a mechanical problem; the second number is the skill to actually repair it. **Basic Skill is 30% to diagnose, 24% to repair +6% (on both) per level of experience.**

Hand to Hand: Basic: This is a fundamental fighting technique taught in the military basic training and self-defense classes. Characters master elementary methods of attack and self defense. ALL bonuses are accumulative.

Hand to Hand Basic Skill Levels
Level 1 Automatic parry and dodge
   2 +2 to parry/dodge
   3 +One additional attack per melee
   4 +1 to strike
   5 +2 to damage
   6 Kick attack does 1-6 damage
   7 +One additional attack per melee
   8 Critical strike from behind
   9 +2 to parry/dodge
   10 +1 to strike
   11 Critical damage on a roll of 19-20
   12 +One additional attack per melee
   13 +2 to damage
   14 +1 to parry/dodge
   15 +1 to strike

Hand to Hand: Expert: An advanced form of self-defense and fighting techniques taught to commandos and special forces. ALL bonuses are accumulative.

Hand to Hand Expert Skill Levels
Level 1 +2 on automatic parry/dodge
   2 +One additional attack per melee
   3 +2 to strike
   4 +2 to damage
   5 +One additional attack per melee
   6 Kick attack does 1-6 damage
   7 Critical strike on a roll of 19-20
   8 +1 to parry/dodge
   9 +One additional attack per melee
   10 +1 to strike
   11 Knock-out/Stun on a roll of 19-20
   12 Critical strike from behind
   13 +2 to damage
   14 +One additional attack per melee
   15 Death blow on a roll of a natural 20

Hand to Hand: Martial Arts: This is a form of ancient Oriental fighting skills such as karate, kung-fu, etc. that teaches advanced hand to hand combat. ALL bonuses are accumulative. NOTE: This skill is available **only** to the Commando O.C.C. as an alternative to Hand to Hand: Expert.

Hand to Hand Martial Arts Skill Levels
Level 1 +3 on automatic parry/dodge
   2 +One additional attack per melee
   3 +1 to strike
   4 Kick attack does 1-8 damage
   5 Body throw/flip does 1-6 damage, victim loses initiative and one attack.
   6 +One additional attack per melee
   7 Karate punch does 1-6 damage
   8 +2 to damage
   9 +One additional attack per melee

10 Critical strike on a roll of 19-20
11 +2 to strike
12 +2 to parry/dodge
13 Critical strike from behind
14 +1 to strike
15 Death blow on a roll of natural 20

Investigation: This is the training in the techniques, principles and theories of investigation, such as how to look for and recognize clues by systematically examining details with care and accuracy. Investigative techniques can be applied to environments, events, the spoken word and body language. A character with the investigation skill is more likely to notice and remember details, locate hidden compartments, locate bugging or other surveillance devices, and recognize inconsistencies (lies) during an interrogation. **Base Skill** is 30%+5% per level of experience.

Locksmith: The practiced study of lock designs, and ability to repair, build, modify and "open" locks. The methods, techniques and tools of lock picking include the old style key and tumbler, combination, and modern electronic locking systems. Time Requirements: 1-4 melees to open an antiquated key type lock; 1-6 minutes to open an elaborate tumbler type; 2-16 minutes to open a simple electronic lock (usually by patching in a by-pass system); and 1-6 hours to break a complex, state of the art electronic lock system such as those used in high security and restricted areas. NOTE: Generally Mechanoid lock systems are the simple electronic type (if any) but are built underneath wall panels and are normally activated by psionic telekinesis. This means that the Locksmith must first locate the lock mechanism and then carefully cut away that portion of the wall plate. Add 4 to 12 minutes using a laser lance or fusion torch.

If an unsuccessful skill roll is made the lock is not opened and the process must be repeated. If an attempt to open an electronic lock fails, roll to see if the lock has been irreparably damaged, 32% chance. If damaged, the lock CANNOT be opened. **Base Skill** is 25%+5% per level of experience. Special Bonus: Add a one time bonus of 5% if the Electronics Skill is also taken.

Mechanical Engineering: A training, understanding and knowledge of how machinery is designed, operated, built and maintained. Characters can attempt to redesign, modify, sabotage, repair or construct mechanical devices. The first percentage is how to operate/analyze/design machinery; the second is how to repair, construct or sabotage. **Base Skill** is 25% design, 20% repair/construct +5% (for both) per level of experience. Special Bonus: Add 10% to A.V. and/or G.V. Mechanics skills, +5% to Locksmith skill and 5% to Surveillance Systems skill.

Medical: First Aid: Rudimentary medical treatment which includes how to bandage wounds, stop bleeding, administer C.P.R./artificial respiration and use antiseptics and common anti-inflammatory drugs and pain killers. **Base Skill** is 60%+8% per level. A failed roll means the patient has not responded to treatment or that treatment was improperly applied.

Medical: Paramedic: An advanced form of medical emergency treatment which includes all first aid techniques, the setting of broken bones, suturing of wounds, use of oxygen and emergency equipment, use of drugs, knowledge of how to move a critically injured person and other life saving techniques. **Base Skill** is 50%+8% per level of experience. A failed roll means the patient has not responded to treatment or that the treatment has been improperly administered. NOTE: For serious injury or coma roll three times consecutively on percentile dice. A roll of two successful out of three means the wound has been properly treated or the patient's condition is stabilized. Failure means the patient's condition is unchanged. Another character can immediately attempt to apply medical aid or the same player can try again, but only after he or she has spent six minutes of examination and/or concentration.

THIS APPLIES ONLY TO SERIOUS INJURY!

P.A.V./Pilot Air Vehicle: This is extensive training in the understanding, operation and basic maintenance of most conventional air vehicles. Included are all conventional hover flying vehicles, hover jet fighters and orbital shuttles. The flying guns and hover tank require special training. NOTE: the skill in sensory equipment is a mandatory prerequisite. **Base Skill** is 35%+10% per level of experience; it indicates the character's overall understanding and flying skill. Players must roll under their P.A.V. skill each time a special maneuver is executed.

P.A.V. Special Maneuvers: Conditions and Penalties:

Evasive Action: Fleeing or dodging another aircraft, obstacle, missile or other attack by moving out of the way. All attacks are lost while engaged in evasive action unless something suddenly flies directly in front of the vehicle, even then the pilot is -4 to strike. NOTE: This tactic will lose any attacker(s), meaning they cannot attack unless the attacker(s) engage in a "dog tail" chase. Skill Penalty: -12% (no attack possible). Maneuver consumes one full melee. A **failed roll** means an ineffective evasive maneuver, attacker(s) still in strike position and/or have struck. The player's attacks are still forfeit from a failed evasive action.

Tilt Dodge: This is a difficult maneuver in which the pilot attempts to avoid an attack by quickly tilting or jerking out of the way at the last minute. In this way the pilot can stay on course and continue his own attacks (if any). Skill Penalty: -35%; -2 to strike. A **failed roll** means no dodge, aircraft is hit and takes full damage. A tilt dodge can be used to attempt to avoid each individual attack. A tilt dodge can not avoid more than one blast from a multiple/simultaneous assault; evasive action is necessary.

Stunts: These are sudden, severe or highly difficult maneuvers including dives, sharp turns, dead man's drop (nearly straight down, high speed drop), tumble, summersault and similar actions. Skill Penalty: -30%; lose attacks that melee. A **failed roll** means the stunt is incomplete and serious difficulties encountered. Roll percentile dice on the following table.

1-40 Engine chokes, stalled out and descending, must make an emergency landing unless the vehicle can be restarted (P.A.V. skill -25%; can try once every melee). All attacks are defensive only, -4 to strike.
41-70 Stunt maneuver botched speed and altitude, reduce by 1/3.
71-88 Engine difficulties, forced to make an emergency landing. Repairs will require 4-24 hours.
89-00 Engine and/or vehicle damaged beyond repair, crash inevitable. Character must parachute to safety. Optional: Can direct vehicle on a suicide crash into an immediate target; P.A.V. skill -20% to strike.

Emergency Landing: Executed when the vehicle or pilot is damaged and flight can not be maintained. Skill Penalty -30%; loses all attacks. A **failed roll** will result in a crash landing. Roll on the following table for Crash Landing:

1-31 Pilot and/or passengers survive, minor injury.
32-57 Crash; pilot and passengers take 5D6 damage.
58-80 Pilot and passengers in critical condition/coma, require immediate, extensive medical treatment. Treat as surviving death and coma.
81-83 No survivors, vehicle exploded.
84-00 Passengers survive with minor injury, pilot dead. Optional: Pilot can opt to parachute to safety rather than attempting a landing.

Shadow: Is a maneuver in which the air vehicle pursues another vehicle without detection. This is usually done by flying above and behind the pursued using clouds as cover. The pursuer will mimic the vehicle pursued in every way so that they will be thought to be a radar shadow or aberration. Skill Penalty: -20%; no attacks possible without revealing true position and nature. While imitating the evasive actions, stunts, and so on of the craft being shadowed roll for each maneuver being copied.

Dog Tail: This is an offensive maneuver in which the pilot closely pursues an enemy air vehicle while locked in combat. This is the only maneuver that can pursue a vehicle taking evasive action. By hanging on the enemy's tail or "dog tailing", the attacker can usually strike with little or no fear of counter attack. This is particularly true of jets and flying guns. **Skill Penalty:** -15%; No strike penalty. A **failed roll** means the target has momentarily slipped out of the striking range/area. Roll once every other melee to maintain dog tail position or for every evasive or stunt action.

P.F.G./Pilot Flying Gun: This is extensive training and understanding in the use and operation of the one-man hover weapon known as the flying gun. This includes all types and variations of the weapon. Because of the specialized nature of the flying gun the conventional P.A.V. skill does not apply; nor does the P.F.G. skill provide sufficient knowledge to pilot any other air vehicle. **Base Skill** is 30% +8% per level of experience.

P.F.G. Special Maneuvers: Conditions and Penalties:
NOTE: All the usual P.A.V. maneuvers apply although limited by the flying gun's size, speed. The flying gun is designed for extremely low altitude combat and maneuverability. SEE P.A.V. For The Actual Maneuver Descriptions.
Evasive Action: Skill Penalty: -10%; no attacks possible.
Tilt Dodge: Skill Penalty: -15%; no strike penalty.
Stunts: Skill Penalty: -12%; lose one attack that melee.
Emergency Landing: Strike Penalty: -20%; lose all attacks. Parachuting to safety not possible. Roll on the following crash landing table if the emergency landing is unsuccessful.

1-10 Pilot survives with minor damage (1D6).
11-17 No survivors.
18-36 Pilot thrown from vehicle takes 3D6 damage from crash; subtract from hit points.
37-50 Pilot thrown from vehicle takes 2D6 damage from crash; subtract from hit points.
51-79 Pilot in critical condition/coma; requires immediate extensive medical treatment.
80-95 No survivors.
96-00 Thrown clear, no damage.
Shadow: Skill Penalty: -20%
Dog Tail: Skill Penalty: -12%; no strike penalty.

P.G.V./Pilot Ground Vehicle: this skill applies to all conventional wheeled vehicles. Characters have an in depth understanding of all the vehicles' operation and basic maintenance. **Base Skill** is 45%+10% per level of experience. NOTE: Sensory equipment skill is NOT required but is a beneficial skill for use of built in radar and such. Without the sensory skill, built in sensory equipment can not be used.
P.G.V. Special Maneuvers: Conditions and Penalties:
Evasive Action: Fleeing or dodging another vehicle, obstacle, missile or some other attack by moving out of the way. Evasive action often involves weaving, zig-zagging and sudden turns at high speeds. A successful roll means the pilot has successfully dodged out of the way. **Skill Penalty:** -15%; pilot/driver cannot attack, passengers are -6 to strike in an attack. A **failed roll** means an ineffective evasive maneuver which in turn means the vehicle has been struck, blasted and/or the attacker is still hot on his tracks. THREE CONSECUTIVE successful evasion rolls mean the pilot has completely lost the pursuer.
Reverse Driving: This is simply driving in reverse/backward. **Skill Penalty:** -25% if driving over 60kmph and roll for each turn, swerve or evasive action. Pilot cannot attack, but passengers are only -2 to strike. A **failed roll** means a minor collision.
Stunts: Include sharp turns at high speeds, sudden-on-the-dime-stops, sudden U-turns at high speeds, propelled leap (such as riding up over an incline or object, sailing 20ft in the air, land and keep on going) and similar maneuvers. **Skill Penalty:** -25%; lose all attacks that melee. A failed roll means the stunt is incomplete and serious difficulties encountered. Roll on the following table:

Loss of Control (Stunt and Side Swipe)
1-38 Minor collision; momentarily stopped; reduce vehicle's S.D.C. by 1/3; occupants shaken, but okay.
39-59 Stunt maneuver botched, reduce speed by half.
60-80 Engine or structural problems develop requiring pilot to pull over and stop. Vehicle needs 2-12 hours of repairs.
81-97 Collision; vehicle is totalled, pilot and occupants receive 3D6 damage (subtract from hit points).
98-00 Collision/crash, all killed.

Sharp Curves: 90 degrees, high speed. Skill Penalty: -10%.
Side Swipe: This maneuver can be used against a stationary object, moving vehicle or person. The purpose of a side swipe is to strike another vehicle, object or person a glancing blow with the body of your vehicle. To strike the swiping player rolls under his P.G.V. skill minus the 20% skill penalty in attempting this dangerous maneuver. NOTE: The target, if controlled by another person, can attempt to dodge via "evasive action" or "stunt" driving. **Skill Penalty:** -20%; no other attack possible. A **failed roll** to side swipe means an automatic miss and the player must roll under his P.G.V. skill -20% to maintain control of the vehicle. If control is lost roll on the Loss of Control Table under stunts (P.G.V.). **Damage** from a side swipe does 2D6 for every 30 kilometers (20 miles) of speed. The side swipe also damages the vehicle which is equal to 1/3 the damage inflicted to the target. Thus, if the side swipe inflicted **24 points** of damage to the target it would also do **8 points** of damage to the vehicle.

P.P. Tank (Pilot Plasma Tank): This is complete training in the understanding, operation and maintenance of the hover tank and its plasma cannon and particle beam turret. NOTE: Anybody with a P.A.V. skill "may" be able to figure out how to fly the plasma tank, but the likelihood of doing so is their P.A.V. skill -40%. Likewise ALL maneuvers are -40% as the movement and response of the plasma tank is unlike any of the much faster and mobile air vehicles. In many respects the plasma tank is more of a ground vehicle than an air vehicle. **Base Skill** is 32%+6% per level of experience; it indicates the character's overall understanding and tank piloting expertise. Players must roll under their P.P. Tank skill each time a special maneuver is expected. Use the same tables as listed under P.G.V.

Pick Pockets: An ability to remove items from a person without their being aware of it. If a pick pocket attempt fails, the item has NOT been removed and there is a 67% likelihood of the intended victim recognizing the intent of the action. **Base Skill** is 30%+5% per level of experience.

Prowl: The practiced ability to move with silence and stealth to avoid human detection. The character uses shadows and objects to cover his movements. A failed prowl roll means that the character has been seen or heard.

NOTE: Prowling cannot avoid detection by sensory detection devices and alarms. **Base Skill** is 40%+5% per level of experience.

Sensory Equipment: Individuals with this training can maintain, understand, operate and "read" or interpret sensory data from all types of conventional sensor devices. These devices include radar, sonar, motion detectors, surveillance equipment, optical enhancement, instrument panels and so on. **Base Skill** is 25%+5% per level of experience. NOTE: Characters without a sensory skill cannot understand nor operate air vehicles, radar or detection/surveillance equipment.

Swimming: Basic: The rudimentary skill of keeping afloat, dives, life saving, and swimming techniques. **Base Skill** is 50%+8% per level of experience. The percentile number indicates the overall quality of form as skill of execution. A special bonus of +1 to parry and dodge while in water applies.

Swimming: S.C.U.B.A.: Individuals with S.C.U.B.A. training have mastered the rudimentaries of basic swimming and are able to swim underwater for prolonged periods through the use of underwater breathing apparatuses. S.C.U.B.A. divers are also trained in the use of other underwater equipment, weapons and swimming methods. **Basic Skill** is 40%+8% per level of experience. **Special bonus** of +2 to dodge or parry underwater.

Swimming: Deep Sea: This is expert training for deep sea exploration. Training includes the understanding, operation and maintenance of deep sea diving suits, E.B.A., weapons, submersibles and other underwater vehicles and equipment. Swimming: Deep Sea counts as TWO SKILLS. **Basic Skill** is 30%+6% per level of experience. **Special Bonus** of +1 to strike and +1 to parry or dodge applies when underwater. NOTE: Because of the special equipment and conditions of deep sea exploration this skill DOES NOT actually teach one how to swim. The best swimming this character can do is to stay afloat with minimal movement. Swimming basic may be desired.

Tracking (outdoors): This skill enables the character to identify tracks; estimate the number of creatures or vehicles, estimate their freshness and follow them. **Basic Skill** is 30%+6% per level of experience. Players must roll for each tracking intention, i.e. identifying the tracks is one roll, estimating their freshness another and following them a third roll. To follow tracks the player must roll once every 180 meters (600 feet). A failed roll means the trail is too confusing or the trail is lost. The character can try to regain his/her bearings by studying the area for no less than five minutes (roll again). A second failed roll means the tracker can not pursue the trail.

W.P. Explosives: Training in the use of explosives for demolition, excavation and as weapons. The character knows how to put together various detonators and explosives, set charges, use fusion blocks and deactivate explosives. **Base Skill** is 42%+8% per level of experience to set or use any explosive. A failed roll means the device is improperly set and does NOT explode. **Deactivating an Explosive** is the base skill -12%. **A failed roll** means one of the following . . . (roll percentile dice)

1-26 Device will explode in 60 seconds, it can not be disarmed.

27-60 The device will explode in 20 seconds, it can not be disarmed.

61-00 The device explodes without warning.

Weapon Proficiency (W.P.) A General Description: Characters trained in the use of a particular weapon type gain a certain degree of skill, marksmanship and understanding of that weapon type. This results in bonuses to strike. Players roll to strike for each "aimed" shot. Shooting wild forfeits all bonuses to strike.

W.P. Handguns: A weapon proficiency in all handguns, i.e. pistols, blasters and laser lance. **Skill Bonus** is +1 to strike at **first level** and +1 to strike for each subsequent three levels of experience. (+1 at level one, again at level four (+2), again at level seven (+3), ten (+4), and thirteen (+5).

W.P. Heavy Weapons: A weapon proficiency in all heavy weapons including the particle beam rifle, all plasma weapons, turrets/cannons and special or experimental weapons. **Skill Bonuses** are +1 to strike at **level two**, again at **level four** (+2), again at **level seven** (+3), **level ten** (+4) and **level thirteen** (+5).

W.P. Knife: A weapon proficiency in small blade weapons including all knives and short swords. **Skill Bonuses** are +1 to strike at **level one**, +2 to parry at **level three**, +1 to strike (+2 total) at **level four**, +1 to strike when "thrown" at **level five**, +1 to parry (+3 total) at **level eight**, +1 to strike (+3 total) at **level ten**, and +1 (+2 total) to strike when thrown at **level thirteen**.

W.P. Laser Rifle: A weapon proficiency in the use of the laser rifle. **Skill Bonuses** are +1 to strike at **level one**, +1 to strike (+2 total) at **level three**, +1 to strike at **level five** (+3 total), +1 to strike at **level eight** (+4 total), +1 to strike at **level eleven** (+5 total) and +1 to strike at **level fourteen** (+6 total).

The Rovers

The humanoids known as Rovers, were discovered by the original Gideon Expedition. Historically the Rovers have always been hostile toward the colonies allowing only the most superficial relations to be established. These relations usually involved trade of goods for information or treaties of nonaggression.

Rovers are an arrogant people steeped in superstition, tribal ritual, and mysticism. The mysticism is rooted in psionic abilities which are much more pronounced and developed than most Earth Espers. It seems that "all" Rovers possess some degree of psionic powers.

The Rover society is tribal and tends to be nomadic in nature. The females are responsible for child rearing, preparation of food and clothes, and gathering of fruits and vegetables. They are also the holders of booty. The males are responsible for making weapons, hunting, protection of the tribe and gathering (stealing) other provisions such as tools and weapons.

In many ways the Rovers are a tribe of "thieves", stealing anything they need or desire from other tribes and the Earth colonies. However, to steal from a member of the same tribe is punishable by death or exile from the tribe. Although males are particularly adept in the arts of thievery, children and females are also skilled in this area. Rovers have the added advantages of being both psionic and ambidextrous.

As part of thieving philosophy, Rovers seldom kill their victims. The concept here is that if you kill an easy mark, that victim can never be victimized again, but if allowed to live, that person can be continually plundered. Or in the words of a Rover; "You can only steal from a dead man once."

This practice holds true even in tribal battles during which hundreds will be wounded and many captured, but only a few dozen are severely injured or slain. Rovers love to capture and ransom people, especially colonists. A typical ransom for a colonist includes: handguns, laser rifles, clothes and candy.

Unfortunately, because of the defoliation of Gideon-E, most animal life and virtually "all plant life" has been destroyed. This presents a critical situation for the Rover tribes. With the exception of the Long Teeth and Sand Pirates, Rover tribes reject most colonial aid (although they will gladly pillage and steal from an unsuspecting supply vehicle). To compound the situation tribal hostility has intensified and it is rumored that some tribes have taken to cannibalism.

Another Aspect Of The Rovers

Perhaps the startling fact about this primitive people is that they are not native to Gideon-E. How they came to this planet is as much a mystery as how long they've lived here. The Rovers have no recollection of any life other than their current tribal ways.

Physiologically the Rovers are among the few known extraterrestrial life forms similar to humans. Of course there are several physical distinctions between the two races. Rovers tend to be very pale, almost stark white in complexion and have 87% less body hair than humans.

These lanky aliens seem accustomed to a lighter atmospheric pressure than that of Gideon-E, which is slightly greater than the Earth's. Consequently, they are often seen slightly hunched and prone to a slower pace of activity interrupted by frequent rests throughout the day. Unlike humans, the Rovers are accustomed to a much lower oxygen atmosphere, acclimating themselves to the high carbon dioxide content quite easily.

The Shaman

Those with the greatest psionic abilities attain high positions within the tribe such as the Shaman or a member of the high circle.

With the exception of the high circle, the Shaman is the single most powerful member of the tribe. His powers are sacred and revered by all. To defy the Shaman is to flirt with death. He is usually surrounded by fanatical acolytes and priests. However, this fanatical devotion to the Shaman is not limited to his devotees. Members of the tribe will gladly lay down their own life at the command of the Shaman.

The Shaman's psionic abilities are easily as extensive as any of the Earth's known Espers. The Black Fist tribe's Shaman is unique in that she is the only female to hold this male dominated position. She is reputed to be a great prophet, allegedly foreseeing the Mechanoid Invasion and defoliation of the planet. This would explain the sudden theft of air filters and other breathing equipment two months before the actual Mechanoid assault.

The High Circle

The high circle is the decision making body of the tribe composed of the wisest and strongest members of the tribe. The head of the high circle is the leader/chieftain of the tribe (often the Shaman) enforcing tribal laws, directing raids, etc.. Subordinate tribe members are expected to accept and obey any decision the circle may invoke. Failure to do so may result in public chastisement, torture, expulsion from the tribe or even death.

Rovers, Humans and Technology

The Rovers are generally a very easy going race, rarely striving for power, greatness or vast wealth. This is reflected in their nonchalant, cavalier attitudes toward hard physical labor and studying or perfecting a skill. In part, the heavy gravity (heavy for rovers) and abrasive atmosphere of Gideon-E are responsible for these nomads' slow and casual pace; while the rest is simply part of the rovers' nature. This is ironic because the rovers are equally as intelligent as any human. Furthermore, they are incredibly fast learners when they find something which intrigues them. Aided by psionic abilities such as object read, speed reading, total recall, telepathy and other psi-powers magnifies their ability to learn and comprehend new ideas far beyond normal humans. A curious rover can master the rudimentaries of almost anything in a third of the time it would take a human. However, few will take that knowledge beyond his or her immediate needs or desires.

Rovers are especially intrigued by the attractive, time and labor saving, high-technology devices of the colonies. The Mechanoid's invasion has suddenly made previously limited human contact and colony access common, enabling them to acquire a vast amount of knowledge and technology. Thus, rovers now have a great variety of human skills and equipment. Many rovers are self taught and able pilots, mechanics and locksmiths. Most are knowledgeable enough to use any of the colonist's weapons and conventional vehicles. Favorite weapons include the LR-20 laser rifle, laser lance and all handguns. Favorite vehicles are the Rosenstein land buggy and hover scout.

Relations with Humans

Prior to the Mechanoids' arrival, only the Arrow Head, Long Teeth and Sand Pirates dealt with the human colonists on any kind of friendly or regular basis. The Mechanoids' destruction of the environment has turned the rovers world upside down. Some tribes, like the Black Fist, believe the humans are responsible for the mechanoids coming and therefore responsible for the annihilation of their world. This has created much resentment and suspicion. The colonists' old rover allies which include the Arrow Head, Long Teeth and Sand Pirates have become even closer allies; trading information, working as scouts and fighting side by side with humans against the Mechanoid menace. Still others, such as the Red and the Black Band tribes view all this with confusion and resentment. They see their old tribal enemies joining with the humans which makes the colonists an enemy tribe too. Rejecting the colonists' aid and shelter has doomed them.

Traditional Weapons

The rovers' traditional weapons are antiquated by human standards. The following is a complete list of weapons with range and damage indicated. Rovers are too lazy to develop any superior weapon skills in combat. Their natural speed and physical prowess tends to make up for any lack of practiced skill. NOTE: Most are ineffective against the Mechanoids or heavily armored humans. The weapons listed do NO damage to Mechanoids.

Knives: Small, hand held blade weapon usually made out of stone, unless it's stolen from the humans which is common. Damage: 1-6 points damage.

War Club: Usually stone and wood; measures approximately .9 meters (3 to 4ft). Damage: 1-8 points damage.

Throwing Sticks: Hard wood sticks, shaped and weighted for balance and throwing. Measure .3 to .6 meters (1 to 2½ft long). Damage: 1-6 points damage. Range: 60 meters (165ft) thrown. NOTE: Throwing sticks are very common among the rovers. Typically six to a dozen will hang at the waist.

Spear: Wood or wood and stone construction. Measures approximately 2 meters (7 to 8ft) long. Damage: 1-6 points damage. Range: 40 meters (135ft) when thrown.

Cross Bow: Wood construction. Damage: 2-12 points damage (2D6). Range: 90 meters (300ft). Rate of Fire: Two per melee at first level, add one for every other level of experience. Example: Third level rover thief can fire three cross bow bolts per melee; at fifth level, four shots per melee and so on.

Energy Weapons

The rovers are enthralled with human weapons, particularly lasers. Warriors have become especially adept in the use of energy weapons. Favorite high-tech weapons among rover espers and thieves are steel knives, laser lance, fusion torch, any handgun and the LR-20 laser rifle. Among warriors, the LP-10 laser pistol, LR-20 laser rifle and PBR-10 particle beam rifle are the most desired.

Rovers and Combat

Since ALL rovers are ambidextrous and agile, they all automatically have FOUR ATTACKS PER MELEE when engaged in hand to hand combat. A hand to hand combat skill will add to the number of attacks per melee. NOTE: The rover warrior also gets an automatic parry and dodge.

Energy weapons are NOT affected by a character's physical prowess, speed or attacks per melee in hand to hand combat. Each weapon is limited by each specific weapon's rate of fire and energy capacity. Some weapons, like the LP-10, can only fire twice per melee while the SB-14 can fire up to seven blasts per melee. The player must decide whether he or she wants to use a multiple hand to hand assault or a more lethal energy attack with a hand held weapon.

Psionics

ALL rovers have some type of psionic abilities even if they are limited to minor psionics (level one abilities only). Except for the determination of psionics; minor, major or master; the psionic powers are the same as those described in the "Psionics" section elsewhere. Likewise, the determination of specific psionic abilities also remains the same as those explained in the "Psionics" section.

To determine the degree of psionics possessed by a rover, roll percentile dice on the following table:
1-75 Minor Psionics
76-90 Major Psionics
91-00 Master Psionics

THE ROVER TRIBES

All rovers are nomads. Although common to the lands that surround Old Gideon, Kucharski and New Gideon, their wandering may take them as far as the Falzon colony in the north and Stelvenson to the north-west. Typical of no-mads, the society is loose knit and self styled. The main tribe group, with its acknowledged leader, shaman and elders, will comprise 40 to 50 percent of the overall peo-ple. The remainder compose a sort of tribal network of much smaller, much more mobile groups, usually family clans. These small groups will range in size anywhere from two dozen to three or four hundred members. It is among the smaller clans that most inter-tribal confrontations occur. For example, a group of a hundred Long Teeth rovers may wander into an area currently dominated by a Black Fist tribe twice their size. Bullying and intimida-tion tactics will be employed by both groups until one backs down and moves on or an actual battle or raid en-sues. Word of the conflict is passed on by word of mouth to each fellow tribesmen (never to another tribe) per-petuating the rivalry and animosity between the various tribes.

Rovers always treat rival tribesmen with disdain and contempt. Insults, put-downs, cat-calls, cruel practical jokes, theft and brawls almost always occur when members of two rival tribes meet. Fortunately, these incidents are usually childish shouting matches or humiliating pranks or brawls rather than deadly serious combat. Sadly, the Mech-anoids' defoliation of Gideon-E has destroyed the rovers' world. This, in turn, has led to greatly escalated hostility and the use of deadly force among the once child-like rovers.

The Talon

The most enigmatic of all the tribes, it is believed that they were a mutant or racial variant of the rovers. The Talon were a foot taller, broader built, had consider-ably more body hair and exhibited even greater psionic abilities than the typical rover, most seemed to be major psionics of esper class. Not a single member of the Talon tribe has been seen since the Mechanoids began their as-sault. The Talon are presumed to be dead or hiding in their secret mountain refuges.

The Red Band and Black Band Tribes

The Red Band and Black Band tribes have always worked together while excluding all others, including the human colonists. Even after the Mechanoids' destruction, the two tribes, hard hit by starvation and disease, refused all aid offered by the colonists. In part, this is because the colonists are viewed as an enemy tribe specifically be-cause they are friends with the Arrow Head and Long Teeth tribes, both of which are ancient enemies of the

Red Band and Black Band tribes. These circumstances would inadvertently doom the two tribes. The megalo-maniac, Long Teeth shaman, Tlepitama, siezed this op-portunity to, at last, slay his enemies. The Red Band and Black Band tribes were slaughtered by the Long Teeth who in addition to superior numbers, were armed with a multi-tude of the colonists' weapons, vehicles and equipment gotten through trade or as support in their own battle to survive the Mechanoids' invasion. Before the humans could put a stop to the battle, the massacre was over.

Currently, only a handful of survivors remain, under one thousand. Now they are continually stalked by the cannibalistic Arrow Head tribes. Understandably, the sur-vivors of the Red Band and Black Band tribes are con-vinced that the humans are their enemies and view all humans and their allies as their sworn "blood" enemies. All communications with the remaining tribesmen have broken down completely, while raids and guerrilla type assaults against humans have increased dramatically. The once independent rovers of the Red Band and Black Band tribes have become killers crazed by revenge.

The Sand Pirates

This unassuming tribe still limits its sphere of in-fluence to the arid vastness of the Muzkie dessert. Con-sidered neutral agents by the other rover tribes, they have adapted to their plight by increasing their already impres-sive merchant trade. Always considered the "merchants" of rovers, Sand Pirates will trade, steal or bargain for anything. Renowned as the most skilled and brazen thieves of any rover tribe, they are denied access to all human colonies and outposts. However, they have still made an incredible living acting as liaisons between the different tribes and the humans, as scouts, robbers and stripping the dead.

They are so clever that they have a fleet of Rosen-stein land buggies (approximately 60) and an impressive supply of human weapons and equipment. Favorite weapons include the LR-20 laser rifle, laser lance, fusion torch, spike launch rod and the traditional cross bow and throw-ing sticks. They also wear padded or soft leather armor or L.B.A. or E.B.A. under their flowing robes.

Unfortunately, the Sand Pirates' refusal to actually work with the humans, rather than simply plunder them, will ultimately be their demise. Estimated numbers of tribe: 1200

The Long Teeth

The Long Teeth are a typical tribe of rovers whose only real distinction is that it's the second largest tribe and led by two charismatic and powerful men. Prior to the Mechanoids' arrival, the tribes' policy toward humans was a sort of cautious, but friendly, aloofness. However, with the generosity and sincere kindness extended to them, they

have accepted the humans as a "friendly" tribe. This relationship has been further cemented by what the Long Teeth perceive as aid, by providing high-tech weapons and equipment, to destroy their enemies, the Red Band and Black Band tribes. The power hungry Shaman, Tlepitama, looks upon their allegiance with the humans as a tactical advantage over the other tribes. This has added to the unrest between the colonists and the Black Fist tribe, especially since the attack on the Red Band and Black Band tribes. Estimated numbers of tribe: 8600.

Maylrick; the Long Teeth Chieftain
12th Level Thief; Self Styled Warrior

Alignment: Unprincipled
Attributes: I.Q. 12, M.E. 16, M.A. 12, P.S. 18, P.P. 22, P.E. 14, P.B. 11, Spd. 16
Age: 30 **Male** **Weight:** 90kg (200lbs)
Height: 2.2m (7ft 8in) **Hit Points:** 58
Disposition: Bold, confident, rippling with energy and charisma. A skilled thief and warrior who's keenly aware of his strengths and weaknesses. Hates and distrusts the Shaman.
Psionics: Master (non-esper class) **I.S.P.:** 146
Abilities: Aura of truth, object read, sense good or evil, meditation trance, bio-regeneration, empathy, limited telepathy, resist fire, bio-manipulation, see the invisible, turn invisible, total recall and ALL extra-ordinary psionic powers except astral projection.
Skills: Prowl 98%, Climbing 98%, P.G.V. 98%, G.V. Mechanics 98%, Pick Pockets 98%, Swimming: Basic 98%, W.P. Knife, W.P. Handgun, W.P. Laser Rifle (the latter W.P.'s are at 8th level proficiency) and Hand to Hand: Basic (sixth level).
Attacks Per Melee: Five; +5 to damage, +4 to strike, +6 to parry and dodge.

Special Equipment:
Steel Knives (2), steel hand axe (1), steel machete (1), LP-10 laser pistol with four extra E-clips, LR-20 laser rifle with six extra charges, laser lance, infra-red distancing binoculars, wrist watch, and a suit of L.B.A. (only 60 S.D.C. for it is somewhat damaged). Maylrick is also skilled in the use of throwing sticks, war clubs and cross bows.

NOTES: Chief Maylrick and the Shaman hate each other. The young chieftain recognizes the scheming Shaman for the conniving and treacherous manipulator that he is. Thus, Maylrick keeps a constant vigil over the deceptive Shaman often thwarting his plans. Fortunately, the young chieftain is so popular among the people that the envious Tlepitama dares not harm him, for even the slightest hint of his involvement in such treachery would spell his own demise at the hands of his own tribesmen.

Tlepitama, the Shaman
10th Level Esper
6th Level Thief
Long Teeth Tribesman

Alignment: Miscreant
Attributes: I.Q. 15, M.E. 18, M.A. 12, P.S. 13, P.P. 14 P.E. 13, P.B. 10, Spd. 14
Age: 61 **Male** **Weight:** 90kg (200lbs)
Height: 2m (7ft) **Hit Points:** 73
Disposition: Cruel, clever, cunning, megalomaniac; a schemer and bully who knows how to use fear and intimidation like a finely crafted weapon. Hates the young chieftain Maylrick.
Psionics: Master (Esper) **I.S.P.:** 153
Abilities: ALL
Skills: Prowl 98%, Climbing 98%, P.G.V. 98%, P.A.V. 98%, Pick Pockets 98%, Swimming: Basic 98%, W.P. Knife, W.P. Handgun, W.P. Laser Rifle (all W.P.'s at 6th level), Audio Communication 88%, Sensory Equipment 84%.
Attacks Per Melee: Four; +2 to save vs. psionic attack.
NOTES: Tlepitama is an evil man corrupted by power. He longs to be the Long Teeths' sole leader, but dares not harm the beloved Maylrick. Still he plans and schemes, and patiently waits for an opportunity in which he can destroy the stalwart chief without implicating himself. The assault

on the Red Band and Black Band tribes was Tlepitama's doing, taking advantage of Maylrick's absence during a meeting with the colonists. It was the chieftain's early return that prevented the two tribes' total obliteration. An event which only fueled the fires of hate and malcontent between these two men. Yet, despite Tlepitama's lust for power, he is not so obsessed as to risk losing everything he has. For the moment, he is the number two man in the tribe; it's a position that must do for the time being while he waits and watches for an opportunity to become the number one man.

The Shaman views the humans as useful pawns; powerful, intelligent but weak and far too trusting. The Mechanoids are seen as destroyers, the ultimate enemy to all life. Tlepitama would never consider joining forces with the Mechanoids, no matter how alluring the proposition may be.

Special Equipment:
PBR-10 particle beam rifle with one extra E-clip, IB-14 ion blaster with two extra E-clips, steel knife, binoculars and a web vest. He also has his own hover scout. The Shaman usually has two, loyal, second level (major psionic) Espers at his side as body guards.

The Arrow Head Tribe

Although they have resorted to cannibalism of other rover tribes, they are still the most loyal and friendly allies of the human colonists. As stalwart human allies they have accepted the Long Teeth and Sand Pirates as friendly tribes because they too are human allies. Since the Long Teeth's devastating assault on the Red Band and Black Band tribes the survivors of these two tribes have become the Arrow Head's main target (food) for hunting. Tribal hatred has always run deep against the Red Band and Black Band tribes as well as the Black Fist and Talon (believed to be extinct).

The Arrow Head are the most nomadic of all the rover tribes. Small and large groups can be found almost everywhere within a thousand kilometer radius around the "Old Gideon" colony. Their aloofness towards humans has given way to an enthusiastic friendship which has resulted from the humans sincere attempts to protect and aid them. These strong feelings of camaraderie are largely the result of Ubar-Que, the Arrow Head's warrior chieftain.

Ubar-Que is an honest, fairly mild mannered person. He is a great warrior, but of little vision and not a very dynamic leader. However, he is greatly respected by his people as a fair and honorable leader, tactician and a warrior without peer.

Ubar-Que, Arrow Head Chieftain
9th Level Warrior
Alignment: Scrupulous
Attributes: I.Q. 10, M.E. 12, M.A. 10, P.S. 16, P.P. 19, P.E. 15, P.B. 9, Spd. 17.
Age: 36 Male **Height:** 2m (7ft tall) **Weight:** 97kg (217lbs)
Hit Points: 56
Disposition: Easy going, clever tactician, somewhat overconfident.
Psionics: Major (non-esper class) **I.S.P.:** 67
Abilities: Presence Sense, Sixth Sense, Bio-Regeneration, Mind Block, and Extended Telekinesis.
Skills: Hand to Hand: Basic (6 attacks per melee, +6 to parry and dodge, +3 to damage, +3 to strike), Prowl 98%, P.A.V. 98%, P.G.V. 98%, Track 98%, Swimming: Basic 98% W.P. Archery (+2 to strike with cross bow), W.P. Throwing Stick (+1 to strike), W.P. Heavy Weapon, W.P. Laser Rifle (both at 6th level proficiency).
Attacks Per Melee: Six; +3 to damage, +3 to strike, +6 to parry/dodge.
Special Equipment:
Steel knife, two fragmentary grenades, LP-10 laser pistol and eight extra E-clips, LR-20 laser rifle and nine extra E-clips, PBR-10 particle beam rifle with six extra E-clips, this weapon is his pride and joy, one full L.B.A. suit, and a hover scout.
NOTE: Ubar-Que is always accompanied by three to twelve trustworthy, 4th level warriors, two of which are his teenage sons; Niibar-Que and Gundar-Que (both are minor psionics). He is also often accompanied by one or two rover espers (major psionics).

Blood-Sand
10th Level Esper
Renegade Shaman and leader of a fanatic splinter group.
Alignment: Miscreant
Attributes: I.Q. 12, M.E. 18, M.A. 12, P.S. 11, P.P. 15, P.E. 12, P.B. 11, Spd. 19

Age: 54 Male **Height:** 2m (7ft 4in) **Weight:** 90kg (200lbs)
Hit Points: 49
Disposition: Cruel, tricky, cunning, a clever liar, excellent speaker. He is a cold-blooded fanatic bent on destroying humans and willing to do anything to achieve his goals, perhaps even ally himself with the Mechanoids.
Psionics: Master (Esper) **I.S.P.:** 127
Abilities: All level one, two and three psionics plus Empathic Transfer, Extended Telepathy, Float, Fuel Flame, Mind Control, Mind Wipe and Telemechanics.
Skills: Climbing 98%, Swimming: Basic 98%, Prowl 98%, Pick Pockets 98%, P.G.V. 98%, Computer Operation 98%, Sensory Equipment 83%, W.P. Laser Rifle (at 5th level proficiency). Speaks the human language fluently 89%.
Attacks Per Melee: Four; +1 to save vs. psionics.
Special Equipment:
Steel knives (2), LR-20 laser rifle with four extra E-clips, laser lance, IB-10 ion blaster with two extra E-clips, fusion torch (2), and a Rosenstein land buggy with extra fuel equal to two full tanks. Also uses a rover war-club and cross bow. In addition, Blood Sand has a long range, wide band radio that he uses to trap and mislead humans.
NOTES: Blood Sand is a cold blooded killer who hunts down human prey with a vengeance. Once a loyal member of the Arrow Head tribe, he was Ubar-Que's right hand man. Unfortunately, the Mechanoids' destruction of the rovers' world (defoliation and more) has driven Blood Sand quite mad. He actually believes the Black Fist tribes leader about the humans drawing the Mechanoids here, causing the ruination of all the rovers hold dear. Unlike the wise Black Fist leaders, Blood Sand has pledged revenge, unrelentlessly hunting his human prey. Although insane, he is much too clever to pit his men against the colonists in an out and out battle. Instead, he prefers to lure his unsuspecting humans to torture and slay slowly. He is a master of disguise and will often pretend to be a friendly Arrow Head, Long Teeth or Black Fist scout in order to lead humans into an ambush, or directly into a group of Mechanoids or some other peril. Blood Sand also uses a stolen, long range radio to trap and mislead his human foes.

Blood Sand is an incredibly dangerous being who wields great psionic powers. He is willing to do anything, lie, cheat, steal or kill, to destroy humanity. If necessary, he may even ally himself with the Mechanoids who will find this new pawn in their games most entertaining. He currently commands about 300 rovers who have joined him out of loyalty or fear. 2-12 new Arrow Head rovers join him on almost a daily basis.

The Black Fist

The largest, most organized tribe is the Black Fist. They are an aggressive, surprisingly well disciplined warrior tribe, led by the infamous female Shaman Li-Amba. It is under Li-Amba's guidance that the Black Fist have grown to become the most feared and war-like tribe rovers have ever seen. So bold are the Black Fist that they have successfully raided the colonies, capturing a variety of tools, weapons and equipment. The first of such raids took place at New Gideon two months before the Mechanoids' invasion. At the time, Li-Amba warned of "demons that will come from the heavens to devour our world. Demons whose spit will kill plant, beast, rover and human!" When none of the humans would believe her premonition she instructed her warriors to raid the colony storage stations, stealing only several thousand air filters, oxygen masks and a handful of vehicles to transport the goods. The entire Black Fist tribe then disappeared into the mountains. At the time, the humans were both puzzled and amused by the ridiculous theft. In retrospect, it is clear that Li-Amba foresaw the Mechanoids' invasion beginning with the global defoliation that would kill thousands of unprepared rovers and strangle most other life forms.

The Black Fist, always cold and defiant toward the colonists, have become even more distant for they believe that the humans are somehow responsible for the Mechanoids' arrival. However, Li-Amba realizes that her tribe's survival is intrinsically linked to the humans. Unfortunately the colonists' close association with their ancient tribal enemies the Arrow Head and especially, the Long Teeth have brutally impaired all lines of communication. Li-Amba suspects that the humans are not aware of the Long Teeth's ambitious, blood thirsty Shaman who has sent clear signals that he intends to crush the Black Fist. Until the Long Teeth Shaman is eliminated, or special action taken, the Black Fist will continue to fend for themselves. Up to this point they have successfully held their own against humans Long Teeth and Mechanoids alike.

Relations with humans continue to be cold, bitter, confused and cautious. Rumors of the Black Fist's collusion with the Mechanoids are completely false, instigated by Tlepitama the Long Teeth Shaman. Unfortunately, many paranoid humans believe the lies to be true. NOTE: The Black Fist would NEVER ally themselves to the Mechanoids which they regard as "blood" enemies.

The Black Fist's tribe Chieftain is an aging thief named Petri-Yag. He is actually a figurehead ruler who puts his full trust in his Shaman.

Petri-Yag, Black Fist Chieftain
15th Level Thief
Alignment: Unprincipled
Attributes: I.Q. 13, M.E. 11, M.A. 9, P.S. 9, P.P. 15, P.E. 10, P.B. 7, Spd. 10
Age: 78   Male   **Height:** 2m (7ft)   **Weight:** 80kg (160lb)
Hit Points: 63
Disposition: Complacent, cranky, alert; trusts Li-Amba completely.
Psionics: Minor (non-esper class)   **I.S.P.:** 88
Abilities: Aura of Truth, Detect Psionics, Presence Sense, Resist Fatigue and See Aura.
Skills: Prowl 98%, Climbing 98%, Pick Pockets 98%, Swimming: Basic 98%, P.G.V. 98%, W.P. Knife, W.P. Archery, W.P. Handgun.
NOTES: Aging, weary, but still partakes in the decision making for the tribe. However, he will follow any suggestions made by Li-Amba.

Li-Amba, Black Fist Shaman
8th Level Thief
Alignment: Unprincipled
Attributes: I.Q. 18, M.E. 14, M.A. 12, P.S. 10, P.P. 16, P.E. 12, P.B. 11, Spd. 16
Age: 29   Female   **Height:** 2m (7ft)   **Weight:** 85kg (170lb)
Hit Points: 44
Disposition: Brilliant, excellent tactician and strategist, bold, confident and dedicated to her people.
Psionics: Master (non-esper class)   **I.S.P.:** 93
Abilities: Detect Psionics, Hypnotic Suggestion, Object Read, Sixth Sense, Bio-Regeneration, Mind Block, Extended Telepathy, Precognition and Empathic Transfer.
Skills: Prowl 98%, Climbing 98%, Pick Pockets 98%, Locksmith 75%, Electronics 87/67%, P.G.V. 98%, Sensory Equipment 77%, Swimming: Basic 98%, W.P. Knife, W.P. Laser Rifle (5th level proficiency), Hand to Hand: Basic (3rd level proficiency).
Attacks Per Melee: Five; +1 to strike, +3 to parry/dodge.
Special Equipment:
Laser lance, SB-14 simple blaster with four extra E-clips, LR-20 laser rifle with six extra E-clips, infra-red distancing binoculars, web vest, Rosenstein land buggy and one Sandwolf Torpedo.
NOTES: Loved and respected by her people. A renowned clairvoyant. Looks upon humans with suspicion, despises the Mechanoids.

Summary Table of Rover Information

Tribe	Population	Humans	Enemies
Red Band	300	Hate	Long Teeth & Arrow Head
Black Band	700	Hate	Long Teeth & Arrow Head
Sand Pirates	1200	Neurtal	Red Band & Black Band
Long Teeth	8600	Very Friendly	Red Band, Black Band & Black Fist.
Black Fist	13,200	Hostile	Long Teeth & Arrow Head
Arrow Head	6,900	Very Friendly	Red Band, Black Band & Black Fist.
Talon		Believed to be extinct.	

Creating A Playing Character

Rather than playing one of the human characters, a player may opt to roll-up a rover character. Rovers have the physical advantage of generally higher physical prowess (P.P.) and the mental advantage of psionics. However, the rover character is limited ONLY to one of the three possible rover O.C.C.s, and limited skill knowledge and equipment.

A rover player character is likely to be considered a friendly "scout" and ally by the humans, but may be considered a traitor by other rovers. Don't forget the tribal rivalry and hatred between the different tribes.

The Eight Attributes

The number after the attribute indicates the number of six-sided dice that are rolled to determine that attribute.

The Eight Attributes	Psionics
I.Q. 3	(Roll percentile dice)
M.E. 3	1-75 Minor Psionics
M.A. 2	76-90 Major Psionics
P.S. 3	91-00 Master Psionics
P.P. 4	
P.E. 3	**Attacks Per Melee:** Four
P.B. 2	**Average Height:** 2m (7-8ft)
Spd. 4	**Average Weight:** 75kg (170lbs)

Alignment: Any, but usually Unprincipled or Anarchist or Miscreant (evil). Players should read the alignments section and choose one.

Tribal Origin

Players may select a tribe or make a random roll on the following table. Roll percentile dice.

1-18 Red Band
19-34 Black Band
35-58 Long Teeth
59-80 Arrow Head
81-00 Black Fist

Ability to Speak and Understand Human Language

Although rovers have no written language, they do have their own distinct spoken language. Roll percentile dice to determine the level of the rover's comprehension and ability to communicate in the humans' common language.

1-12 **Rudimentary understanding** (like a 3 or 4 year old child).
13-30 **Basic understanding** (good comprehension, broken speech).
31-50 **Good understanding** (good comprehension, easy communication).
51-75 **Perfect understanding** (excellent comprehension and command of the spoken word. Not literate).
76-00 **Perfect understanding and literacy** (can speak, read and write the human language equal to a high school student).

Rover Thief

ROVER THIEF O.C.C.

ALL rovers are thieves although the number of thieving skills and abilities may vary. Some may be more mechanically inclined while others may be more combat oriented; this is especially true of the Black Fist, Red Band and Black Band tribes. Still others may be more developed as Espers (See rover esper) All rovers are psionic.

Attribute Requirements: P.P. 11 (characters with a P.P. below 11 can still be thieves but suffer a skill penalty of -5% on ALL skills)

Psionics: Usually minor, but can be a major psi as well.

Major Areas of Expertise:

Prowl	+30%
Climbing	+20%
W.P. Knife	

Elective Skills: Choose four at level one, two at level three, one at level six and one at level nine.

Audio/Visual Communications	+10%
A.V. Mechanics	+5%
Computer Operation	+5%
Electronics	+5%
G.V. Mechanics	+10%
Hand to Hand: Basic	
Locksmith	+20%
Medical: First Aid	+6%
P.A.V. (Pilot Air Vehicle)	+10%
P.G.V. (Pilot Ground Vehicle)	+15%
P.F.G. (Pilot Flying Gun)	+10%
Pick Pockets	+20%
Sensory Equipment	+5%
Swimming: Basic	
W.P. Handgun	
W.P. Laser Rifle	

NOTE: Often use primitive weapons; See rover weapons and combat.

Combat and Weapons

Most rovers are trained in basic hand to hand combat and skilled in the use of knives, spears, bow and arrows, war club and throwing sticks (both blunt). The use of these primitive weapons are restricted to the number of attacks per melee and the specific weapon limitations (See rover combat and weapons). Rovers have also adopted the colonists' handguns and laser rifles (See W.P. skills)

Attacks Per Melee: Four; as always this applies only to hand to hand combat not energy weapons. ALL rovers are ambidextrous, thus the extra number of attacks.

Use of Battle Armor: Any, but rarely use stolen E.B.A.'s most common are treated leather, studded leather, web vest (stolen) and stolen L.B.A. The usual penalties apply if E.B.A. is worn (See commando).

Common Equipment:

Bow and Arrow
Knife (1 or 2)
Throwing Sticks (2 to 8)
Additional weapons are possible
Leather Armor
Baggy hooded garments
Water skin
Mini Tool pouch (usually stolen)

Stolen Equipment Commonly Used Include:

Laser Lance
Binoculars
Air Filters
Flash Light
Knife
Nylon Cord
Various Tools

Not as common, but coveted items include:

Handguns
Laser Rifle
Particle Beam Rifle (rare)
Web Vest
L.B.A.
Land Buggy
Hover Scout

Rover Scouts

The colonists often enlist the aid of friendly rovers as scouts or extra hands. This may result in the issuing of or payment in the equipment listed in the "Stolen Equipment" list. Paid at the job's completion.

Psionics: ALL rovers are psionic. Be certain you have determined the degree of that psionic power before you determine your O.C.C. A master psionic is automatically a rover esper. See rover information and psionics section.

Rover Warrior

ROVER WARRIOR O.C.C.

The rover warrior concentrates his or her attention on combat, weapons and lastly, thieving. They are usually excellent archers and masters with throwing sticks. NOTE: The W.P. skill of archery and throwing sticks is automatic providing a one time bonus to strike as listed. The other rover O.C.C.'s do not get any automatic weapon proficiences other than knife.

Attribute Requirements: P.S. 9; Psionics: Usually minor or possibly major.

Major Areas of Expertise:

Hand to Hand: Basic	
Prowl	20%
W.P. Archery (+2 to strike)	
W.P. Throwing Stick (+1 to strike)	

Elective Skills: Choose three at level one, two at level three, one at level six and one at level nine.

Audio/Visual Communication	
Climbing	+10%
Computer Operation	+5%
Locksmith	+10%
Medical: First Aid	+6%
P.A.V. (Pilot Air Vehicle)	+10%
P.G.V. (Pilot Ground Vehicle)	+10%
P.F.G. (Pilot Flying Gun)	+10%
Pick Pockets	+15%
Sensory Equipment	
Swimming: Basic	
Tracking (outdoors)	20%
W.P. Handgun	
W.P. Laser Rifle	
W.P. Heavy Weapons	
W.P. Knife	
W.P. Explosives	+10%

Combat and Weapons

All rover warriors have a basic hand to hand knowledge and are skilled in the use of knives, spears, war club throwing sticks, and the bow and arrow. They have also adopted the colonists' handguns, laser rifle and particle beam rifle, while rovers rarely use the much larger and bulkier plasma ejectors. The favorite of all the colonists' weapons is the LR-10 laser rifle because of its light weight and great range. Remember, **any** weapon can be used by **any** character of any O.C.C., however he/she will have no bonuses to strike unless skilled in that weapon type (W.P.).

Attacks Per Melee: Being ambidextrous, rovers have four attacks per melee in hand to hand combat. The number of attacks or blasts from an energy weapon is limited by the weapon itself.

Use of Battle Armor: the most common is treated leather, studded leather or a stolen web vest or L.B.A. Rovers rarely use E.B.A. because its bulk impairs their movement. Same penalties are noted under the Commando O.C.C.

Rover Scouts

Rovers will often trade their services as scouts or even a temporary soldier type in trade for the colonists' high-tech items. Most desired will be the laser rifle, laser pistol, binoculars and L.B.A.

Common and Stolen Equipment List:
Identical to the Rover Thief.

Rover Esper

THE ROVER ESPER O.C.C.

This Rover O.C.C. is nearly identical to the human colonists' Esper O.C.C. with the main difference in that there is no prejudice or preferential treatment because all rovers have some degree of psionics. Since rovers are generally nomads living off the land by gathering fruit, stalking small game and plundering other tribes, there is little social distinction from a minor psionic thief or warrior to a master psionic. Remember, ALL rovers, including the rover esper, are practiced thieves.

Attribute Requirements: Major or Minor Psionic.

Major Areas of Expertise:

Use of Psionic abilities.

Elective Skills: Choose five at level one, two at level three, one at level six and one at level nine.

Audio/Visual Communications	+10%
Climbing	+10%
Computer Operation	+10%
Hand to Hand: Basic	
Locksmith	+10%
Medical: First Aid	+6%
P.A.V. (Pilot Air Vehicle)	+8%
P.G.V. (Pilot Ground Vehicle)	+10%
Pick Pockets	+15%
Prowl	+15%
Sensory Equipment	+8%
Swimming: Basic	
W.P. Knife	
W.P. Handgun	
W.P. Laser Rifle	

Combat and Weapons
Same as rover thief O.C.C.

Common Equipment and Stolen Equipment
Same as rover thief O.C.C.

Rover Scout
Same as rover thief O.C.C.

Determining Psionics
See opening explanation about rovers and their psionic abilities. Also see psionic descriptions.

GUSTOVICH

34

Psionics

Players familiar with the original Mechanoid Invasion game will notice that psionics is one of the areas of major change. If you prefer the old rules, then stick with them. However, I think the psionics presented in this book offer even more opportunities in game play.

ALL players should roll percentile dice to determine if their character has any psionic abilities (as explained in the character creation section).

1-59 No psionic abilities
60-79 Minor Psionic (not considered an Esper)
80-89 Major Psionic (Esper material)
90-00 Master Psionic (Esper material)

DETERMINING PSIONIC ABILITIES

Minor Psionics are individuals with latent psionic potential, but do not have the strength or ability to develop their mind powers. Although these characters CANNOT become an Esper (choose a different O.C.C.), they still retain a limited number of psionic abilities. **Choose any FIVE abilities from level one psionics.** Minor psionics do not gain any new abilities as they grow in experience levels. However, their I.S.P. does increase with each new level of experience.

Determining Inner Strength Points (I.S.P.): Base I.S.P.: M.E. plus the roll of a 20 sided die (M.E.+1D20). Add the roll from a six-sided die (1D6) to the I.S.P. base for each level of experience.

Major Psionics (non-Esper) are individuals with great latent psionic abilities. If the character chooses NOT to develop his psionic powers by choosing an O.C.C. other than Esper, his or her abilities are severely restricted. **Choose any TWO abilities from Level one and Level two psionics.** There's also a 60% chance of possessing one extra-ordinary psi-power (1-60; roll percentile dice, one time only). If this is the case, roll again on the following table.

1-14 Mind Control
15-25 Create Force Field
26-39 Float
40-55 Fuel Flame
56-67 Extended Telekinesis
68-80 Pyrokinesis
81-90 Empathic Transfer
91-00 Telemechanics

Determining I.S.P. is identical to the minor psionic.

Major Psionics (Esper) are individuals who develop their full psionic powers under the O.C.C. of Esper. **Choose SIX level one psionic powers at first level; SIX second level psionic powers at second level and choose ONE extra-ordinary psionic power at third level.**

Determining Inner Strength Points (I.S.P) Base I.S.P.: M.E. plus the roll of a 20 sided die (M.E.+1D20). Add the roll from an eight-sided die (1D8) to the I.S.P. base for each level of experience. NOTE: although the major psionic can NEVER gain any additional abilities other than those previously stated, his I.S.P. increases with each level of experience as may the strength or duration of his psi-powers.

Master Psionics (non-Esper) are the most powerful of all natural psionics. Even the untrained master psionic has the following abilities. **Choose FOUR first level psi-powers at first level, choose TWO second level psi-powers at second level, TWO third level psi-powers at third level and ONE extra-ordinary psionic ability at fourth level.**

Determine Inner Strength Points (I.S.P.) the same as for Master Psionic Esper.

Master Psionic Esper O.C.C. characters have developed his/her psionic powers to their full potential. Psi-powers: All first level psionics at level one, all second level

powers at level two, all third level powers at level three, choose ONE extra-ordinary psi-power for each additional level of experience.

Determining Inner Strength Points (I.S.P.): Base I.S.P.: M.E. plus the roll of a 20 sided die (M.E.+1D20). Add ten I.S.P. points for each level of experience.

INNER STRENGTH POINTS (I.S.P.)

The use of each particular psionic ability requires concentration and will power, drawing upon the astral body or "inner strength" of the individual. Each specific psionic power will indicate exactly how many I.S.P. are required to perform that ability. When a psionic has exhausted all of his I.S.P. he is unable to perform anymore psionic feats until he has had sufficient rest.

The recovery of I.S.P. can be done in one of two ways: **total relaxation** and/or sleep, recovering I.S.P. at a rate of TWO I.S.P. for every hour; or through psionic meditation. **Meditation** is a psionic skill ability in which the psionic places himself in a simple hypnotic trance. This meditative trance provides maximum relaxation recovering THREE I.S.P. per every hour of relaxation.

SAVING THROWS AGAINST PSIONIC ATTACKS

There is always a chance of fighting off a psionic attack or probe through the force of one's own will and mental endurance. Psionic attacks that fall into this category include empathy, empathic transfer, mind wipe, mind control, telepathy, hypnotic suggestion and bio-manipulation. Some psionic powers for which there is no saving throw are telekinesis, levitation, pyrokinesis, presence sense and mind block.

Those who have psionic abilities have a much better defense against such attack than those who do not possess psionic powers.

Non-Psionics must roll 15 or higher to save.
Minor and Major Psionics must roll 12 or higher to save.
Master Psionics must roll 10 or higher to save.

AN ALPHABETICAL LIST OF PSIONIC ABILITIES

Level One

Aura of Truth (2)
Detect Psionics (2)
Hypnotic Suggestion (2)
Meditation Trance (0)
Object Read (4)
Presence Sense (4)
Resist Cold (2)
Resist Thirst (2)
Resist Fatigue (2)
See Aura (4)
Sense Good or Evil (2)
Sixth Sense (4)

Level Two

Bio-Regeneration (6)
Death Trance (4)
Empathy (4)
Levitate (6)
Limited Telepathy (6)
Limited Telekinesis (6)
Mind Block (4)
Resist Fire (4)
Resist Hunger (4)
Speed Reading (4)

Level Three

Bio-Manipulation (12)
Extended Telepathy (8)
Mental Bolt of Force (8)
Precognition (8)
See the Invisible (8)
Teleport Object (20)
Turn Invisible (8)
Total Recall (4)

Extra-Ordinary Psionic Powers

Astral Projection (10)
Create Force-Field (12)
Empathic Transfer
Extended Telekinesis (10)
Float (air/water) (8)
Fuel Flame (8)
Mind Control (10)
Mind Wipe (special)
Pyrokinesis (10)
Telemechanics (12)

LEVEL ONE

Aura of Truth
Range: 10 meters (35ft)/line of vision
Duration: Two melees
I.S.P.: 2 per two melees

This enables the psionic to differentiate lies from the truth by intensely observing the person's aura. Base chance 30% (+10% per additional two I.S.P. applied).
Saving Throw: Standard, non psionic must roll 15 or better, minor or major must roll a 13 or better, and a master psionic must roll a 10 or better to save. A successful save means the person is not affected.

Detect Psionics
Range: 580 meters (1800ft)
Duration: Two melees
I.S.P.: 2 per two melees

This mental probe will detect psionics in others. Unfortunately there is a 75% chance that the probe will be detected by a fellow psionic revealing your own psionic nature.
Saving Throw: None. However, a mind block reduces such a detection to 9%.

Hypnotic Suggestion
Range: 3.6 meters (12ft)
Duration: Unknown
I.S.P.: 2 per suggestion

With this ability the psionic may induce his will upon another through the power of suggestion. This is a subversive mental attack that requires eye contact and verbal suggestion. The verbal suggestion should be weaved into a conversation and take the form of a simple request or demand.
Saving Throw: Standard

Meditation/Trance
Range: Self
Duration: Varies
I.S.P.: None

This is a simple self hypnotic trance which allows the psionic to completely relax. During such trances the psionic regains 3 I.S.P. per hour.
Saving Throw: None

Object Read
Range: Touch
Duration: Instant (about 2 melees)
I.S.P.: 4

This uncanny ability enables the psionic to tap into the psychic emanations of the object's owner. This is done by holding the object and concentrating on the owner or history of the object. If successful, the psionic instantly receives impressions and images revealing bits of information such as whether the previous owner is dead or alive, or in danger, etc. In addition to impressions, the psionic will actually see images of isolated events which have happened in the past. However, very specific blocks of information or events must be concentrated on with each new block of info, requiring a new object read. It is important to point out that the entire life of the owner CANNOT be explored through object read, only small, isolated bits. Traumatic experiences are the easiest impressions to get.
NOTE: The object must be a personal item which has been in the person's possession for some time or a very important item to the person. Human beings and animals are NOT objects and cannot be read. Dead bodies can be construed as objects, but will only provide images of the last few moments before he/she died. This may indicate the cause of death and an impression of if the assassin was friend, foe or a complete surprise/stranger.

Object reading machines will produce an image of someone operating the machine, thus providing a rudimentary idea of its purpose and basic function. It will NOT reveal a complete detailed schematic or instruction book like information.
The following is a list of the types of information and base success ratio.
35%   Operation and history
20%   Present location of previous owner
30%   Present condition of previous owner
The more I.S.P. spent, the better the percentage of success. Add 10% for every 3 additional I.S.P. applied to the reading. NOTE: Only one object can be read per minute.
Saving Throw: None. However, another psionic may use a mind block to prevent the discovery of his present location or condition.

Presence Sense
Range: 36.6 meters (120ft) radius
Duration: 8 melees
I.S.P.: 4

Presence Sense enables the psionic to detect the presence of any person or creature, visible or invisible, hiding or not within the area. Unfortunately, the ability is far from exact, providing only a very general idea of numbers and location. Because only a vague impression is possible, the psionic will perceive one or less than six entities as a few, while a dozen or more as many. Likewise, it cannot perceive the difference between an insect or a human being, thus both would register as a presence of equal intensity. Robots will not register as a presence, but the Mechanoids, both flesh and machine, do. Remember, while it is excellent for determining if anyone is behind closed doors, it will not indicate how many are there. Being indoors also reduces the range somewhat (1/3).
Saving Throw: None

Resist Cold
Range: Self
Duration: Two Hours
I.S.P.: 2

This mental discipline is one of many mind over matter abilities. It enables the psionic to suffer no ill effects or discomfort from even prolonged exposure to cold conditions. Two I.S.P. are required for every 10 degrees below freezing. The psionic will suffer half damage from extreme or unnatural cold. Five full minutes of concentration is required to prepare for the resistance.
Saving Throw: None

Resist Fatigue
Range: Self
Duration: Four Hours
I.S.P.: 2

This ability also enforces the psionic's will over physical matter. This allows the psionic to operate normally even under taxing conditions. It takes five minutes to prepare.
Saving Throw: None

Resist Thirst
Range: Self
Duration: Eight Hours
I.S.P.: 2

This ability allows the psionic to suspend any desire for water. Although the ability may be handy wandering through a desert, it does not negate the physical dehydration of the body. It takes five minutes of concentration to prepare.
Saving Throw: None

See Aura
Range: 36.6 meters (120ft) within line of vision
Duration: One melee
I.S.P.: 4

All things, organic and inorganic, possess an aura. The aura indicates many things, such as health or power of a creature or object. Seeing an aura will indicate the following:
- The general alignment (good or evil)
- Estimated level (never exact).
- Physical condition (sick or healthy).
There is a 15% chance per level of the psionic to recognize an aura he has seen before. Even if the person is in disguise he can be recognized by his aura.
Saving Throw: None

Sense Good or Evil
Range: 27 meters (90ft)
Duration: Instant
I.S.P.: 2

The psionic will instantly know the general alignment (good, evil) of any person or object within range.
Saving Throw: None except mind block.

Sixth Sense
Range: 27 meters (90ft)
Duration: Two melees
I.S.P.: 4

This unique ability will alert the psionic to any potential danger, traps, ambush, etc., within a 90 foot radius. Unfortunately, while it indicates any threat to the psionic, it DOES NOT indicate what the danger is, nor where it is.
Saving Throw: None

LEVEL TWO

Bio-Regeneration
Range: Self
Duration: Permanent
I.S.P.: 6

This is the ability to mentally heal oneself of disease, poison, or physical damage. Unfortunately this ability is limited to the healing of oneself and cannot help others. The process requires one full minute of concentration meaning the character cannot use any other psionic power during that time. Bio-Regeneration does not restore missing limbs, but does restore 2-12 hit points. In addition, when cuts and scrapes are healed through bio-regeneration there is NO scarring. The psionic can regenerate as often as once every other minute.
Saving Throw: None

Death Trance
Range: Self
Duration: Ten minutes
I.S.P.: 4

This takes the slowing of the metabolism to the maximum degree. The process places the psionic in a temporary state of suspended animation, slowing his body's metabolism to a crawl, simulating death. While in this deathlike state the psionic will not respond to any type of stimulation, making the illusion of death complete.
Saving Throw: None

Empathy
Range: 160 feet or line of vision
Duration: Eight melees
I.S.P.: 4

The psionic is able to receive emotion within a 38 meter area. In some ways empathy is a primitive telepathy, allowing the psionic to read emotions rather than words or images. It is incredibly difficult (but not impossible) to emit a false emotion enabling the psionic to sense a person's true feelings; hate, fear, sorrow, anger, nervousness, etc. Of course, reading emotions is no easy task. Just because a person is nervous doesn't mean that he is guilty or lying.

Despite the potential inaccuracy in reading emotions, it can be incredibly useful to identify strong emotions. Consequently, empathy can be used as a lie detector in many instances. While questioning a person the empathic can sense nervousness and much more.

A wide spread emotion scan can also help identify someone in a crowd or someone hiding by picking up fear, hate or nervousness. Unfortunately, empathy will not enable the psionic to pin-point the exact person on location, but it can narrow things down or alert him to potential trouble.

The duration of an empathic scan, whether on an individual or the maximum 38 meter area, is eight melees To extend the duration will require another 4 I.S.P. for an additional eight melees.
Saving Throw: Victims of an empathic scan are allowed a savings throw each time or question. If a successful save is made the psionic gets no reading or an uninterpretable one. The savings throw is standard.

Levitate
Range: Self or other person/object 27 meters (90ft) away
Duration: Six Minutes
I.S.P.: 6

Levitation can be used by the psionic to lift himself, an object or another person into the air. Levitation is limited to moving straight up and down and should not be construed as a limited flying ability. Height limitation: 4.6 meters (15 feet) per each level of the psionic. Weight limitation: 113kg (250lbs) per each level of the psionic.

Levitation can be used in many ways, to reach a height (rooftop, ledge, etc.), to avoid an attack, for a better view, to immobilize an opponent by suspending him in the air, and so on. Dropping someone or thing from a great height will do 1-6 damage for each 4.6 meters of height. The psionic can cancel, or raise or lower his victim at will. If he is knocked out or killed the levitation effect is immediately cancelled.
Saving Throw: None. Victims of levitation are caught in an invisible force for which there is no defense. Attacks Per Melee: 2

Limited Telepathy
Range: 38 meters (160ft)
Duration: 8 melees
I.S.P.: 6

This ability allows the psionic to pick up the surface thoughts of others as well as send simple messages. Remember, because this is limited to surface thoughts,

the person/creature whose thoughts are being read will reflect only what is on his mind at the time.
Saving Throw: Any non-psionic with an M.E. of ten or higher, as well as all psionics, get a saving throw against a psionic attack, even if he is not aware that his thoughts are being read.

Limited Telekinesis
Range: 36.6 meters (120ft)
Duration: Eight melees
I.S.P.: 6

Telekinesis is the ability to move physical objects through the power of thought. This means the psionic is able to cause objects to float, hover, fly, slide, etc. by mental manipulation. The only requirements are that the object must be clearly visible and within 120 feet of the psionic. The psionic can manipulate up to 10 pounds per level. This means that the psionic can manipulate as many objects as desired so long as they do not exceed his weight limitation. Objects under three pounds can be used as missile weapons.
Saving Throw: None

Mind Block
Range: Self
Duration: Eight melees
I.S.P.: 4

The mind block is a mental wall that prevents the penetration of telepathy, empathy, sense good or evil, and detect psionics. It can be a valuable protective mask when dealing with other psionics.
Saving Throw: None

Resist Fire
Range: Self
Duration: Ten melees
I.S.P.: 4

This is the amazing mind over matter ability that allows the psionic to juggle hot coals or walk through a wall of flame unharmed. This ability is self induced and cannot be cast upon others. The psionic will take half damage from intense heat (above 400 degrees). The psionic can raise his heat tolerance at the cost of 4 I.S.P. per 100 degrees.
Saving Throw: None

Resist Hunger
Range: Self
Duration: Eight hours
I.S.P.: 4

This is yet another example of mind control in which the psionic can wipe out the desire for food. This can be particularly handy if caught in a situation with limited food supply. The person employing resist hunger will function normally even while dying of malnutrition. As with resist thirst, this ability does not negate the physical damage of starvation.
Saving Throw: None

Speed Reading
Range: Self
Duration: Ten minutes
I.S.P.: 4

This is the ability to read and comprehend the written word extremely quickly. Speed of reading is 30 pages per minute. The psionic will retain the information as he would normally. Highly technical texts will reduce the speed reading by half (15 pages per minute) and may require two readings.

Extended Telepathy
Range: 79 meters (330ft)
Duration: Ten melees
I.S.P.: 8

Extended telepathy functions much like limited telepathy except that the psionic can delve deep into another's mind. Likewise, conversations can be transmitted through extended telepathy.
Saving Throw: Any non-psionic with an M.E. of 10 or higher automatically gets a saving throw against a psionic attack, even though he is not aware of having his thoughts read. The same save applies to all psionics.

Bio-Manipulation
Range: 38 meters (120ft)
Duration: 4-16 melees (4D4)
I.S.P.: 12

There are seven types of bio-manipulation effects. Each affects only one person per attack and can be used in any combination. Intended victims must be within line of vision or their exact location known to the psionic.

This psionic power ebables the psionic to temporarily manipulate specific biological functions or conditions in humans and animal life-forms. Each costs 12 I.S.P. to inflict. The duration can be extended 4-16 minutes per additional I.S.P.
Blind: Temporarily knocks out the victim's optic nerves, rendering that person quite helpless. Victims are -9 to strike, parry and dodge.
Deafness: Can be caused by manipulating the ear drum. Victims cannot hear anything and are -6 to parry or dodge attacks from behind. In addition, the shock of suddenly becoming deaf makes them -3 to strike, parry or dodge any other attacks and they automatically lose the initiative on all attacks.
Mute: Impairs the victims vocal cords making speech impossible. Victims are likely to be shocked and panic making them -2 to strike, parry and dodge for the first melee ONLY.
Pain: By manipulating the nerve centers the psionic can induce terrible pain shooting throughout the body. Victims are -6 to strike, parry and dodge, and take one point of damage off their hit points (not S.D.C.) per each minute affected.
Paralysis: Immobilizes the motor part of the brain causing legs and arms to stop functioning. Victims are completely incapacitated for the duration.
Stun: This attack disorients and confuses its victims. Victims forfeit one attack per melee, speed is cut by half and are -4 to strike, parry and dodge.
Tissue Manipulation: Affects the tissue connecting nerve fibres which can cause a variety of effects. By irritating the nerve fibres a victim will suddenly feel itchy as if suddenly breaking out in a severe rash. Through endothermic manipulation the victim can be made to suddenly feel cold or hot while everyone around him feels fine. This is done by manipulating the body chemical which absorbs heat. ALL three conditions are more annoying or frightening than physically impairing. In each case, the victims are -1 to strike, parry and dodge.
Saving Throw: Standard; if a character successfully saves against the attack he is not affected at all. This applies to all seven bio-manipulative attacks.
NOTE: The psionic can use this power only once per melee.

Mental Bolt of Force
Range: 36.6 meters (120ft)
Duration: Instant
I.S.P.: 8

The psionic is able to tap into his own electromagnetic force and fire an energy bolt capable of inflicting 2-12 points of damage. The target must be within the line of vision; the bolt has a +4 to hit.
Saving Throw: Dodge Only

Precognition
Range: Self
Duration: Two melees
I.S.P.: 8

This is the ability to pick up psychic emanations and glimpse a few moments of the future. This future insight may be a few moments or a couple of hours; time is a very tenuous element caught up in continual change. This means the potential future can be altered or avoided.

Using precognition on an unopened door may reveal what lays beyond. The psionic may actually see himself engaged in battle or working on something. (Gamemasters: Try not to reveal the actual outcome of an incident or event. Describe the inception of a battle or the elements that may lead to danger or success. The fewer hard facts, the better, after all, the future is open to speculation).
Saving Throw: None

See the Invisible
Range: 60 meters (200ft)
Duration: Ten melees
I.S.P.: 8

This simply allows the psionic to see invisible creatures/objects. As with most psionic abilities, only the psionic is affected.
Saving Throw: None

Teleport Object
Range: Touch
Duration: Immediate
I.S.P.: 20

This is the ability to cause physical matter to disappear and reappear at a different location. Such teleportation is limited by the level of psionic. A psionic can teleport 10 pounds per level of experience a distance of 50 feet per level of experience. This is one way teleportation, since, to teleport an object, it must be touched by the psionic. (NOTE: A personal possession that has belonged to the psionic for at least two years may be brought back, 46% chance).
Saving Throw: None

Turn Invisible
Range: Self
Duration: Ten minutes
I.S.P.: 8

The powers of the mind are awesome and this is but one of the more spectacular abilities. Scholars are not certain exactly how this effect is achieved but apparently light is manipulated in such a way as to create the illusion of invisibility. The physical body is still corporeal though unseen. The invisible psionic can still be struck by a weapon or heard moving or speaking. Attackers against an invisible foe have a -5 to hit and a -3 to dodge/parry.
Saving Throw: None

Total Recall
Range: Self
Duration: Twenty minutes
I.S.P.: 4

The psionic is able to remember small blocks of information in absolute detail. The memory of the information recalled is retained for 20 minutes and then fades away unless recalled again.

EXTRA-ORDINARY PSIONIC POWERS

Astral Projection
Range: Self
Duration: Four minutes per level of the psionic
I.S.P.: 10

When a person astral projects, the physical body falls into a death-like trance while the astral body enters the vast plane of the astral world. The astral world seems to be an infinite world of rolling clouds and yellow sky. No up, no down, just endless sky.

While in the astral world the person can fly great distances in the blink of an eye. The astral traveler has a 50% chance of being able to sense locations of the physical world, parallel them in the astral plane, stop and peer into the physical. In doing so the astral traveler can see and hear everything that's going on in a room. The usual visual and audio limitations apply while in the astral plane so a character cannot hear or see any farther than he could in the physical dimension. However, he can hover above, or at any angle, to literally get a bird's eye view.

While in the astral plane the person cannot be heard, seen or detected by any conventional means. Only a psionic presence sense can detect an astral traveler and only psionic attacks can harm or affect him. This makes astral projection the perfect spying method with little chance of even being detected, let alone harmed or captured.

Of-course there are both limitations and hazards in astral projection. Although the traveler cannot be seen or heard this also means he cannot communicate to the physical plane unless he also possesses telepathy or empathy. No other psionic ability will function or affect the physical world. Likewise, the astral body is completely intangible, unable to pick-up or move the lightest of objects. Remember, the astral body does not exist in this world. Even so, it is susceptible to psionic assaults and can be killed.

The hazards are two fold. First, if the physical body is killed the astral body is forever lost and will die, fade away, within six hours. The real danger is the second and most common hazard, becoming lost in the astral plane. There is a time limit as to how long a person can exist in the astral plane, four minutes per level of the psionic. If the full time elapses before he has returned to the physical body, he will be forever lost in the astral plane. Yet, even if conscious of the time, there is always the danger of becoming lost. If the person does become lost and can not return to his body, the astral body is eternally trapped in the astral plane. The physical body will die within 1-6 days. It is not wise to wait until the very last minute to return to the physical body.

Roll percentile dice to determine the state of mind and sense of direction. The percentile dice can be rolled up to three times per minute to find the physical body. The player may keep trying until he succeeds or time elapses. The player must roll "definitely certain" to return.

  1-30 Hopelessly lost
31-50 Uncertain, confused
51-79 Fairly certain of location
80-00 Definitely certain of location.

Create Force Field
Range: Self
Duration: Eight melees per level of the psionic
I.S.P.: 12

The force field will have an S.D.C. of 20 and an A.R. of 8. The S.D.C. of the field can be increased by one for each additional I.S.P. expended. The force field blocks all attacks before any personal armor is affected.
Saving Throw: None

Empathic Transfer
Range: 38 meters (120ft)
Duration: 2-12 minutes (2D6)
I.S.P.: 10

This ability allows the psionic to project false emotions into one individual. By increasing the I.S.P. to 18 he can influence as many as six characters (each one gets a savings throw). The duration can also be extended 2-12 minutes by expending another 6 I.S.P. Attacks Per Melee: One.
Despair or Deep Sorrow: Invokes great emotional upheaval, deep sorrow and a sense of loss. There is a 50% chance of the victim surrendering or leaving without a battle; furthermore, victims are -2 to parry and dodge.
Confusion: Disorients the person so badly that he has no sense of direction, time or of what is exactly going on.

Victims are -3 to strike, parry and dodge, and loses initiative in any combat.

Fear: Invokes unreasoning terror in all those affected. Victims are -3 to strike, parry and dodge, plus there is a 66% chance that those affected will turn and run.

Hate or Anger: Will prompt those affected to act rashly, charge, attack, argue violently, etc. Victims are likely, 60% chance, to attack, kill, harm, or betray those he dislikes; +1 (yes, that's plus) to strike, -1 (minus) to parry and dodge.

Love or Peacefulness: Will induce a deep feeling of serenity dispelling anger, hatred, sorrow and so on. Hostile opponents are likely, 60% chance, to reconsider their actions, deciding not to attack, show mercy, leave without being overtly cruel or destructive, halt a rampage, and so on. It does NOT make its victims docile sheep, but curbs hostility.

Trust: Will make its victims believe everything the psionic tells them, but only while under the empathic influence. Life threatening suggestions that go against deep seated fears or ideals provide an additional savings throw against the suggested action with a bonus of +3 to save.

Float
Range: Self
Duration: Two hours
I.S.P.: 8

This ability controls the distribution of body weight and creates a mild sort of telekinetic field which enables the psionic to effortlessly float on water or one foot in the air per level of experience. Floating in air can break a fall by slowing the rate of descent until he is gingerly hovering above the ground.
Saving Throw: None

Fuel Flame
Range: 60 meters (200ft) per level of the psionic
Duration: Two melees
I.S.P.: 8

This pyrotechnic ability quadruples the size of the flame by feeding it with psychic energy. The area affected is a 45 meter (150ft) radius per level of experience.
Saving Throw: None

Mind Control
Range: 12 meters (40ft)
Duration: Five minutes per level of the psionic.
I.S.P.: 10

This psi-power affects any intelligent creature but can only be used on one person at a time; it is not an area affect power. The affected person will fall under the complete control of the psionic. Victims of mind control will obey the psionic without question and answer all questions truthfully. They can even be made to combat friends and allies although the controlled person's reaction and reflexes are somewhat impaired, -2 to strike, parry and dodge.
NOTE: If an evil character should try to make another person under his control commit suicide or do something which is obviously certain death, that person will hesitate and is given a chance to break free of his control. This provides an extra saving throw to break the mind control. The person is +4 to save. If the saving throw is unsuccessful the person will do exactly as told.

As the psionic grows in experience he can control more than one person simultaneously. He can control two people at third level, another at fifth level, and one more at every other level thereafter. A psionic can attempt to control one person or several simultaneously, once per melee.

Mind Wipe
Range: Touch
Duration: Special

I.S.P.: Special

To mind wipe an intelligent creature the psionic must make physical contact, touching his victim's temples to erase whatever he desires. This is done by suggestion and can erase any past event, knowledge, skill and so on. The process takes about three minutes to complete.

The loss of memory is temporary, lasting 1-4 days for every 10 I.S.P. expended. The memory can be permanently erased if the psionic exerts 50 I.S.P. at once. A psionic can also permanently wipe a mind completely blank by expending 50 I.S.P. and four Mental Endurance (M.E.) points. This is an extremely grueling process for the psionic and the loss of the four M.E. points is permanent, even if the opponent successfully saves against the wipe and is not affected.
Saving Throw: Standard; a successful save means the person is unaffected and still retains his memory.

Pyrokinesis
Range: 27 meters (90ft)
Duration: Special
I.S.P.: 10

Pyrokinesis is the impressive and terrifying ability to create fire through force of will and molecular agitation. Psionics with pyrokinesis abilities have a variety of fire creating powers.
Fire Eruption: This is the ability to cause something to erupt and be engulfed by fire. Even non-combustible materials or objects can be affected. Range: 27.4 meters; Duration: Combustibles, until it burns itself out or is put out. Non-combustibles like brick, metal, etc., 6 melees; I.S.P.: Combustible items 6. Non-combustible items require 10 I.S.P.
Saving Throw: As dodge, but intended victims are -6 to dodge because the fire erupts out of nowhere, engulfing its target and setting it ablaze; Damage: 5-30 per melee, until the fire is extinguished.

Telemechanics
Range: Touch or up to 1.5 meters (5ft)
Duration: Ten minutes plus two minutes per level of psionic
I.S.P.: 12

This ability allows the psionic to mentally communicate and understand machines. This psi-power is a bizarre combination of object-read and telepathy except that it applies to mechanical devices only.

By touching any non-artificially intelligent machine, whether it be a bicycle, gun, car or airplane, the psionic will instantly have a complete (although temporary) knowledge of exactly how the machine operates. I must stress that the psionic knows everything about the machine; the complete schematic diagram and operation knowledge are clearly seen in his mind's eye. The level of skill expertise is equal to 80% scholastic skill.

When touching an artificially intelligent machine, i.e., computers, the psionic not only understands everything about its operation, repair, access codes, etc., but can actually communicate with it telepathically. This means he can tap into a computer's memory bank without using a terminal because the information would be sent directly into the psionic's mind. Remember, the telepathic link and memory are temporary abilities (although a total recall would be able to call up small bits of information). The psionic's skill knowledge is equal to 88% skill proficiency and applies to all aspects of the machine, its operation, repair, special codes, etc.

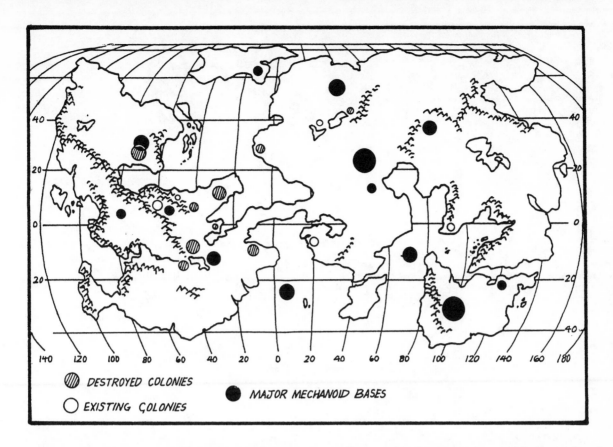

DESTROYED COLONIES

EXISTING COLONIES

MAJOR MECHANOID BASES

A CHRONOLOGICAL SEQUENCE OF THE MECHANOID INVASION

The First Month

1. Appearance of unidentified extraterrestrials on the outer edge of the Galevetti Galaxy.

2. Contact with space station Alpha Q lost. (Now presumed destroyed by Mechanoids).

3. Attempt at radio communication with advancing extra-terrestrials futile.

4. Observations intensified. Gideon-E placed on yellow alert.

5. Aliens orbit Thelos, the largest of Gideon-E's sister satelites.

6. All radio communication with aliens negative.

7. S.O.S. continually sent to Intergalactic Federation.

8. Immense spacecraft, about the size of Earth's North America appears.

9. Thalos is broken down into fragments, gathered, and re-moved. Supposition: Mining operation. Length of operation: 3 Earth months.

10. Process repeated on Mio-5.

11. Radio interference may have prevented S.O.S. from reaching I.F. All comunication satellites destroyed by aliens.

12. Invasion divided into two sections. One prepares the destruction of Lea Pox. The second prepares the destruc-tion of Gideon-E.

13. Gideon-E placed on battle alert. Evacuation to moun-tain retreats initiated.

14. First wave alien attack staved off.

15. Second wave alien attack is devastating. Defenses crumble:
    Human Casualties: 39%
    Property Loss/Damage: 72%

16. Evacuation to mountains and tunnels 82% successful.

17. Faint radio communique received by the original Gideon colony. The Intergalactic Federation (I.F.) is aware of the

situation (at least in part). Six months till I.F. intervention. Interference and disruption of communications by aliens.

18. Aliens now classed as mechanoids. Cybernetic in nature.

19. Mechanoids begin defoliation of planet Gideon-E.
    Human Casualty: 3%
    Rover Casualty: 7%
    Vegetation Casualty: 98.5%
    Animal Life Casualty: 74.9%

Second Month

1. Defoliation of planet Gideon-E completed.

2. Falzon colony falls. Human casualty 96.3%, property 100%. Major Mechanoid base established.

3. New Gideon falls. Human casualty 87%, property 98%.

4. Maykanok outpost falls. Human casualty 100%, property 100%.

5. Williams outpost falls. Human casualty 100%, property 100%.

6. Manbiji sea coast colony partially evacuated before it falls. Human casualty 47%, property 92%.

7. Balent Bay outpost successfully evacuated to Gideon colony before it falls. Human casualty 0%, property 63%.

8. Major Mechanoid base established in Northern Hemisphere.

9. Undersea Mechanoid activities noted in Aldonease Ocean Speculation: Undersea base.

10. Remaining human colonies: Gideon colony - Kucharski - Muzkie desert outpost - Stelvenson - Orz - Malibar.

11. Muzkie desert outpost limited to minimal maintenance personnel falls to Rover Raid (Red and Black tribe). Human casualty 22%, property 18%.

12. Muzkie outpost destroyed by Mechanoids. Human cas-ualty 0%, property 98%.

13. Mechanoid undersea base in Aldonease Ocean confirmed.

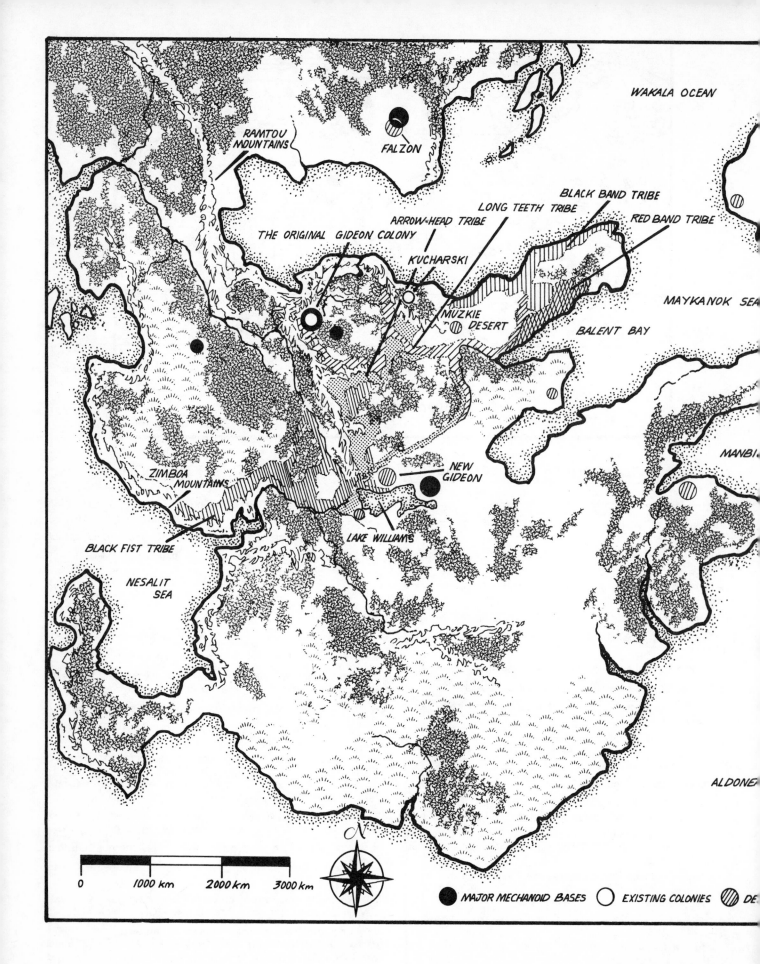

WAKALA OCEAN

RAMTOU
MOUNTAINS

FALZON

BLACK BAND TRIBE

LONG TEETH TRIBE

ARROW-HEAD TRIBE

RED BAND TRIBE

THE ORIGINAL GIDEON COLONY

KUCHARSKI

MUZKIE
DESERT

MAYKANOK SEA

BALENT BAY

ZIMBOA
MOUNTAINS

MANBI

NEW
GIDEON

BLACK FIST TRIBE

LAKE WILLIAMS

NESALIT
SEA

ALDONE

N

0   1000 km   2000 km   3000 km

● MAJOR MECHANOID BASES   ○ EXISTING COLONIES   ◍ DE

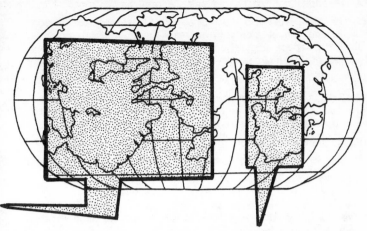
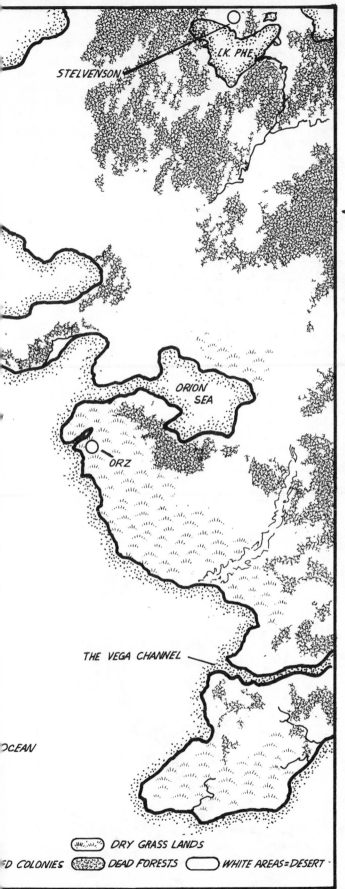
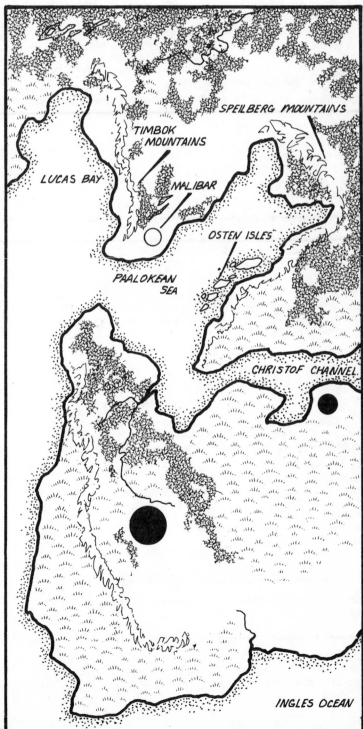

14. 10 additional Mechanoid bases established.

15. Partial evacuation of **Orz** and **Stelvenson** to Gideon colony and tunnel mountain retreats (near Gideon) successful. Both reduce population by 36%, while still maintaining full manufacturing capacity.

16. Malibur colony totally isolated. Evacuation impossible.

17. Frequent encounters with Mechanoids indicate they do not consider humans a threat, but rather a plaything to vent their psychotic hatred of all humanoid life forms.

18. Mechanoids continue to display psionic nature.

19. Mechanoid bases located over deposits of fossil fuels and gas reserves. Begin mining operations.

20. Rover situation: Black Fist increasingly hostile to colonists - Arrowhead tribe and Long Teeth have allied themselves to colonists - Red Band, Black Band and Sand Pirates slowly perishing, refuse colonial aid.

21. Major confrontation off the Pallakean Sea 2000km from Malibar. Human casualty 59%, Mechanoid 88%.

Ancient surface dwelling sentient computer and global tunnel system discovered after battle, but was lost after infiltration by Mechanoid assault team of Wasp and Brutes. System self-destructed. Thermonuclear (tapping into planet core) area effected 200km.

22. Timbok mountains (entire 2800km length) leveled by Mechanoid mothership as show of power. Malibar colony 400km away untouched.

23. Colonies increase production of experimental and high powered weapons.

Third Month

1. Massive Mechanoid devices (diggers) begin to carve the planet Gideon E into sections. Devices cut an unbroken line/canyon 2km deep and 1km wide across the entire planet. Bridge and bridge fort areas built approximately every 1800km (5900ft).

2. Increasing geological disturbances indicate Mechanoids have tapped into Gideon E's molten core as a power source.

3. Long Teeth Rover tribe wipes out Red and Black Band tribes. Only scattered fragments of these tribes remain. Extremely hostile.

4. Black Fist tribe may have allied itself with Mechanoids.

5. Colonial assaults have only minimal effects against Mechanoid mining and construction.

6. Gideon colony discovers 21 Balrog Destroyers.

7. Humans successfully destroy Mechanoid base at the old Falzon sight and damage Mechanoid outpost near the ruins of New Gideon. Four Balrog Destroyers are lost.

8. Mechanoid assault atomizes the Kucharski colony and damages the Gideon colony.
Kucharski: Human casualty 89% (43,857 die)
         Property 99%
Gideon colony: Human casualty 13% (10,346 die)
         Property 20%
Rover tribes: Black Fist 42%
         Sand Pirates 95%
Six Balrog Destroyers lost in battle.

9. 11 Balrog Destroyers remain in good working condition.

10. Intergalactic Federation aid will not arrive in time (2 months too late).

Present Situation Of Colonies

1. Plan to evacuate Gideon E via orbital shuttle dock and penetrate the massive Mechanoid mothership (This ship is approximately the size of North America). Target Date: 48 days.

2. Shuttle operations will be directed from Orz and Gideon colonies.

3. Escort for evacuation and diversionary forces include hover jet fighters and both types of I.L.R.M.

4. Objective: Penetrate enemy and destroy from within, even if means of escape is not available. Estimated penetration success ration 74%; subverting ship .05%. See Book Two: The Journey for this adventure.

5. Not all colonists can be evacuated; while others desire to remain and fight till the end. These people comprise the suicide assault forces. Stelvenson is base headquarters; Gideon and Orz are back-up. The 11 Balrog Destroyers are dispersed as follows: 6 at Stelvenson, 2 at Gideon and 3 at Orz.
Gideon has 3 times as many jet fighters (360) and dreadnoughts (73) as Stelvenson and Orz, thus Gideon will act as air command.

6. Malibar remains completely isolated. Aid is impossible. Defense of remaining colonies is top priority. All "major" assaults against the Mechanoids have been suspended. Suicide assaults will begin on the day evacuation to the Mechanoid mothership begins. Colonel Elijah Gideon will be commander in chief of this final assault.

7. Total ecological imbalance.

8. Increased hostility of environment.

9. Increased hostility of Rovers.

10. Objective One: To delay Mechanoid operations until help can arrive. Impossible.

11. Two: Gather as much data on the Mechanoids as possible for further defense/offense of other I.F. properties. Satisfactory.

EUSTOVICH

GIDEON-E

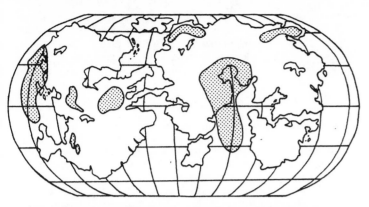

KNOWN NATURAL GAS RESERVES

Gideon-E is a fascinating planet because it is almost a twin Earth. It is actually one of four satellites (moons) orbiting the giant liquid planet, Alva.

The diameter of Gideon-E is 11,987km and its average density is 5.12 times that of water. The core is composed of nickel and iron like that of the Earth. Geological probes have revealed large deposits of fossil fuels; most notably: coal, oil and natural gas. Additional probes were expected to uncover even more such deposits on this mineral rich planet.

The surface temperature of Gideon-E is presently 25% higher than Earth's and increasing annually. The temperature has risen 23 degrees in the last 120 years. This increase is attributed to the dense atmosphere which traps incoming solar radiation and prevents heat from being reradiated into space. It was feared that this "greenhouse effect" would lead to the eventual evacuation of the planet as it became increasingly inhospitable for human life.

Some geologists believe that Gideon-E was an ice laden world as recently as 2.5 million years ago, until something radically altered its atmosphere.

However, a growing number of scientists feel that the present greenhouse effect may not be the result of natural phenomena. The atmosphere's condition is reminiscent of Earth's past problems with industrial pollution and the deterioration of the ozone layer.

The atmosphere is primarily composed of carbon dioxide, oxygen and nitrogen with trace elements of argon, chlorine and hydrocarbons. While breathing this dense atmosphere unaided by filters or oxygen supplements is not initially deadly, it is extremely hazardous. Nasal and eye irritation results in two or three hours, increasing in severity. Labored breathing occurs within five to eight hours accompanied by intense irritation of the eyes, throat and lungs. Prolonged exposure (two to four Gideon-E days) may result in permanent respiratory problems, brain damage or death.

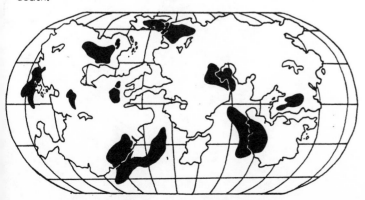

ADDITIONAL FOSSIL FUELS

Gideon-E was first explored by the infamous Gideon expedition and later used by the estranged Colonel A.E. Gideon when he turned renegade.

Despite the increasing temperature, the satellite planet proved stable and fairly suitable for colonization. Fourteen colonies/cities were established over the last 120 years.

The surface varied from arid mountains to deserts, to vast grasslands, to tropical and sub-tropical jungles. That was before the coming of the Mechanoids. With the defoliation of the planet, the terrain has become dry and barren. Vast dusty desert and shrivelled grasslands have replaced the prairies and lowlands. Black twisted husks claw at the sky, a grim mockery of the lush jungles that once flourished there.

The Ecological Imbalance Of Gideon-E

Since the Mechanoids have defoliated the entire planet, it is unnecessary to delve into the thousands of plant, animal, bird or insect species catalogued by the Gideon colony. The more delicate life forms died as a result of the toxic defoliant. Others perished because of the dramatic ecological imbalance of the environment and food chain.

Surviving life forms include most aquatic species and a handful of carnivores. Yet perhaps the greatest threat to humanoid life, other than the Mechanoids, are the Sand Beetles. These dog size insects were seldom found beyond the Muzkie desert. Unfortunately, the Mechanoids defoliation has created the type of arid dusty environment the Sand Beetles thrive in.

Dangerous Indigenous Animal Life

SAND BEETLE LARVA

The Sand Beetle

The adult Sand Beetle is actually quite harmless to animal or humanoid life. Its small mouth is designed for the consumption of Sand mites only. While the adult male's life cycle may last as long as 10 months, the female's cycle is limited to a few short days.

The female has no mouth. Her only purpose is to lay 300 to 900 eggs before she dies. These eggs are layed in pockets of 15 to 35, about 2 to 4 meters under the sand or dry earth. There the eggs will lay dormant for up to six weeks, until a burrowing male happens upon them and fertilizes them.

The gestation cycle of the fertilized egg is very rapid larva emerging within five days. It is the larva which present the danger to mammals. The larva, like the adult mosquito of Earth, lives on the blood of other animals, consuming "four times" its weight a day. Since the once natural predators no longer exist, the Sand Beetle flourishes. However, the mammoth mammals they once fed upon are also eliminated. Thus the larva must feed upon the last remaining mammals on the planet, humans and rovers.

The larva and adult Sand Beetle are very adaptable and quite resistant to poisons or radiation.

	Adult	Larva
Size	1.2m long	0.3m to 1.2m (1-4ft)
A.R.	6	4
Hit Points	4-24	1-6 Young; 2-12 medium
Speed	30kmph	18kmph

Attacks Per Melee	None	one bite does 1-6 damage, +3 per melee
Weapons	None	Bite
Bonuses	None	+2 to dodge, prowl 57%
Function	survival/predator	Same
Operation	Insect	Insect

or impaled in its victim no other attacks are available.

Damage: 1-6 from each tentacle followed by one additional point of damage every other melee.

Size: Body size varies widely from as small as one meter to as large as 4.6 meters (15ft). Tentacles' length are equal to the body size.

Weight: 13kg (30lbs/4 gallons of water) per each meter in size.

Speed: 3 slow crawl/burrow

Bonuses: +2 to strike

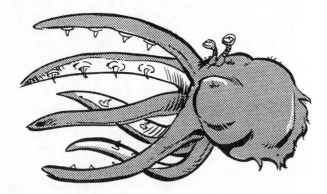

The Water Trap

The water trap is an unusual creature found in deserts and other arid areas. The Sand Pirates and other rovers hunt water traps, for beneath its tough leathery hide it holds one to twenty (1D20) gallons of reasonably fresh water. Indeed, the creature itself resembles a giant bag of water with tentacles or a massive wad of chewing gum.

Water traps draw moisture from every conceivable source; living animals, vegetation, morning dew, etc. Once fat with water, at least 4 gallons, it buries itself in the sand often near rocks, awaiting its prey. The water trap has no sense of fear or proportions and will strike out at a small lizard, human, rover or tunnel rat with equal zeal. When a creature walks over a buried water trap, one to six tentacles will move up through the sand to ensnare it. At the same time the four thorny barbs under each tentacle will dig into the animal's flesh. The barbs are strong bone-like tubes in which it attempts to suck out all moisture in its prey's body. The water trap is not physically powerful, consequently, it will attempt to bind its prey with its tentacles, preventing movement and slowly drink all its precious body fluids. As long as a person caught by a water trap does not panic and has one or both arms free the experience is not likely to be lethal. Only the initial strike of the tentacles can inflict severe damage (1-6 points each) but, afterwards, very little additional damage occurs (one point every other melee) unless the tentacles are carelessly torn or pulled off the person (which does another 1D6 points of damage each). Although tough skin protects the creature; its tentacles can be easily severed with blade or energy weapons. A water trap will usually release its foe if it loses two or more tentacles, tentacles which will regenerate within a few months. Most vulnerable to harm are its two tiny eyes mounted on short stalks, but blinding it is not likely to cause it to release its grip. Least vulnerable is its bloated, water filled body which seems to be primarily blubber and tissue. A person can stab or blast the body with little effect other than the release of water. Its internal organs are actually very small and hidden in another sack-like envelope of tissue, near its eye stalks, under approximately eight inches of blubber. NOTE: The tentacles' barbs CANNOT penetrate hard leather armor, web vests, L.B.A. or E.B.A. doing little more than scratch the armor's surface.

A.R.: 9; rovers often use these tough hides to make leather armor.

Hit Points: Main body 100; each tentacle 4-24

Attacks Per Melee: Initial attack, up to six (one for each tentacle), but once all the tentacles are wrapped around

Sandspear

Another dangerous desert insect is the sandspear. This creature resembles an earthworm with a thick leathery skin and amazing speed. It slithers through the sands of Gideon E in search of food, navigating by following vibrations. It only occasionally pokes its head above the sand to sun itself or for a quick glance around. When prey has been found it will race towards it at astounding speed, suddenly shooting out of the sand to plunge head long into its unsuspecting prey, resembling a thrown javelin. If it successfully strikes its target it will burrow through its victim, dropping into the sand for another attack until its prey is dead. It feeds by entering the carcass and absorbing the body fluids. A sandspear will never remain in a living creature, but strikes repeatedly until it is slain. Because of Gideon-E's severe ecological imbalance and now vast, arid wastelands, the sandspear's numbers are increasing at an alarming rate and have been found as far as 1000km from their usual desert haunts.

NOTE: The sandspear is so tough its attack so powerful that it can even penetrate a web vest or suit of L.B.A.

A.R.: 10

Hit Points: 6-36+2 (6D6+2)

Attacks Per Melee: One by impaling itself in its victim.

Damage: 3-18

Bonuses: +4 to Dodge

Size: to 1.8 meters (4 to 6ft) long

Weight: 8kg (18lbs)

Speed: 25, can leap up to 4 meters (15ft)

Moss Men

These mysterious creatures were discovered only 25 years ago by the Stelvenson Colony. Humanoid in appearance, they are, in reality, an as of yet undefined form of plant life.

To heap mystery upon mystery, the creatures possess great psionic ability. Perhaps this indicates intelligence, although other investigations seem to indicate otherwise.

It is believed that these creatures instinctively assume the shape of the dominant life-form around them as a sort of camouflage, in much the same way that an Earth chameleon changes its color. In this case the humans of the Stelvenson colony are the dominant life form in the region.

These are no signs of inter-communication, culture, society, nor inter-action between one another. Each simply dwells in its own shallow burrow (3 meters deep/5 meters long) and minds its own business.

A.R.: 6
Hit Points: 6-36+20 (6D6+20)
Attacks Per Melee: Two psionic attacks per melee are possible. Moss Men NEVER use a physical attack or even parry or dodge.
Psionic Abilities: All level 1, 2, and 3 plus empathic transfer. I.S.P.: 225
Bonuses: +2 vs psionic attack.
Average Attributes: I.Q. 4, M.E. 10, M.A. 10, P.S. 6, P.P. 6, P.E. 6, P.B. 6, Spd. 10
Notes: The Moss Men are generally passive, attacking only when they feel threatened. The entire community will rise against intruders/threats even if only one of its fellows are attacked.

They are not physical creatures employing only the simplest of movements. They use no tools or weapons and attack psionically only when threatened. Because of their psionic nature they are particularly receptive to strong emotion (fear, hate, anger) and will react accordingly.

Moss Men feed off molds, lichen, and decaying organic substances. 1247 burrows have been counted within a 10km area around Stelvenson. 6000 more are estimated to exist within a 200km radius of Stelveson.

Qual-Rogg

This nocturnal hunter blinds its prey by spitting an acidic solution into the face/eyes of its victim. It then rends and slashes its prey apart with the razor sharp claws of its bony forearm and feet.

The Qual-Rogg's toothless maw is incapable of biting or chewing; thus, it feasts upon its victim's blood, bone marrow and swallows small organs such as the liver, spleen and bladder.

Qual-Roggs roam forest regions, travelling with a mate and 2 to 4 offspring. They are virtually blind when exposed to intense light (day light) and are forced to rely on the sensitive touch of their antennae.

Size: 2.2 to 2.8 meters tall (9ft)
A.R.: 4
Hit Points: 6-48+30 (6D8+30)
Attacks Per Melee: Four; with razor sharp claws or two acid attacks every other melee. **Claws** do 2-12 points of damage each; **acid** temporarily blinds its victim until the eyes are flushed clean with ordinary water. -7 to strike, parry and dodge while blinded. Eyes will become permanently impaired unless thoroughly cleansed within six hours.
Range of Acid: is 9 meters (30ft), Claw's reach is about 2 meters (7ft)
Bonuses: +1 to strike, prowl is 40%, terrible climbers and swimmers.
NOTE: Claws will do full damage to L.B.A. and half damage to E.B.A.

47

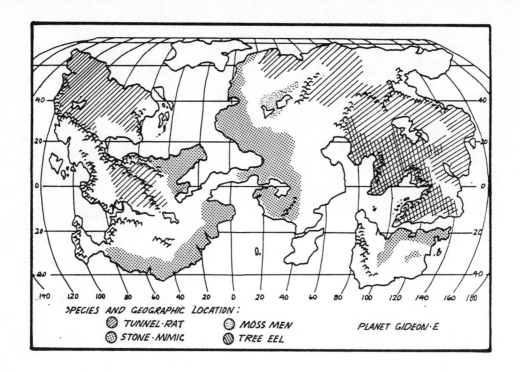

SPECIES AND GEOGRAPHIC LOCATION:
TUNNEL·RAT   MOSS MEN
STONE·MIMIC   TREE EEL   PLANET GIDEON·E

Stone Mimic

These bizarre mammals thrive in arid regions across the planet. The tongue like appendage is an ultra sensitive organ able to detect vibrations created by nearby movement as well as possessing keen olfactory faculties. When movement or smell indicates another mammal is near, the Mimic launches itself into the air via the tongue impaling its prey with its 6 inch fangs. A lethal poison is then injected which can kill a human size victim within 3 minutes.

Saving vs Poison: The colonists do have an anti-toxin with a 92% success rate if administered immediately. Survival Without Toxin: is the Physical Endurance rating of the character. This means if P.E. is 12 there is a 12% chance of surviving. P.E. of 18 or greater has a bonuses vs coma/death (i.e. P.E. 20+17% = 37%).

Attacks Per Melee: One and poison; fangs do 2-12 damage this applies only to the first attack. Poison does 5-30 damage per melee.

Range: Leaps up to 4 meters

Bonuses: Camouflage among stones 82%; Camouflage is effective even when being actively sought - 60%

Size: .3 long to .7m long

Armor Rating: 10

S.D.C./Hit Points: 36 average (roll 4D6+36 for larger species)

Speed Factor: Crawl 19.8 meters per hour
Leap 140 meters per hour.

*Fangs can not penetrate plastics, metals, or fibres with an AR of 6 or greater.

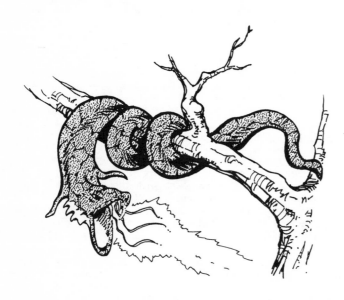

Tree Eel

The tree eel is found through the forests of the southern hemisphere. They are generally harmless to human preferring to prey upon larger mammals such as the Tunnel Rats. They attack by dropping from a tree and attaching themselves to the body. Three long (177.8mm/7 inches) needle sharp tendrils are sunk into its victim drawing upon its life fluids. This parasite operates much like the Earth leech.

The tree eel derives its name from its appearance and ability to generate electric energy through its tendrils and body.

A.R.: 2

Hit Points: 3-18 (3D6)

Attacks Per Melee: One; by bite doing 1-4 damage or electric discharge doing 1-8 damage with a 25% chance of stunning its victim, humans included. Duration 2-8 melees; range of electric discharge is one meter.

Speed: 6; climbing 90%

Size: 1.5 meters long

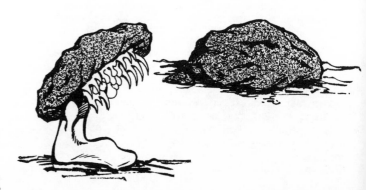

Tunnel Rats

These large mammals are commonly found throughout the ancient tunnel systems and the great northern forests.

Originally scavengers feeding on both vegetation and dead meats, the ecological imbalance of Gideon-E has made them increasingly vicious predators. They now prey upon smaller mammals including humanoids. Although cautious of humans, Tunnel Rat packs (6 to 20 rats) have become alarmingly bold and have been sighted at colony disposal dumps. (NOTE: The Black Fist and Arrow Head tribes have been known to use the rats as mounts.)

A.R.: 6
Hit Points: 6-36+22
Attacks Per Melee: Three; by bite 1-8 damage or claws doing 3-18 damage.
Size: 6 meters long (20ft), 2.4 meters tall (8ft).
Speed: 24
Other Abilities: Climb 96%, burrow 4 meters per melee, swim 58%, leap 4 meters (13ft)

The Colonists

The planet Alva and its four satellites are located at the edge of the **Intergalactic Federation's** sphere of influence. It was discovered, by Colonel A.E. Gideon, that the largest of these moons had a lush, hospitable environment that could easily support human life. It was also Colonel A.E. Gideon who led the first exploration teams and accurately mapped the satellite world. Named after the colonel, the moon, Gideon-E, was soon populated by an ever growing research colony. In addition to the usual planetary studies, Gideon-E seemed to offer a wealth of mineral resources and the recently discovered technological wonders of a lost alien civilization the humans call the "Ancient Ones". (SEE the Ancient Ones and Ancient Tunnels sections for more details).

The world yielded no threats to human life other than animal predators in the wild and an occasional, minor difficulty with the alien primitives known as the rovers. The most distressing problem was the abrasive atmosphere which was compensated for by using simple air filters, protective eye goggles and air purification systems. The land itself was not unlike Earth's South America and southern United States.

Gideon-E is located in the outbacks of the Intergalactic Federation's (I.F.) territory and surrounded only by a handful of uninhabited worlds. Its location held absolutely no strategic significance and, while it appeared to have a rich mineral resource, it was not so rich as to be a susceptible target of plunder. This meant that Gideon-E sat in the middle of what's called "Dead Space". Classification: safety zone AAA; absolutely no hostiles within several light years distance and no military significance. Consequently, the Mechanoids' arrival was a devastating surprise to everyone from the colonists to the highest head

of the I.F. Because the colonies were in "Dead Space" they had minimal military protection.

In the 120 years that followed its discovery, Gideon-E had become a prospering research network of colonies without experiencing the slightest acts of aggression from within the community or from outsiders. The colonies themselves were a combination of residences, research complexes, manufacturing plants and food processing facilities, which made them almost completely self sufficient.

Entire families of researchers and laborers alike came, went and some even settled permanently. Gideon-E was considered to be a model example of successful colonization.

The giant, orbiting space station, Alpha Q, was the colonists' sole link and means of communication with the outside world. It also served as a cargo bay for incoming supplies and rest stop for new arrivals pending approval clearance. Alpha Q was also intended to be a military deterrent against attacks from pirates or other rogues. Not a single fighter managed to take off before the entire space station was atomized by the Mechanoid Mothership.

NOTE: Unknown to most colonists, Gideon-E was believed to have been used as an occasional hideaway, drop point, by pirates and black marketeers. One black market network, specializing in high-tech and weapons, was allegedly established by 'the' Colonel A.E. Gideon turned renegade and may have used Gideon-E as a transit point for especially "hot" items as recently as a decade ago. This could explain the discovery of the Balrog Destroyers packaged in non-military crates marked "Agricultural Pumper". Apparently that particular shipment was lost or the bandits slain.

OLD GIDEON: The Original Gideon Colony

In the old days of the colonization of Gideon-E there was only one spaceport, one hotel, one trading center and they were all located in the one center of population; Old Gideon. Originally, when less was known of the rovers, the human population built "Old" Gideon as a fortress city. By the time the population started to decline 60 years later, the ancient tunnels were half forgotten and the urban sprawl extended out a good sixteen kilometers beyond Mount Casper. New Gideon and Falzon were the new centers of the research colony's activities prior to the Mechanoid's arrival.

It's because of the ancient tunnels and defensive structures of Old Gideon that it is now the main refuge and base of surviving humanity. Yet even with its natural and artificial defenses it could not survive a full assault from the Mechanoid mothership. Thus, the sense of security is an uneasy one.

Spaceport: Pilot's called this area the "Devil's Doorway" and too many shuttle craft pilots have impacted on Glass Rock for anybody's comfort, Devil's Doorway had been used only occasionally in recent years. Until the Mechanoid invasion most traffic was routed through New Gideon.

One major advantage of the Doorway is that the shuttle bays are built directly into the base of Mount Casper. The spaceport control and communications crew operates from the top of Glass Rock. Major sensory and satellite signals are relayed from the peak of Mount Casper. Only the Mechanoid Wasps can easily maneuver around the Devil's Doorway.

The one Mechanoid raid on the Devil's Doorway was driven off by the heavy Mount Casper plasma defenses. No significant damage was done to the spaceport.

Airfield: Five kilometers northeast of downtown Old Gideon is the airfield. Because of its central location it has remained a thriving and busy terminal in spite of the overall decline of Old Gideon's economy. Initial Mechanoid raids have destroyed much of the airfield's structure but the main control tower continues to operate.

Any aircraft needing repairs or long term storage are moved into the bays at the foot of Mount Casper. Although the airport is still quite busy no one stays on the ground any longer than absolutely necessary.

Suburbs: The large suburbs of Old Gideon were built during the city's boom days. Before the Mechanoid invasion less than two houses in three were occupied. Since then the entire area has been evacuated of humans. However, at least a couple of hundred citizens have refused to leave their homes. In addition, the rovers have adopted the area as a major settlement. Quite a few supposedly 'abandoned' houses are filled with rover families.

Most of the houses in this area are prefabricated one story buildings with connecting garages.

Old Gideon's Central Business District has also survived because of it's proximity to Mount Casper. Even the 48 story Commonwealth Insurance Building has remained undamaged by recent attacks.

This area covers about 36 square blocks and was used to house the bulk of Gideon's financial, banking, and commercial business. The area is pretty much abandoned at this point although a few skyscrapers continue to operate.

I.F. Region: According to Intergalactic Federation (I.F.) law a certain parcel of land must be legally granted to the I.F. government before a colony can be considered for membership. This area contains all of the main I.F. buildings including Customs and Immigration, the military recruitment and training compound, and all other official I.F. buildings. The entire area is fenced off and guarded by the remaining I.F. marines (approx. 640 E.B.A.)

Old Town: All of the oldest building on Gideon are in this area. At the time of the Mechanoid invasion it was a mixed neighborhood of residences and shops. Because of a protective overhang of Mount Casper it is still largely populated.

South Side: All of the southern reaches of Old Gideon have been badly chewed up by Mechanoid attacks. To the far west, Gideon's upper class housing is completely destroyed. Both the new and old industrial parks have been hit with nuclear strikes. Of the three different warehouse and shipping areas only the northern section is relatively undamaged.

Road System: Major multilane highways go east to Kucharski and southeast to the destroyed New Gideon. More primitive roads extend in other directions.

Tunnel Complex: Previously abandoned, the ancient alien tunnels of Mount Casper have become a bee-hive of activity. Almost 80,000 people have taken refuge here. In addition most of the surviving industrial machinery, vehicles, weapons and supplies have all been stored in the lower levels.

Level 1 - Sensory Station: Various satellite and microwave dishes, communication and sensory antennas are fixed to the peak of Mount Casper. Each has already been replaced at least once after various Mechanoid attacks. The old observation deck, once a popular tourist spot, has been mostly destroyed. The 16 large lights that circle the peak are used for navigation and signaling.

Level 1a: The elevator stop for the observation deck at the peak.

Level 1b: A series of tunnels close to the outside walls. Used for maintenance only.

Level 1c: Tunnels connect various maintenance and observation rooms. Off-limits to all but security cleared personnel.

Level 2: This is Old Gideon's primary weapons station. On upper level (2a) there are 18 laser cannon (12-120+40 damage, range 3500 meters) circling the mountain. Level 2b is criss-crossed with large tracked tunnels. Of the original 6 plasma cannons (2-24 X 10+100 damage, range 3200 meters) only 5 now survive. The cannon can be moved between 28 different emplacements.

Inside tunnels on level 2 there are a variety of military offices, briefing rooms, and armories. This entire level is restricted to military personnel only.

Level 3: This is still in the process of being excavated. Formerly it held only a few refrigeration units, now it's being outfitted for a military command center.

Level 4: This was used for archival storage of Gideon's administrative records. Most of the chambers have been converted to residences. All the schools and child care facilities have been set up here.

Level 5: Even in the early days many scientific laboratories were located on this level. Now virtually all of the human community research takes place here. In the very center is MC-090, Gideon's largest operating computer. Terminals and smaller computers are scattered throughout the labs.

Level 6: This is the level with the outside surface. Large vehicle doors and personnel hatches are all heavily guarded. Large caverns near the spaceport house all maintenance and hanger facilities for both space and aircraft. The southern areas are now used for ground vehicle maintenance and storage.

Level 7: This was a vast series of storerooms but is now being used and expanded for refugee housing.

The entrance to the natural caverns lies to the far west of the tunnel complex on this level.

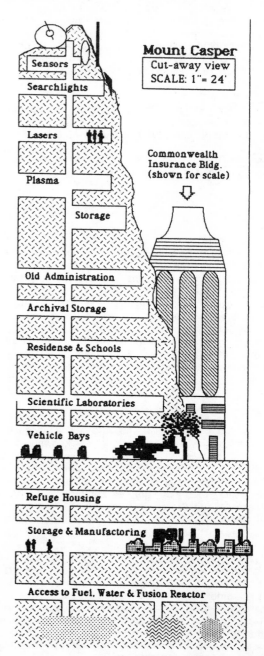

Mount Casper
Cut-away view
SCALE: 1"= 24'

Commonwealth Insurance Bldg. (shown for scale)

Sensors
Searchlights
Lasers
Plasma
Storage
Old Administration
Archival Storage
Residense & Schools
Scientific Laboratories
Vehicle Bays
Refuge Housing
Storage & Manufactoring
Access to Fuel, Water & Fusion Reactor

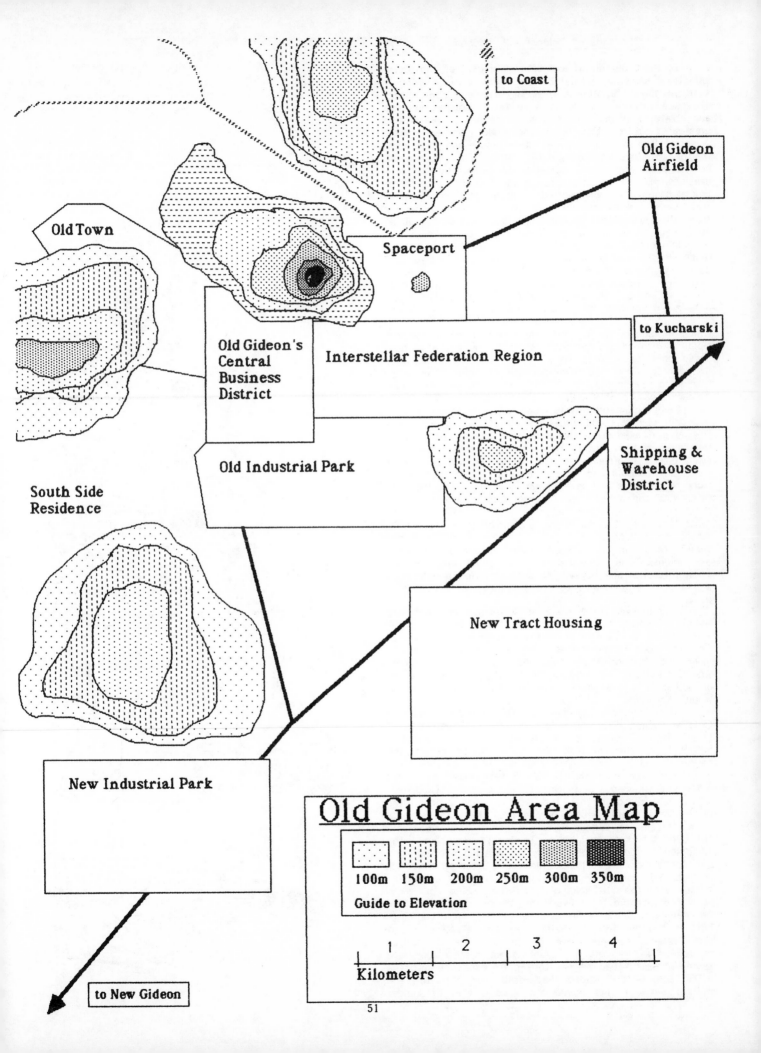

to Coast

Old Gideon
Airfield

Old Town

Spaceport

to Kucharski

Old Gideon's
Central
Business
District

Interstellar Federation Region

Shipping &
Warehouse
District

Old Industrial Park

South Side
Residence

New Tract Housing

New Industrial Park

Old Gideon Area Map

| 100m | 150m | 200m | 250m | 300m | 350m |

Guide to Elevation

1   2   3   4

Kilometers

to New Gideon

The Saga of Colonel A.E. Gideon

To most Earthlings and other members of the Intergalactic Federation (I.F.), Colonel Allan Elisia Gideon is a larger than life, almost legendary figure in the history of space exploration. He is a renowned combat veteran and strategic genius. He is a space pioneer, explorer and amateur field scientist. He is the modern universal man. A hero. He's said to have become a pirate and some say traitor. Whatever the enigmatic colonel may have been, he has stimulated the imagination and admiration of generations. He has become a space age folk hero, an indestructible maverick who defied the odds and won. Colonel A.E. Gideon wrestled with all the challenges of space from alien encounters to the bleak loneliness of the black void he came to call home. Always he met the challenge on "his" terms, boldly, confidently and ultimately, in triumph. In the end he would even challenge the power and authority of the Intergalactic Federation. To most humans he is the greatest hero of the century . . . a super hero . . . a legend. Like most legends, Colonel Allan Elisia Gideon did not die, but simply vanished.

In reality, Colonel Gideon, the man, is much the things of legend. He is a brilliant and charismatic speaker rippling with an energy that seems to radiate with bold faced confidence, superiority, genius and an unsurpassed lust for life. He has been accused of being a megalomaniac, a psychopath, pirate and traitor. Indeed, each has its own measure of validity.

Colonel Gideon always expressed his thoughts with impudent openness and made a habit of seizing opportunities at the expense of his superiors. In his rise through the ranks of the military he continually rebuked his superior's direct commands to implement his own tactics or scheme. He would undermine the authority of these superiors through his own overwhelming successes, astute observations and subversion. Colonel Gideon would earn a reputation of accepting and successfully executing the most difficult and dangerous assignments. His constant, intentional disregard for authority, and military daring would brand him an arrogant megalomaniac (a reasonable assessment). This same behavior, combined with his hair raising tactics and pursuit of death defying assignments, would mark him as an uncontrollable maverick and psychopath.

It might be said that his arrogance and defiance would ultimately destroy him. For while becoming the youngest person in military history to attain the rank of Colonel, deep space commander, at age 26, he would never rise beyond that rank. His multitude of enemies who had suffered embarrassment, humiliation manipulation or demotion at his hands would see to it that his career would stop here.

After several long and fruitful military campaigns Colonel Gideon could no longer contain his frustration at this impasse... defeat ... and became even more blatantly antagonistic. This, in turn, led to his assignment to the toughest and/or farthest reaches of I.F. territory. Yet even here the indomitable A.E. Gideon would carve his place into the pages of history. It would be the Colonel who would discover that the largest moon orbiting the planet Alva could support human life. It would later be named after him, Gideon-E. Only Colonel Gideon was able to route the Yree pirates of Tandar 9 and prevent the Andersbil incident; a potentially devastating political crisis that could have crippled the young Intergalactic Federation. Yet even then he was ostracized to the relative obscurity of the out-backs of I.F. territory.

Too late did the powers that be realize that an unchecked A.E. Gideon had established his own little kingdom in the out-backs utilizing the political power, weapons, vessels, and men loyal to him that the I.F. had so conveniently provided.   A kingdom that would have remained secret had he not thrown its existence into the I.F.'s face. Colonel Gideon had established a pirate/black market network that made the Yree pirates of Tandar

K. SIEMBIEDA · 85

9 look like penny-ante thugs. A criminal network that would last over 90 years after his untimely disappearance. Ironically, it would be through Gideon's network that the mysterious race of techno-wizards known as the Po-tang would be introduced to the I.F. Eventually the Po-tang would become the I.F.'s greatest allies, yet, prior to Colonel Gideon's efforts, their existence was completely unknown to the federation.

Just as extreme measures were about to be taken against the Colonel, he disappeared. Countless reports of his whereabouts, activities and death would flourish over the next 70 years. In order to preserve the legend, the ideal that Colonel Gideon had become, the I.F. report would read that "Colonel A.E. Gideon is missing in action after a heroic confrontation with pirates at the edge of I.F. territory. A media funeral and eulogy equal to the greatest heads of state marked his passing.

Now; one hundred years later, the legend returns from the dead to defend his name-sake world. What had happened a century earlier was that Colonel Gideon had discovered the ancient tunnels that honeycomb the moon. Having puzzled out the use of the phase balls and the transit tunnels, he and a hand picked team of his most loyal men set out to uncover more of these potentially marketable commodities. It's in one of these ancient, underground chambers that he accidentally trapped himself in a stasis field which has held him frozen in time all these decades. It was only the Mechanoids' dissection of the moon world that happened to disrupt the field, releasing its captive. What happened to his men remains a mystery.

Among the living once again, he is ready to accept his greatest challenge. The mere presence of "the Legend" has boosted morale, making the impossible seem plausible. Colonel Gideon will stay behind to orchestrate the final battle against the Mechanoids.

Colonel Allan Elisia Gideon
12th Level Commando
5th Level Field Scientist
I.Q. 15, M.E. 20, M.A. 24, P.S. 14, P.P. 13, P.E. 17, P.B. 16, Spd. 9
Alignment: Anarchist
Age: 59   **Male**   **Weight:** 81kg (180lbs)
Height: 1.9 meters (6ft 4in)   **Hit Points:** 89
Dispostion: Bold, impudent, cocky, super confident and reassuring, courageous, daring, fast thinking. excellent persuasive speaker. Capable of almost any act if it will save the lives of his men or people that he's directly responsible for. The same applies to his own well being, Gideon is NOT the self sacrifice type, without having some last ace in the hole or some chance to destroy his opponents as well. This means he will lie, cheat, steal, kill, back-stab, etc., if he feels the circumstances require it. Excellent strategist.
Psionics: None
Bonuses: +3 save vs psionics (M.E.), +1 save vs toxins/+6% save vs coma/death (P.E.), 84% likelihood of instilling trust & confidence, very charismatic (M.A.). 40% to charm and impress by his mere physical presence (P.B.)
Skills: (commando) W.P. handguns, W.P. laser rifle, W.P. heavy weapons, W.P. explosives (all at 10th level proficiency), prowl 98%, climbing 98%, locksmith 95%, pick pocket 95%, sensory equipment 98%, audio visual communications 80%, investigation 90%, P.A.V. 85%, P.F.G. 80%, surveillance systems 95%.
Hand to Hand: Martial Arts: 5 attacks per melee, +5 to parry and dodge, +3 to strike, +2 to damage, karate kick does 1-8 damage, body throw does 1-6 damage, karate punch does 1-8 damage, critical strike on a roll of 19 or 20.
(field scientist): computer operation 95%, computer programming 85%, medical: paramedic 98%, E-clip recharging 92%, A.V. mechanics 60/55%, mechanical engineering 70% design/65% construct, electronics 85/65%, swimming:basic 90%, tracking outdoors 75%, P.G.V. 75%.

Personal Equipment: PBR-10 particle beam rifle, IB-10 ion blaster, along with his laser lance these are his favorite weapons. He's also fond of the M.A.A. and fusion blocks. Armor: L.B.A. or E.B.A. the latter is always worn into certain combat. NOTE: has access to ALL vehicles, weapons and equipment. Preferred vehicles include the hover scout, flying gun and the new alien needle racer.

Personal Profile: The mere presence of the living legend has boosted morale among the colonists. This, in turn, has fed his tremendous ego, cementing Colonel Gideon's loyalty and resolve to vanquish the enemy or die in a blaze of glory. It has been his decisive actions that have seen several difficult battles to victory. However, his usual disrespect, ego and know-it-all attitude has created a tremendous rift between him and the established administration/military leaders. He and Commander Winston Bromelli, in particular, have engaged in several heated heated arguments. It is clear to all that both men despise each other which has shaken some of the military personnels' confidence in Bromelli.

Colonel Gideon has elected to stay behind, with the majority of the colonists and rovers, to direct the final battles against the Mechanoids. Bromelli will direct his force of several thousand to attempt to gain access to the mothership and sabotage it from within. Col. Gideon views Bromelli's plan as pure stupidity, but has surprisingly kept his sentiments to himself for he believes it has given a goal and hope to everyone. Since everybody is likely to die in the end, he sees it pointless and cruel to take away the one thread of hope that so many cling to.

Despite Col. A.E. Gideon's ego and sense of self preservation, he always fights at his men's side never asking them to do what he himself would not do. He demands his peoples' loyalty and his actions win it.

NOTE: Col. Gideon has found and secreted away his personal means of escape, an "ancient ones" space vehicle. He and an Esper friend (rover) have been able to determine its operation and should be able to pilot it. Its important to note that this is an extreme last measure! Col. Gideon will NOT abandon his men unless 90% have died and all is clearly lost. "If" the slightest chance of defeating the Mechanoids exists he will remain.

The ancient alien space vessel is a tiny spacecraft probably a scout or a lifeboat, designed for long deep space travel. It can hold a maximum of sixteen passengers. Its cargo hold is already packed with the necessary supplies to make the long journey to a safe port. Because of the ship's miniscule size and alien nature, the success of such a journey is, at best, 50-50.

Commander in Chief - Winston Bromelli
10th Level L.B.A. Officer
28 years experience as the head of staff for various top military and political agencies/committees. 8 years as executive of the Gideon-E colony administration. (supposed to have been a gravy retirement position).
Attributes: I.Q. 16, M.E. 13, M.A. 20, P.S. 15, P.P. 12, P.E. 10, P.B. 12, Spd. 11
Alignment: Unprincipled
Age: 66   **Male**   **Weight:** 68kg (152lbs)
Height: 1.7 meters (5ft 10in)   **Hit Points:** 64
Disposition: Smug, pompous, arrogant, condescending toward most personnel of inferior rank; organized, excellent administrator, excells at the utilization of human resources. Tends to be conservative. Fair strategist. Not well liked but respected.
Psionics: None
Bonuses: +3% skill bonus (already included in skills), 65% likelihood of instilling trust and confidence.
Skills: W.P. handgun, W.P. laser rifle, sensory equipment 98%, computer operation 98%, P.F.G. 98%, P.P. tank 98%

tracking 98%, audio communication 73%, P.G.V. 98%, P.A.V. 48%

Hand to Hand: Expert: 5 attacks per melee, +2 to parry and dodge, +3 to strike, +2 to damage, kick attack does 1-6 damage, critical strike on a roll of 19 or 20.

Personal Equipment: LP-20 laser rifle, LP-10 laser pistol (also experienced in all types of handguns).

Armor: L.B.A. or Web Vest. Preferred vehicles include the Rosenstein land buggy, flying gun and hover scout. NOTE: has access to ALL vehicles, weapons and equipment. As commander in chief he can deny or approve the assignment of any item from the balrog destroyer to a simple blaster.

Personal Profile: Commander Bromelli is a competent military commander, fair strategist and excellent administrator. He is trying to make the best out of a horrifying situation.

The hatred between Commander Bromelli and Col. A.E. Gideon grows from Col. Gideon's arrogance and presumption that since he is the best there is (at least in his own opinion), he should be given full charge or at least free reign. Commander Bromelli refuses to relinquish "his" command, especially to a brigand such as Gideon. He has tried to overlook the colonel's abrasive, rash behavior, but finds it unforgivable. The conflict between both men has been compounded by what Col. Gideon views as Commander Bromelli's indecisiveness. In truth, the Commander is simply more conservative, taking much more consideration in his thoughts before making a decision. Col. Gideon has also embarrassed Bromelli and has made it painfully clear that he believes Bromelli's plan to sabotage the Mechanoid mothership is garbage.

Sadly, Commander Bromelli views most of Col. Gideon's astute observations, strategies, comments and ideas with contempt and disregard; foully on both counts. The Commander's personal feelings and need to be in absolute control has blinded him to the vast potential of the mouthy Col. Gideon. NOTE: Bromelli is not a fool, thus he does provide Col. Gideon with as much personal power as any of the other top officers under his command. He has also agreed to place Col. Gideon in charge of the decoy operations, in order to penetrate the mothership, as well as the final ground battles.

Commander Sheldo Schwab
Chief of Experimental Weapons Design Division
8th Level E.B.A. Division Officer
6th Level Field Scientist
Attributes: I.Q. 16, M.E. 16, M.A. 12, P.S. 10, P.P. 11, P.E. 10, P.B. 9, Spd. 10
Alignment: Scrupulous
Age: 42   Male   Weight: 90kg (200lbs)
Height: 1.7 meters (5ft 10in)   Hit Points: 67
Disposition: Dedicated, hard worker, honest, trustworthy, respectful to authority, clever and inventive, extremely resourceful.
Psionics: Major (non-esper O.C.C.) I.S.P.: 74
Abilities: Object read, resist fatigue, see the invisible, and total recall. No extra-ordinary psi-abilities.
Bonuses: Save vs psionic attack +1, +3% skill bonus (included in skills)
Skills: (E.B.A.) W.P. handgun, W.P. laser rifle, W.P. heavy weapons and W.P. explosives (all 8th level proficiency), audio visual communication 93%, P.P. tank 94%, P.G.V. 98%, climbing 92%, swimming: basic 74%.
Hand to Hand: Expert: 4 attacks per melee, +3 parry and dodge, +2 to strike, +2 to damage, kick attack does 1-6 damage, critical strike on a roll of 19 or 20.
(field scientist) computer operation 98%, computer programming, sensory equipment 98%, medical: paramedic 98%, E-clip recharging 98%, electronics 93/78%, mechanical engineer 78% design/73% construct, A.V. mechanics 68/63%, G.V. mechanics 84/78%, surveillance systems 90% P.A.V. 78%, swimming: scuba 52%, locksmith 33%.
Personal Equipment: PBR-10 particle beam, LP-10 laser pistol, laser lance; mini-tool pack. He's also extremely

familiar with ALL experimental weapons especially the M.A.A. and fusion blocks which he helped design and the HAVOC camouflage system which he assisted on. Commander Schwab is also considered to be an expert in the artifacts of the "Ancient Ones". Armor: E.B.A. under battle conditions, L.B.A. otherwise. Favorite vehicles include the A.T.V. walker, hover scout and ancient alien needle racer (to which he has personal access and is an expert pilot). The portable laboratory is always brought along for any field operations.

Personal Profile: Commander Schwab is a weapons expert and experimental weapons master. It is Schwab's responsibility to supervise the development and testing of experimental weapons. Prior to the Mechanoids' arrival he was in charge of the excavation of the ancient tunnels. Generally, assignment of experimental or alien devices must be cleared with him first.

Surprisingly, Commander Schwab gets along well with both Commander in Chief Bromelli and Col. A.E. Gideon. Both men view Schwab as a creative genius and palladin-like person. He is the ONLY officer truly respected by Col. Gideon.

GUSTOVICH

Weapons

COLONY WEAPONS

Gideon E was a peaceful colonization operation unprepared for a full military confrontation. Consequently, many weapons, particularly assault vehicles, are limited in scope and magnitude. Many are modifications of existing, peace time equipment, while others are experimental and still others are remnants of the ancient alien race that built the subterranean tunnels millions of years earlier.

Important Notes On Energy Weapons

1) **Weapons are limited** to those listed in this book.
2) **Automatic weapons** have not been used for centuries and are considered to be obsolete. They will NOT be manufactured.
3) **Weapons of antiquity** such as knives, swords, axes, bow and arrow, spear, sling, and so on are generally considered to be tools or objects for hobbyists and sportsmen. Only the "rovers" use them as weapons. Such weapons are useless against Mechanoids, although still quite lethal to humans and rovers.
4) **ALL energy weapons**, except the fusion torch and experimental weapons, have automatic safety mechanisms that makes intentional or unintentional overloading/explosion IMPOSSIBLE!
5) All energy weapons are powered by an **energy clip**, also known as an "E-Clip", or a portable generator of a fusion or plasma nature. An E-clip can only be recharged at an established base or by somebody with an E-clip recharging skill (SEE P.G.V.M. O.C.C.). Once an energy clip is used up the weapon is powerless until a new one is "clipped" in. Empty E-clip are kept to be recharged later. Recharging usually costs half as much as a brand new E-clip.

Weapons By Category

Side Arms/Handguns	Special or Experimental Weapons
SB-14: Simple Blaster	I.L.R.M.
IB-10: Ion Blaster	Tiger I.L.R.M.
LP-10: Laser Pistol	Sandwolf Torpedo
	E.M.B. (Bore Rifle)
Rifles	Fusion Blocks
LR-20: Laser Rifle	Fusion Block Projector
GP-14: Glop Projector	Remote Multi-Firing Unit (RMF-1)
	Multi-Arm Antagonizer (M.A.A.)
Heavy Weapons	M-1 Juggernaut E.B.A.
PBR-10: Particle Beam	M-2 Juggernaut E.B.A.
PE-6: Plasma Ejector	
PE-M8: Plasma Ejector	
Explosives	
Grenades	
Flying Gun	

Utility Tools
Fusion Torch
Laser Lance
Spike Launch Rod
Survival Knife
Hand Axe
Machete
Grappling Hook & Line
Flares
Nylon Cord
Protective Head Gear
Medical Kit
Food Ration Pack
Hand Held Communicator

Side Arms/Handguns

SB-14/Simple Blaster
Range: 120 meters (400ft)
Damage: 2-12+2 (2D6+2) points
Attacks Per Melee: up to seven blasts, maximum
E-Clip Capacity: 14 blasts
Weight: 0.9kg (2lbs)
Cost: 500 credits, widely available; E-clip 700 credits

This is a common side arm in the earth colonies. Perhaps its most attractive feature is its rapid firing capabilities, able to fire seven times per melee. This means the wielder can squeeze off one or two blasts or seven per melee.

IB-10/Ion Blaster
Range: 180 meters (600ft)
Damage: 3-18 (3D6)
Attacks Per Melee: up to four blasts
E-Clip Capacity: 10 blasts
Weight: 0.9kg (2lbs)
Cost: 600 credits, widely available; E-clip 70 credits

The IB-10 is often called the "heavy duty" blaster because of its damage and range.

LP-10/Laser Pistol
Range: 300 meters (1000ft)
Damage: 4-24 (4D6)
Attacks Per Melee: Two
E-Clip Capacity: 10 blasts
Weight: 0.7kg (1½lbs)
Cost: 800 credits, moderate availability; E-clip 100 credits. Illegal cost: 1200 to 1500 credits, moderate availability.

The LP-10 is a light weight precision laser weapon. It is a common side arm for L.B.A. and E.B.A. officers.

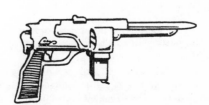

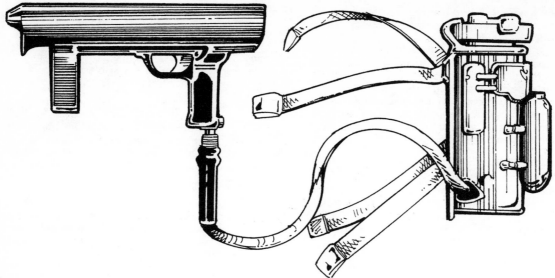

Rifles

Heavy Weapons

Glop Projectors
__Classification:__ Special: Low Clearance (not field tested)

This weird sounding device, developed by Professor Rad McCall, resembles an old-fashioned flame thrower. However, instead of shooting flame it throws a stream of what's called glop. The glop is a sticky substance that can be sprayed on Mechanoids, blocking their normal optics and impairs their infra-red and ultra-violet sensors as well as other mechanical scanning processes. The "glop" wears off within two hours or can be removed with a simple solvent.
__Range:__ 9 meters maximum (30ft) most effective within 4.6 meters.
__Attacks Per Melee:__ Two
__Bonuses:__ None
__Damage:__ Effectively blinds mechanoids and sensory equipment. Makes the mechanoid -5 to strike, parry and dodge.
__Weight:__ With glop tank back pack 11kg (25lbs); the projector gun part itself weighs 2.3kg (5lbs).
__NOTES:__ A glop back pack holds enough glop for a total of 28 blasts. It takes at least two blasts to completely blind a mechanoid brain, brute, exterminator or mantis. Only one well placed shot can blind a runner, tunnel crawler, seeker pod, assault probe, thinman, runt skimmer or weavel.

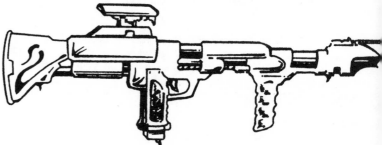

PBR-10/Particle Beam Rifle
__Range:__ 1400 meters (4620ft)
__Damage:__ 5-50 or 5-50+25*
__Attacks Per Melee:__ Two
__E-Clip Capacity:__ 10 blasts
__Weight:__ 5.4kg (12lbs)
__Cost:__ Not available for civilian use. Illegal purchase will cost approximately 3800 credits, while an E-clip runs about 200 credits. Possession of an illegal PBR-10 in this war torn situation is confiscation of the weapon, a reprimand and it is permanently recorded on the person's record.

The destructive power of this weapon is so awesome that its use is generally restricted to the combat forces (L.B.A., E.B.A. and commando) and persons on special assignments. The PBR-10 comes equipped with an infra-red telescopic targeting scope.
*__Damage from a Particle Beam Weapon:__
THE FOLLOWING RESTRICTIONS APPLY TO ALL PARTICLE BEAM WEAPONS:

When rolling a twenty sided die to strike an opponent/ target, the normal rules are modified when using a particle beam weapon. ONLY a roll of 11 through 20 hits; and even then, a roll of 11-17 is only a nick. A roll of 18-19-20 is a direct hit.

__Damage from a nick__, a roll to strike of 11-17, indicates that the particle beam merely grazed its target which probably means part of it is atomized. A so called "nick" does 5-50 points of damage (5D10).

LR-20/Laser Rifle
__Range:__ 1200 meters (4000ft)
__Damage:__ 5-30 (5D6)
__Attacks Per Melee:__ Two
__E-Clip Capacity:__ 20 blasts
__Weight:__ 3.2kg (7lbs)
__Cost:__ 1800 credits, wide availability; E-clip costs 120 credits. Illegal purchase will cost around 2600 credits, moderate availability.

This light weight energy weapon is standard issue for commandos, L.B.A. and E.B.A. Divisions, investigation in the field/exploration and combat situations. The LR-20 comes equipped with an infra-red telescopic scope.

Damage from a direct hit, on a roll to strike of 18, 19 or 20, is even more devastating; doing 5-50+25 points of damage (5D10+25).

Double damage or a critical hit occurs when a "natural 20" is rolled to strike. A natural 20 is a die roll that is not modified by the character's weapon skill bonus (W.P) or attribute bonuses. Players can either roll 5D10+25 points and multiply those numbers rolled by two, or roll 10D10+50.
NOTES: 1) A.R. and S.D.C. rules still apply to particle beam weapons.
2) All human and mechanoid P-beams do the same damage unless otherwise indicated.
3) Anything destroyed by a particle beam will be a hunk of half dissolved slag and far beyond salvaging. We're talking total annihilation. A person would be lucky to even recognize the object after a particle beam assault.

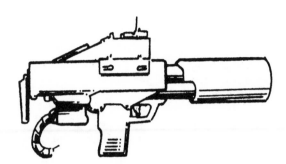

PE-6/Plasma Ejector
Range: 2200 meters (7260ft)
Damage: 4-24+10 per each blast
Attacks Per Melee: up to 6 maximum; +1 to strike
Plasma Generator Capacity: 6 blasts
Weight: gun ejector with opticals 2.5kg (5½lbs); plasma generator 18kg (40lbs)
Cost: Not available for civilian use. Illegal purchase will cost approximately 3800 credits while a second generator or replacement generator costs about 1600 credits.

The PE-6 is a high powered distance weapon with built in laser tracking and radar (4km area), infra-red distancing scope with digital display. Its greatest disadvantage is its limited firing power and its weight. The generator is designed for use as a portable back-pack unit.

The PE-6 is able to fire a single fiery ball of plasma or a full volley of six. When more than one blast is fired per melee; the plasma balls will merge into one larger sphere of energy, all of which will strike the same target. For the sake of quick game play in determining damage from a multiple blast, I recommend rolling 4D6 times the number of blast(s) plus 10 damage points for each. For example: firing half the payload, three, would be 4D6 X 3+30 points of damage.
NOTE: Once the generator has released all six charges it will require a full 24 hours to recharge and be usable again. Of course the exhausted generator can be detached and a fresh fully charged one connected, but this takes 1-4 minutes and only a mechanic (P.G.V.M. or P.A.V.M.) or someone with a W.P. Heavy Weapon skill can do so.

PE-M8/Multiple Plasma Ejector
Range: 2200 meters (7260ft)
Damage: 4-24 X 10 (4D6X10) or 8-48 X 10 (8D6X10)
Attacks Per Melee: One (total of two); +2 to strike
Plasma Generator Capacity: 8 plasma charges
Weight: Gun ejector on tri-pod 8.6kg (19lbs); generator 90kg (40lbs)
Cost: Not available to civilians. Illegal purchase will cost about 5600 credits while a second or replacement generator costs about 3000 credits.

The PE-M8 is a multi-firing heavy assault weapon with a built in laser tracking scanner and radar (4km area) The PE-M8 is capable of firing a half load of four simultaneous charges (two attacks); or its maximum fire power

of eight plasma charges (one attack). These simultaneous, rapid fire plasma ejections expand as they travel to create one massive wall of plasma, filling approximately, a 5 meter area (18ft).

As with all plasma weapons its firing power is very limited. This means the PE-M8 can only fire once (a full load of 8 charges) or twice (two half loads). Once all eight charges are expended the weapon must have its generator replaced with a new, fully charged one. Changing generators requires 2-8 minutes and can only be done by a mechanic or person with a W.P. Heavy Weapon skill.

Flying Gun
See Vehicles

CONVENTIONAL EXPLOSIVES

Concentrated Blasting Caps

There are three types of blasting caps, each denoted by the magnitude of the explosion. Each type comes equipped with a timer which can be set for as little as 60 seconds or as long as three hours.
Type One: 4-24+10 damage (4D6+10) to 0.9 meter (3ft) area.
Type Two: 6-36+24 damage (6D6+24) to a 1.2 meter (4ft) area.
Type Three: 6-60+24 damage (6D10+24) to a 1.8 meter (6ft) area.

Shape Charges

This is a form of plastic explosive that can be shaped and molded as needed.
S.C. Type One: 6-36+24 damage per 0.5 kilogram (1lb), affects a 1.5 meter (5ft) area.
S.C. Type Two: 5-50+50 damage per 0.5 kilogram (1lb), affects a 2.1 meter (7ft) area.
S.C. Type Three: 8-80+50 damage per 0.5 kilogram (1lb), affects a 3 meter (10ft) area.

Grenades

Being a non-military outpost, the types of grenades available are limited. Furthermore, conventional explosives are not as effective against the mechanoids as the equally powerful, long range energy weapons.
Explosive Hand Grenade: "Effective" range thrown: 21 meters (70ft) or 48 meters (160ft) maximum, but -2 to strike when thrown beyond 21 meters. Damage: 6-36 points damage to a 4.6 meter (15ft) area.
Fragmentation Grenade: Specially designed to hurl hundreds of tiny fragments to inflict greater damage. Same range limitations apply as previously stated. Damage: 7-42 (7D6) points damage to a 6 meter (20ft) area.
White Phosphorous: Ignites/flames on contact with air setting a 6 meter (20ft) area ablaze. Damage: 3-18 points damage; does NO damage to the mechanoids but does disrupt infra-red and heat detecting sensors.
Smoke Grenades: Creates great billowing clouds of smoke

filling approximately a 9 meter (30ft) area. Can be used as a signal or as a smoke screen to impair normal optics and infra-red scans.

Ion Grenade: This energy grenade unleashes a blinding and destructive blast of ion energy. Damage: 4-40 (4D10) points damage to a 6 meter (20ft) area.

Plasma Grenade: Unleashes a fire ball of plasma energy. Damage: 4-40+2 to a 9 meter (30ft) area. The plasma grenade is usually restricted to L.B.A. and E.B.A. Divisions or commandos on special assignment. Unlike white phosphorous, the plasma grenade will do FULL damage to the mechanoids.

Signal Flare: Fires an illuminating flare into the sky, dropping down and lighting up a 27 meter (90ft) area. Does 3-18 points damage as a weapon (does not damage mechanoids).

Grenades are available only on assignment. However, they "may" be available illegally for 120 credits each for explosive, frag, white phosphorous; 60 credits for smoke and flares; 200 credits for ion and 300 credits for plasma. Costs may be much higher in some cases (G.M.'s discretion).

Utility Tools

Fusion Torch
Range: 30 meters maximum
Damage: 2-12+4 (2D6+4)
Attacks Per Melee: Two (considered the same energy charge for both).
Energy Capacity: 200 charges (special)
Weight: Torch .5kg (1lb); fusion energy pack 7kg (17lbs)
Cost: Torch 50 credits, energy pack 1200 credits.

The fusion torch is a common tool used by mechanics for welding and body work. However, it can also make a formidable, close range weapon.

Conditions and Special Damage as a Weapon:
When used as a normal, acetylene type torch the flame is only a few centimeters long (approximately two inches), does 1-8 points of damage (1D8) but DOES NOT drain the energy pack.

To extend the flame, simultaneously increasing the heat, requires only a simple adjustment. The fusion torch has thirty one settings; normal and numbers one through thirty. These additional settings of 1-30 regulate the length and intensity of the flame. Each setting burns up "5 charges" of energy while increasing the flame's length one meter for each setting. This means that if the torch is placed on setting number one the flame will reach one meter (about 3½ft) and cost five energy charges/units per melee. At setting number two the flame extends to two meters (7ft) and costs ten energy charges per melee. At the maximum setting of thirty the flame will shoot out thirty meters (100ft), but will burn up a huge amount of energy, 150 charges per melee. Once all the energy is expended the fusion torch is useless unless a reserve energy tank is connected (takes two or three minutes if you know what you are doing). Used in this manner, the fusion torch can shoot fiery bursts at a rate of twice per melee. It can also shoot a sustained stream of fire, like a flame thrower, by holding the trigger mechanism down. The amount of energy used is the same per each melee the torch is on.
NOTE: The fusion torch can only fire a sustained stream of flame for a maximum of FIVE melees. Use in this manner will cause the device to overheat and explode.

Another optional setting is FREE-FLOW. This fires a continuous stream of flame inflicting triple the normal damage (6D6+12), but will always overload the system. The initial energy expended is 50 and will continue to expend 50 energy charges per melee until it explodes (in the 5th melee). The flame's length is the maximum 30 meters.

Overloads
The fusion torch begins to overload if it is in continual use or expends a great amount of energy in a rel-

atively short time. If the device uses 120 charges or more within one hour, it will visibly begin to smoke and should be allowed to cool for at least four hours. If it is continued to be used there's a 64% chance of its locking into the free flow mode and exploding within two melees. Roll to determine if it locks into free flow once for every five energy charges used.

The Explosion
The fusion torch will explode within one or two melee of having expended its normal number of energy charges (200). The seathing energy reserve and gases will ignite in a searing mini-thermonuclear explosion. Damage: 120 points to the core area of six meters (20ft) and 70 points of damage within an additional 10 meters (35ft) beyond the blast center.

Laser Lance (tool)
Range: 90 meters maximum (300ft)
Damage: 1-6 or 2-12 (two settings)
Attacks Per Melee: Two
Energy Capacity: 30 charges
Weight: 113.4 grams (4 ounces)
Cost: 350 credits, readily available

The laser lance is a common utility tool, often used by mechanics and communications engineers. This handy all purpose tool is slightly longer than a normal writing pen (about 8 inches) and twice as wide. It can be easily carried in pockets, clipped onto utility belts, mini-tool packs or even one's boot. Because it is so easy to conceal it is a favorite item coveted by the rovers and always the first item stolen.

The laser can fire a short laser beam burst of varying intensity or it can unleash a continual beam.
Short Burst: Damage: 1-6 (1 energy charge) or 2-12 (2 energy charges).
Continual Beam: Damage: 1-6 (2 energy charges) or 2-12 (3 energy charges per melee)

SLR-60/Spike Launch Rod
Range: 60 meters maximum (200ft)
Damage: 2-12 (2D6)
Attacks Per Melee: One
Energy Capacity: 30 charges
Weight: .9kg (2lbs)
Cost: 300 credits, high availability

This small, .6 meter (2ft), rod-like device is commonly used by commandos, for planet exploration and recreational mountain climbing. The SLR-60 can effectively fire a small (6 inch) metal spike up to 60 meters away carrying a high test line along with it for scaling surfaces. It comes equipped with 130 meters of heavy duty cord, detachable spool and feeder with digital counter. Additional spikes are available at 30 credits a dozen while additional clip-in, prewound spools of 130 meter line costs 75 credits each.

Survival Knife
Range: Hand held, 30 meters (100ft) thrown
Damage: 1-6
Attacks Per Melee: Equal to number of hand to hand attacks
Weight: .5kg (1lb)
Cost: 50 credits, widely available

This well balanced stainless steel blade is used by all military type personnel and in the field. It is designed to take as well as dish out punishment.

The other edge is serrated for cutting wood, etc. and the handle is wrapped with nylon line (4 meters, 15ft) that can be used for snares, fishing line, trip wire etc. There is also a small compass that screws onto the end of the handle.

Hand Axe
Range: Hand held or 18 meters thrown (60ft)

Damage: 1-6
Attacks Per Melee: equal to hand to hand attacks
Weight: .9kg (2lbs)
Cost: 40 credits, fair availability.

The hand axe is a small axe used for field expeditions and camping.

Machete
Range: Hand held or 12 meters thrown (40ft)
Damage: 1-8
Attacks Per Melee: Equal to hand to hand attacks
Weight: 1kg (3lbs)
Cost: 60 credits, fair availability

This is a short sword-like blade made of tough, durable steel and designed to retain its sharpness. The machete was used exclusively for chopping through dense vegetation.

Grappling Hook & Line
Range: 30 meters maximum (100ft)
Damage: 1-4
Attacks Per Melee: equal to hand to hand attacks
Weight: .9kg (2lbs)
Cost: 80 credits for hook and 90 meters (300ft) of line. Fair availability.

This is your typical grappling hood and line for scaling surfaces.

FLARE GUN

Flares (tools)
Three Types: Flare Gun
Hand Held Flare
Rocket Flare

Flare Gun
Range: 90 meters (300ft)
Damage: 2-12 per melee ignited (5 melees)
Attacks Per Melee: Two
Energy Capacity: Charge contained in the flare itself.
Weight: .9kg (2lbs)
Cost: 100 credits for the gun only, flares cost 10 credits each. Wide availability.

The flare gun has not changed much over the decades and is basically like those we use today. It is generally used as a signal or to light up an area. Used for luminescence: lights up 90 meter area (300ft) for about five melees (45 seconds). It is not intended to be a weapon thus it is not balanced for aiming; W.P. handgun skill bonuses do NOT apply.

Hand Held Flares
Range: Hand Held
Damage: One point
Attacks Per Melee: equal to hand to hand attacks
Weight: 170 grams (6 ounces)
Cost: 3 credits each, wide availability.

The hand held flare is generally used to mark an area or for signaling. They are similar to those used by present day truck drivers.

Rocket Flare
Range: 90 meters straight up (300ft), 20 meters diagonally
Damage: 2-12
Attacks Per Melee: One
Energy Capacity: one
Weight: 141 grams (5 ounces)
Cost: 10 credits each; wide availability

This hand held flare has a disposable, one time; launch mechanism which fires the flare gun. Commonly used for

expeditions in the wild. A minus 3 to strike penalty applies if used as a weapon.

Nylon Cord
A variety of heavy duty, all purpose, nylon rope or cord is available. Average tension strength is 270kg (600 lbs). Average length is 90m (300ft) at a cost of 50 to 100 credits. Good availability.

Protective Head Gear
Padded Helmet: A.R. 10; Cost: 25 credits
Protective Goggles or Tinted Visor: Designed for use outdoors or for welding. Unbreakable plastic lenses. Cost 20 credits.
L.B.A. style face protector and gas mask: The mask can attach to most standard helmets providing added protection to the face and eyes. Tinted visor and detachable air filter are standard. Costs 70 credits. With gas mask modification and independent oxygen supply (2 hour), 195 credits.
Conventional Air Filter: Fits over nose and mouth; Costs 8 credits.
Conventional gas mask: With a superior filtering system; Costs 25 credits.

Medical Kit
A comprehensive first aid kit that contains six doses of each of the following: antibiotics, anti-inflammatory, sedative, pain killer. Assorted mini-instrument pack, with scalpels, scissors, probes, etc., a dozen in all. Tape, bandages, sutures, a precision surgical laser lance (20 charges) and four air filters.
Not available on the open market with the drugs.

Food Ration Packs
A standard food pack contains enough concentrated, vitamin enriched, freeze dried rations to easily last two weeks. The food supply can be stretched to last four weeks if necessary. Geared for two man consumption. Costs 200 credits on the open market. Limited availability.

Hand Held Communicator
This is essentially a souped-up walkie-talkie, short range directional communicator. Range: 4.8km (3 miles). Independent energy source. Costs 200 credits; wide availability.

BATTLE HELMET WITH DIRECTIONAL COMMUNICATOR.

LASER PISTOL

RE-ENFORCED BODY PLATES

UTILITY BELT

HOLSTER

Experimental Weapons

Experimental Weapons are generally a variation or jury-rigging of existing technology and devices modified for combat use. Most are not field tested and many are plagued with irregular malfunctions (see malfunction tables for specific items. If there is no table the device is stable, without flaws). Most fall into the classification of Heavy Weapons which would limit its authorized use to E.B.A. division and commando. However, authorization to use these devices are often given to field scientists and L.B.A. division on special assignment or for field testing. Experimental weapons may also be assigned to any other O.C.C. but this is not as likely as the former.

The same is also true in the assignment of alien technology.

The original Mechanoid Invasion and the Journey books presented a handful of experimental weapons and vehicles which are included in these pages (some with adjusted statistics). Another dozen or so new devices are also presented for the first time. These devices are indicative of the colonists' frantic research and pursuits to vanquish the Mechanoids.

EXPERIMENTAL MISSILES

Intelligent Limited Range Missiles (I.L.R.M.)
Classification: Special (experimental)

These intelligent robot missiles have been fitted with a sophisiticated computer that can actually search out its target. If its target is beyond its strike range of 1800 kilometers, the I.L.R.M. will land and "wait" until a programmed target comes into range. All I.L.R.M.s are equipped with radar/sonar (40km range), infra-red, ultra-violet, radio wave and micro wave scanners.

I.L.R.M.s are designed for maximum speed and mobility (see bonuses), enabling it to skillfully execute high speed pursuits, sharp turns and maneuvers at both high and low altitudes. Although experimental, it has been extensively tested and has an impressive strike record of 89%.
Speed: 1800kmph
Range: 1800km
Attacks Per Melee: One (self-destruct)
Bonus: +4 to strike and +4 to dodge
Damage: 110 on impact
Weight: 148kg (330lbs)
    Size: 1.5 meters long (5ft)

S.D.C.: 25
A.R.: 10

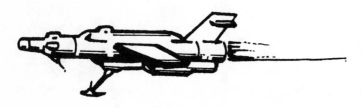

I.L.R.M.

The Tiger I.L.R.M.
Classification: Special (experimental)

The Tiger I.L.R.M. is a slightly larger, more powerful, intelligent missile. It has all the same tracking/scanning capabilities as a normal I.L.R.M. but is a little slower and its maximum range a little shorter.

On the plus side, the Tiger has a much greater strike and damage potential. In addition to its own explosive power, it also has two heat seeking, **mini-seeker missiles** that it can fire at will. Like the Tiger, the mini-seekers are programmed to attack only specific targets.
Speed: 1650kmph
Range: 1200km
Attacks Per Melee: Two with mini-seeker missile and one by the Tiger I.L.R.M.
Bonuses: Mini-seekers are +3 to strike; the Tiger I.L.R.M. is +4 to strike and +3 to dodge.
Damage: Mini-seekers 25 points of damage each, (range 10km, +3 to strike, speed 1800kmph); Tiger I.L.R.M. 150 points of damage.
Weight: 180kg (400lbs)
Size: 2.1 meters long (7ft)
S.D.C. of the I.L.R.M. 30; mini-seekers 10
A.R. of the I.L.R.M. 10; mini-seekers 8

TIGER I.L.R.M.

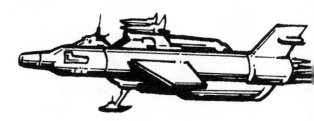

The Sandwolf Land Torpedo (S.L.T.)
Classification: Special (missile)

Another modified weapon developed by Rad McCall is the Sandwolf Land Torpedo or "wolf" as it's been dubbed by some. The S.L.T. is a small hovercraft-like weapon equipped with an I.L.R.M. brain. Fast and clever, the S.L.T can be launched as a low altitude missile against a specific target or it can be sent out as a roving land-mine. It is for this last function that the S.L.T. is called wolf; for it can be sent out to hunt a particular prey, lying in wait and detonating only when the target is within its blast range.

Although the S.L.T. lacks the speed and range of an I.L.R.M., it is an equally devastating smart bomb. The sandwolf torpedo is designed for maximum mobility at low altitudes, enabling it to skirt as low as one meter (4ft) above the ground, skillfully avoiding any obstacles in its path until its target is found. Like the I.L.R.M., the S.L.T. can land and wait for its preprogrammed target. Unlike the I.L.R.M., the S.L.T. can camouflage itself by shooting out powerful jets of air, covering itself in sand, loose dirt, leaves and so on. This makes it an ideal weapon for the desert (hence its name sandwolf) and the barren wastelands which resulted from the Mechanoids' defoliation and mining.

The sandwolf's usual programmed tactic is to be launched into a particular area where it hides itself in what appears to be a traveled area. If its scanners indicates the targets have moved, it will rise and fly to that area, bury itself again and wait until a target is near or on top of it and detonate. Or it will wait, hidden under

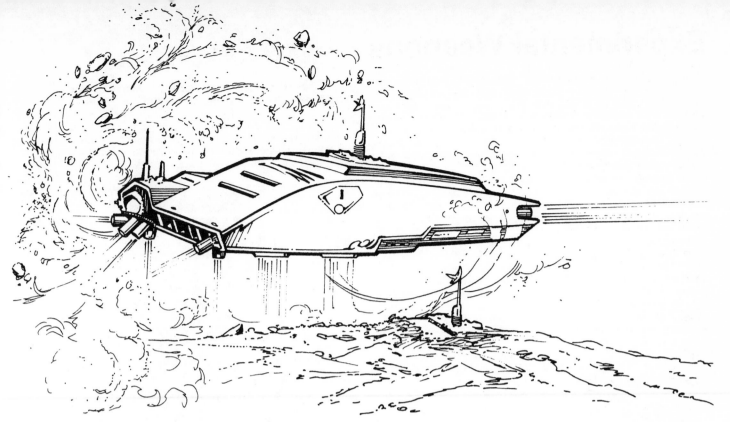

sand or leaves, and launch itself or attach itself to a near by target (60 meters) and detonate. In effect the S.L.T. is an artificially intelligent roving land mine, able to pick-up and reposition itself wherever it's most effective. Of course, as a smart bomb, it will NOT detonate even if stepped on by humans, rovers, animals, earth vehicles and so on. Its only targets are the distinctive Mechanoids and their vehicles. When out of fuel it will just sit and wait, although the S.L.T. is rarely foolish enough to completely exhaust its fuel supply.

Maximum Range: 804km (500 miles)
Maximum Speed: 321kmph (200mph)
Attacks: One only.
Bonuses: +3 to strike, +2 to dodge +6 to strike as a hidden land mine.
Damage: 80 points of damage in a 4.6 meter area (15ft)
Weight: 45.36kg (100lbs)
Size: 1 meter (approximately 3½ft) long
S.D.C.: 30 **A.R.:** 10
NOTES: Sensors include radio monitoring, heat, infra-red and radar/sonar with a one kilometer range. The S.L.T. can also be fitted with a fusion block if conditions warrant it. The usual problems with fusion blocks apply.

Electro Magnetic Borer (E.M.B.)
Classification: Rifle (experimental)

This energy rifle fires an interchangeable projectile that can be used as a weapon or for information gathering. This is done by inserting a particular type of projectile. Both types will attach themselves to a metallic surface and then releases a short, high intensity laser burst which will cut or bore into the metallic substance. Once the hole is cut the projectile fires its payload into the hole. This can be either an explosive or scanner.

The explosive head fires an explosive charge into the laser bored hole and directly into the internal workings of the machine or mechanoid mechanism. This will often cripple a machine (52% chance) or instantly slays a mechanoid (31% chance). Damage is 8-80+40 (8D10+40).

The scanning head fires a miniature sensory device into the laser bored hole. The sensor will then continually transmit data for up to four hours and has a transmission range of 16 kilometers (10 miles). Minimal damage is inflicted by the scanning head projectile doing a mere 2-12

points of damage.

Malfunction Tables:
Explodes On Impact: Roll for each projectile fired whether it's the explosive head or scanner head. 33% likelihood of exploding; Damage from explosive is 8-80 (no +40 because it impacted on the outer shell/outside). 3-8 from scanner.
Rifle Jams 10% of the time; roll for each time fired. Requires 2-8 melees to unjam.
Awkward Balance: -1 to strike
NOTES: Anyone with a W.P. Laser Rifle skill can use this weapon with the greatest level of skill, although anyone can use the gun.
Attacks Per Melee: One
Range: 540 meters (1200ft)
Weight: 3.6 kilograms (8lbs), each projectile weighs .7 kilograms (1½lbs).

Fusion Blocks
Classification: Explosives (experimental)

This compact explosive device is as dangerous as it is devastating. However, the awesome damage potential and flexibility of its use is very alluring. Each block measures 0.6 meters (2ft) long by 0.3 meters (1ft) wide and 19cm (7½ inches) tall. Average Weight is 7.7kg (17lbs). Each block comes equipped with a built in timing and detonation mechanism.

The major drawback in using the fusion block is its unstable detonators and timers. A yet undetermined flaw in these basic mechanisms can cause a fusion block to explode prematurely or not at all. Ironically, one of the fusion block's fail-safes is that the block can NOT be detonated by ANY means other than its built in detonators or a direct blast from a particle beam.

Roll on the following table EACH TIME a fusion block is used.

Fusion Block Malfunction Table

1-4	Explodes immediately
5-18	Explodes in 30 seconds from moment set
19-30	No problems; will detonate as set
31-36	Dud; does not detonate
37-48	No problem; will detonate as set
49-56	Faulty timer; will explode within 60 seconds
57-64	Dud; does not detonate
65-70	Faulty timer; will explode within half the time set
71-80	No problem; will detonate as set
81-88	Faulty timer; will explode within double the time set.
89-92	Dud
93-95	Explodes immediately
96-00	Okay; will detonate as set

Fusion Block Damage Tables

Type One does 160 points of damage at the center of the blast, 9 meter (30ft) area, and 5-50+20 points of damage for an additional 12 meters (40ft).

Type Two does 200 points of damage at the blast center, 9 meter (30ft) area, and 5-50+50 points of damage for an additional 15 meters (50ft).

Type Three does 500 points of damage at the blast center, 10.7 meters (35ft) area and 6-60+120 points of damage for an additional 21 meters (70ft).

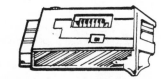

FUSION BLOCK PROJECTOR

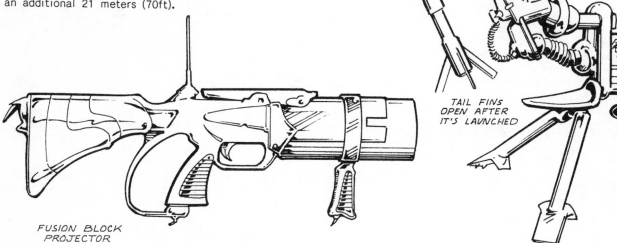

A TYPICAL FUSION BLOCK

Fusion Block Projector
Classification: Heavy Weapon & Explosives (not field tested).

In an attempt to extend the use of these destructive fusion weapons in battle, researcher Matt T'Nelab developed the fusion block projector. The projector is a simple device that can launch or hurl a fusion block up to **40 meters** (approx. 135 feet) away. The sturdy fusion block is not affected by the impact, but the usual timer and detonator problems still apply (roll on malfunction table).

Special Requirements: Only characters with a W.P. Heavy Weapons can use the projector with any real skill; all others are -2 to strike. MUST have W.P. Explosives to activate the blocks.

Attacks Per Melee: One

Weight: 11kg (25lbs)

Length: 1.5 meters (5ft)

Remote Multi-Firing Unit/R.M.F.-1
Classification: Heavy Weapon (experimental)

Another weapon developed by Matt T'Nelab is a radio controlled mini-launcher which fires a volley of explosive projectiles. The RMF-1 can fire its payload one at a time, sequentially or simultaneously. Although T'Nelab is continuing his work to perfect an automated ammunition feed system, presently the RMF-1 must be manually loaded.

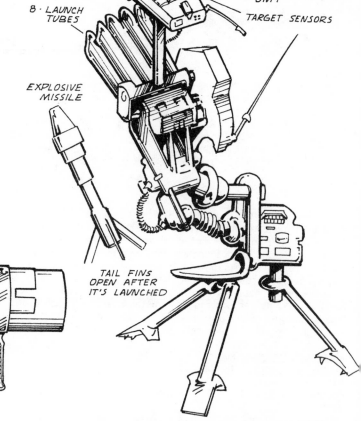

REMOTE MULTI-FIRING UNIT

TARGET SENSORS

8 - LAUNCH TUBES

EXPLOSIVE MISSILE

TAIL FINS OPEN AFTER IT'S LAUNCHED

A computer targeting device is mounted at the top of the RMF-1 with an automatic range finder, laser targeting and infra-red scanner. The unit can be strategically placed and activated via radio signal or set on computer target monitor which will fire at any preprogramed target, or manually operated.

Range: 200 meters (660ft)

Attacks Per Melee: 1 to 8 (takes 4 melees to completely reload).

Strike Bonuses: +2 via laser targeting computer or W.P. Heavy Weapon bonuses if operated manually. Manual operation without a W.P. Heavy Weapon skill is -3 to strike.

Damage: Each individual projectile does 4-40+10 points of damage. Or can fire smoke projectiles for cover.

Weight: 77.1kg (170lbs) for the RMF-1 unit; 2.7kg (6lbs) per each projectile.

Height: 1.5 meters (5ft)

S.D.C.: 50

A.R.: 10

RMF-1 Malfunction Table

0-18	No problem
19-34	Misinterprets target, fires at any target (only if the targeting computer is used).
35-50	No problem
51-60	Jam; try to fire again next melee
61-80	No problem
81-00	Jam; try to fire again next melee

The Multi-Arm Antagonizer (M.A.A.)
Classification: Experimental; top security (high risk)

The M.A.A. is so named for its many distinctly different functions. The scientist's original intent was to develop an artificial exo-skeleton as a tool for handling heavy equipment and space exploration. The exo-skeleton has been combined with present state of the art technology and another experimental weapon, the continual plasma generator

The continual plasma generator is somewhat misleadingly named as it is actually limited to a total of forty-two charges. However, this "new" plasma generator is capable of generating seven times the fire power of the conventional plasma ejector weapons. Other weapons built into the M.A.A. include a retractable laser lance and a projectile firing mechanism.

Each weapon and function of the arm is activated or triggered by a verbal three digit code. To avoid accidental triggering or outside influence each specific M.A.A. is keyed to the voice pattern of its wearer. This prevents any unauthorized use or attempts to over-ride the arm. In case of a systems break down, or successful outside interference, a manual override command pad is provided. This small digital key pad attaches directly into the arm. The secret access code will complete the connection allowing the operator to activate and control the multiple functions of the M.A.A. by simply punching in the three digit code.

Attacks Per Melee: Vary with each particular weapon.
Weapons:

The continual Plasma Ejector
Attacks Per Melee: Once every 8 melees (requires 8 melees/2 minutes to regenerate the plasma charge).
Total Number of Charges: 42
Damage: 4-40+4
Range: 900 meters (3000ft)
Bonuses: +1 to strike plus any W.P. Weapon bonuses

The Laser Lance (modified)
Attacks Per Melee: Two per melee, 15 blasts total charges
Damage: 3-18; one setting only
Range: 90 meters (300ft)
Bonuses: +1 to strike
Notes: Independent limited power source. A spring mechanism fires the lance into the palm of the hand. Retractable from housing unit.

Armor Piercing Projectiles
Attacks Per Melee: One, two or three
Damage: 4-24+6 per each projectile
Range: 50 meters (170ft)
Bonuses: +1 to strike
Notes: A new modification allows for the projectile unit to be manually reloaded. Takes one melee to reload.

Exo-Skeleton
The exo-skeleton increases the strength of that arm to equal P.S. 30. Padded armor reinforcement of the hand, fingers, wrist and arm enables the character to forcefully strike/punch inflicting severe damage. Damage: 2-12+15.

The M.A.A. exo-skeleton also enables its wearer to lift as much as 270 kilograms (600lbs). Lifting additional weight is impossible because of the weakness of the human body. Remember only the arm and shoulder are reinforced by the exo-skeleton.

Additional M.A.A. Features

Dosimeter
M.A.A. manual adaptor (override key pad)
Signal beacon homing device (radio signal)

M.A.A. Malfunction Table

The instability of the continual plasma generator is a hazard that cannot be eliminated. The more often it's used the more likely the risk of radiation poisoning or even an explosion. The player rolls percentile dice each time a critical use level is reached. Rolling under the percentage listed means radiation and a potential explosion (roll again). A roll higher than the percentage means no problems yet but the risk of disaster is much higher at the next critical level.

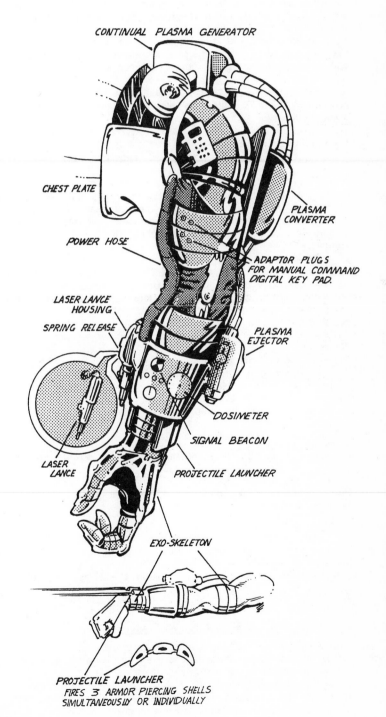

CONTINUAL PLASMA GENERATOR

CHEST PLATE

POWER HOSE

LASER LANCE HOUSING

SPRING RELEASE

LASER LANCE

PLASMA CONVERTER

ADAPTOR PLUGS FOR MANUAL COMMAND DIGITAL KEY PAD.

PLASMA EJECTOR

DOSIMETER

SIGNAL BEACON

PROJECTILE LAUNCHER

EXO-SKELETON

PROJECTILE LAUNCHER
FIRES 3 ARMOR PIERCING SHELLS SIMULTANEOUSLY OR INDIVIDUALLY

	Critical Use Level	Radiation	Explosion
Level 1	6 plasma blasts	4%	--
Level 2	10 plasma blasts	9%	2%
Level 3	14 plasma blasts	18%	6%
Level 4	20 plasma blasts	36%	18%
Level 5	26 plasma blasts	47%	36%
Danger Zone	Roll for each Additional Blast	62%	59%

NOTES: The radiation poisoning cannot be shielded from beyond the safe zones of levels one and two. At critical use levels three and four the radiation levels are hazardous and will result in nausea and sluggishness within 1-4 hours of exposure. Penalties: -1 to strike, -3 to parry and dodge, and speed is reduced by 1/3. Permanent damage occurs after 5 hours or more, reduce P.E. by 2 points, P.S and P.P. one point. Fatal if exposed for more than twelve hours. Affects a two meter area.

Level five and the danger zone cause the same nausea symptoms and penalties within 4-16 melees (4D4) and is fatal within three hours. Affects a six meter area (20ft).

The M.A.A. is almost always reserved for use by L.B.A. and E.B.A. divisions and commandos on special assignments.

The M-1 Juggernaut E.B.A.
Classification: Heavy Weapon E.B.A. (experimental/high risk)

The basic prototype of this environmental battle armor was a sort of all purpose, super tough, exo-skeletal space suit which would protect the astronaut from the most severe conditions. It has since been refitted with a plasma ejector, tri-laser and other modifications for combat.

Besides the many possible malfunctions that plague this battle armor, it is extremely slow moving with mobility and dexterity at an absolute minimum. The wearer can not bend at the waist, neck or wrists nor can he turn his head. With weapons mounted in place of hands it is impossible to pick up or carry anything.

Attacks Per Melee: Vary with each particular weapon.
Weapons:
Plasma Ejector (left arm)
Attacks Per Melee: One; 20 blasts capacity generator
Damage: 4-40+10 (4D10+10)
Range: 1200 meters (4000ft)
Bonuses: +1 to strike plus any W.P. Heavy Weapon skill bonuses.

Tri-Laser (right arm)
Attacks Per Melee: Three; 60 blasts capacity power cell.
Damage: 6-36 each blast
Range: 1600 meters (5900ft)
Bonuses: +2 to strike plus any W.P. Laser Rifle or Heavy Weapon skill bonuses.

Exo-Skeleton
All joints are reinforced and armored to provide additional strength and protection. The strength of the exo-skeleton is equal to a P.S. of 23 inflicting impressive damage when it strikes something (using the arms as clubs).
Damage: 4-24+8 points of damage. This considers both the raw physical strength and weight of its metal limbs.

Additional M-1 Juggernaut E.B.A. Features
Computer controlled life support system.
Purge system and independent oxygen supply with an eight hour limit.
Radiation shielded
Computer optics (basic infra-red, ultra-violet and telescopic)
Short range (4km) directional communicator
Radar/sonar (10km range)
Internal cooling system
External heat resistance of up to 1300 degrees fahrenheit (600 celsius)

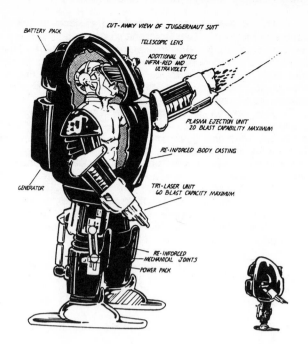

CUT-AWAY VIEW OF JUGGERNAUT SUIT

BATTERY PACK
TELESCOPIC LENS
ADDITIONAL OPTICS INFRA-RED AND ULTRA-VIOLET
PLASMA EJECTION UNIT 20 BLAST CAPABILITY MAXIMUM
RE-INFORCED BODY CASTING
GENERATOR
TRI-LASER UNIT 60 BLAST CAPACITY MAXIMUM
RE-INFORCED MECHANICAL JOINTS
POWER PACK

Overall S.D.C. 1180 (body shell 600, arms 300, legs 200)
A.R.: 16
Weight: 110kg (260lbs)
Speed Limitations: Reduce the character's natural speed by 75%; climbing is impossible. Penalties: -4 to dodge, -2 to parry, peripheral vision reduced by half. It requires 45 minutes to suit-up and 10 minutes to completely unsuit.

M-1 Juggernaut Malfunctions

In addition to its numerous mobility problems the Juggernaut E.B.A. M-1 is beset with other, irregular defects.

The reinforced mechanical leg joints freeze from time to time. The player should roll once every twenty minutes to check on the joints.

1-20	No problems . . . okay
21-40	Temporarily immobilized 2-8 melees (2D4)
41-60	Temporarily immobilized 3-12 melees (3D4)
61-80	Temporarily immobilized 4-24 melees (4D6)
81-90	Temporarily immobilized 6-36 melees (6D6)
91-00	Permanently locked, no movement possible until repairs are made.

The cooling system can also fail. The player should roll once after every third plasma blast.

1-30	Okay; no problems
31-50	Temperature rises 5 degrees fahrenheit
51-70	Temperature rises 10 degrees fahrenheit
71-00	Temperature rises 3 degrees EVERY minute from this point on.

NOTE: All affects are accumulative. Temperature begins at 60 degrees.

The Tri-Laser jams often. Roll percentile dice for each melee round in which the character wants to fire the laser. 20% chance of jamming, but the difficulty is only temporary lasting one melee (15 seconds). If the tri-laser jams it can not fire that melee. Next melee try again (roll percentile; 21-00 okay, no problem).

The M-2 Juggernaut E.B.A.
Classification: Heavy Weapon (experimental)

The M-2 is a greatly modified version of the juggernaut environmental battle armor. Its design is loosely based on the first juggernaut model, but is not built from the egg-shaped environmental space suit. Instead a completely new body shell or armor has been designed which combines elements of the traditional E.B.A. and L.B.A. and the fundamentals of the first juggernaut.

This second juggernaut E.B.A. is much more mobile allowing its wearer to turn at the waist (and even bend a little), turn the head at the neck both up and down as well as from side to side, grasp with the right hand and much greater speed and agility in general. The optics are also improved. ALL these improvements have made the M-1 juggernaut E.B.A. obsolete.

Yet even with all these improvements and modifications, the M-2 juggernaut still has its share of debilitating difficultes. Like its predecessor, the body armor is heavy and still impairs movement when compared to conventional E.B.A. Paradoxically, the greater mobility enjoyed by the M-2 is at the expense of its structural damage capacity and fire power.

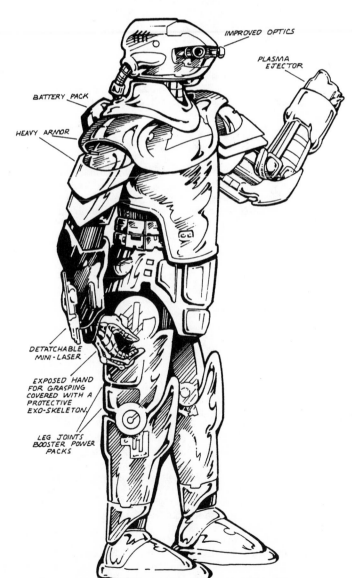

IMPROVED OPTICS

PLASMA EJECTOR

BATTERY PACK

HEAVY ARMOR

DETATCHABLE MINI-LASER

EXPOSED HAND FOR GRASPING COVERED WITH A PROTECTIVE EXO-SKELETON.

LEG JOINTS BOOSTER POWER PACKS

GREATER MOBILITY

Attacks Per Melee: Vary with each particular weapon.
Weapons:
Plasma Ejector (left arm)
This is a somewhat more limited version of that used in the M-1 Juggernaut. However, its smaller energy capacity is much less taxing on the overall system of the battle armor which has eliminated the cooling system problems of the M-1

Attacks Per Melee: One; 10 blast capacity generator
Damage: 4-40 (4D10)
Range: 360 meters (1200ft)
Bonuses: +2 to strike plus any W.P. Heavy Weapons skill bonuses

Mini-Laser (detachable)
Attacks Per Melee: Three; 30 blast capacity power cell when attached to the right arm; 10 blasts if detached from the arm's power link.
Damage: 4-24 (4D6)
Range: 1600 meters (5400ft)
Bonuses: +2 to strike plus any W.P. Laser Rifle bonuses.

Exo-Skeleton
The strength of the exo-skeleton is equal to a P.S. of 23.
Damage: 2-12+8 points of damage from a punch.

Additional M-2 Juggernaut E.B.A. Features:

All of those listed under the M-1 Juggernaut PLUS:
Improved optics infra-red, ultra-violet, telescopic distancing and laser targeting sights, (these elements are all part of the weapon's bonuses to strike).
Independent oxygen supply; six hour capacity.
Overall S.D.C.: 800 (body shell 400, arms 200, legs 200).
A.R.: 14
Weight: 81kg (180lbs)
Speed Limitations: Reduce the wearer's natural speed by one third; climbing by half. **Additional Penalties:** -2 to dodge. It requires 30 minutes to suit-up and 10 minutes to completely unsuit.

M-2 Juggernaut Malfunctions:

The only remaining problem is the locking of the leg joints. Roll percentile dice on the **"M-1"** leg joint freeze table every 20 minutes the M-2 is worn.

Experimental Equipment

Personal Energy Weapon Shields (P.E.W.S.)
Classification: Experimental (not field tested)

This expermintal device developed by professor D.R. Wilson deploys an electro-reflective refraction shield which covers the entire body of the operator, including clothing and items held or on that person. There are two types of P.E.W.S. the **Limited P.E.W.S.** and **M.A.A.-P.E.W.S.**

The limited P.E.W.S. is powered by a small independent power pack which can be strapped to the waist or back. Unfortunately the energy supply is limited which restricts the shield's use to a total of fifteen minutes.

The Energy Shield: A.R.: 17; S.D.C.: 150; **Duration:** 15 minutes total; **S.D.C. of the Power Pack** is 50; **A.R.** is 10. **Weight:** 5kg (11lbs)

Limitations: 1) Requires a special under suit with connecting circuits for the P.E.W.S. system. 2) CANNOT fire any energy or projectile weapon while the P.E.W.S.'s engaged. Any hand held weapon will automatically be enclosed in the energy shield, if it's fired the energy blast will be contained, inflicting the wearer with two times the normal damage inflicted by the weapon. 3) When engaged the shield is extremely easy to pick-up on even the most basic energy scans, because of its unique emanations. 4) Plasma attacks do half damage to both shield and wearer. 5) The S.D.C. cannot regenerate. All damage is an accumulative reduction of S.D.C. 6) The energy shield must be on for at least 30 seconds once it's engaged.

The M.A.A.-P.E.W.S. is an energy weapon shield that can hook directly into the Multi-Arm-Antagonizer (M.A.A.). The greatest advantage to doing this besides making a formidable weapon even more so, is that the energy shield is stronger and lasts longer. By linking directly into the plasma generator for power the P.E.W.S.'s duration is extended by at least twice as long (30 minutes), A.R. is increased to 19 and S.D.C. to 300. However, the use of the P.E.W.S. also contributes to the malfunction of the continual plasma generator. **Each five minutes of use is equal to one plasma blast.** Players should be certain to keep track of this counting each five minutes of use as a plasma blast which depletes the M.A.A.'s plasma charges and increases the risk of malfunction (see continual plasma generator malfunction/radiation chart).

The Energy Shield: A.R.: 19; S.D.C.: 300; **Duration:** Varies; **No power pack,** no special suit. Power drawn from M.A.A.

Limitations: 1) As usual the wearer cannot fire an energy or projectile weapon when the shield is up. 2) The shield cannot be clicked on and off for a few seconds at a time. Once turned on the shield must remain on for one full minute (60 seconds). 3) The shield does NOT automatically regenerate, but unlike the limited P.E.W.S. the M.A.A. version "can" regenerate by tapping into the energy of the continual plasma generator. However, doing so can place a dangerous strain on the plasma generator. Regeneration of 50 S.D.C. is equal to two plasma blasts/charges. The A.R. remains constant at 19.

Plasma Weapons vs. P.E.W.S.

A weakness common to both limited P.E.W.S. and the M.A.A. version is that it cannot provide full protection against plasma attacks. This means that the energy shield will absorb half the damage inflicted while the other half will affect the person (i.e. hit points or S.D.C. of additional body armor).

The Phoenix Charge
Classification: Heavy Weapon

This unique weapon is a common mining and excavation mechanism modified and shielded for use in combat by professor Rad McCall. Though common, the phoenix charge represents the state-of-the-art technology in mining. The device creates a ball of temporarily self-sustaining plasma energy. This plasma ball measures approximately 1.2 meters in diameter (4ft) and will eat through almost any matter regardless of armor ratings. The plasma ball remains active for 4 to 16 melees (4D4) inflicting 4-40+20 damage (4D10+20) EVERY melee.

The plasma ball travels at a rate of 1.2 meters per melee, slowly tunneling through walls, earth, stone, support struts and so on. The energy ball can even cut through Mechanoid vehicles, walls and the giant Mechanoid digger.

The greatest disadvantages of the phoenix charge are its extreme lack of mobility, size and limited range. The phoenix device is quite large, 3 meters tall by 1.8 meters wide (10X8ft), plus its connecting generator which measures another 2 meters in length and .9 meters high and 1.5 meters in width (7X3X5ft). The combined weight is 3 metric tons. This means the phoenix charge can only be mounted or transported on large vehicles such as the MLR-120 land rover, hover transport, jet or orbital shuttle. The phoenix is further limited by its minimal range of fire. Even modified for combat, its maximum range is a pitiful 30 meters (100ft). Thus the weapon is generally limited to special operations, and defense of the colonies and the alien tunnels. NOTE: A half dozen phoenix charge weapons were recently deployed to successfully destroy a Mechanoid digger while a second attempt was able to severely disable another digger.

Range: 30 meters (100ft)
Attacks Per Melee: One charge
Bonuses: None; most effective against large or immobile targets.
Damage: 4-40+20 each melee for a duration of 4 to 16 melees. NOTE: The phoenix charge is an extreme plasma concentration that will burn through any substance regardless of the substance's A.R. The charge cannot be directed to move in any direction other than the direction it was fired.
Weight: 3 metric tons (heavily reinforced with armor); generator one ton; plasma ejector two tons.
Size: As previously described.
S.D.C.: Plasma ejector (the firing mechanism) with reinforced battle armor. S.D.C. 600. **A.R.:** 14. Generator also battle shielded. S.D.C. 400, A.R. 14.
NOTES: There are no apparent bugs/malfunctions, but the modified phoenix has had only moderate field testing. **The Unmodified Phoenix Drill** is basically the unarmored commercial version used for mining and excavation; Weight: two metric tons, S.D.C. 300+200 on the generator, A.R. 10, Range: 20 meters (66ft). All other stats are the same.

H.A.V.O.C. Camouflage System
Classification: Special/experimental

This extremely experimental cloaking device was Professor Rad McCall's pet project prior to the mechanoid's invasion. The basic principles were derived from the Professor's understanding of some of the alien artifacts unearthed in the tunnels of Gideon-E. Even after 22 years of research the cloaking system is far from perfected. The H.A.V.O.C. camouflage system or **Human Audio-Visual Occlusion Computer** is a small back pack that generates an energy field which renders the wearer invisible to all electronic scanning and probes. The H.A.V.O.C. energy field also creates an unexplained light refraction effect that makes the wearer appear semi-invisible in bright light (daylight or artificial).

Unfortunately the H.A.V.O.C. system is plagued with **problems** that can be more of a liability than an asset. The odd light affect while handy in light glows like a shimmering beacon in the dark.

More serious problems include a communication and sensory black-out. Although the H.A.V.O.C. system cloaks its wearer from detection it also prevents him or her from receiving any radio or other signals. This means that while the H.A.V.O.C. is turned on the wearer cannot send or receive any radio communication or use ANY sensory equipment. The H.A.V.O.C. energy field also affects the wearer's metabolism, thankfully without any permanent damage. For reasons not yet determined the wearer of a H.A.V.O.C. system is prone to short, periodic black-outs. Of course this can be a most dangerous side effect in combat conditions. The system is also prone to temporary signal feed backs which clearly signal its wearer's location (this is always accompanied by a sizzling sound and static electricity so the wearer is likely to be aware of the problem) and a temporary systems overload which will momentarily shut the unit off.

Players with characters using the H.A.V.O.C. camouflage system must roll on the following table EACH time the device is used and/or for EVERY 30 minutes of use.

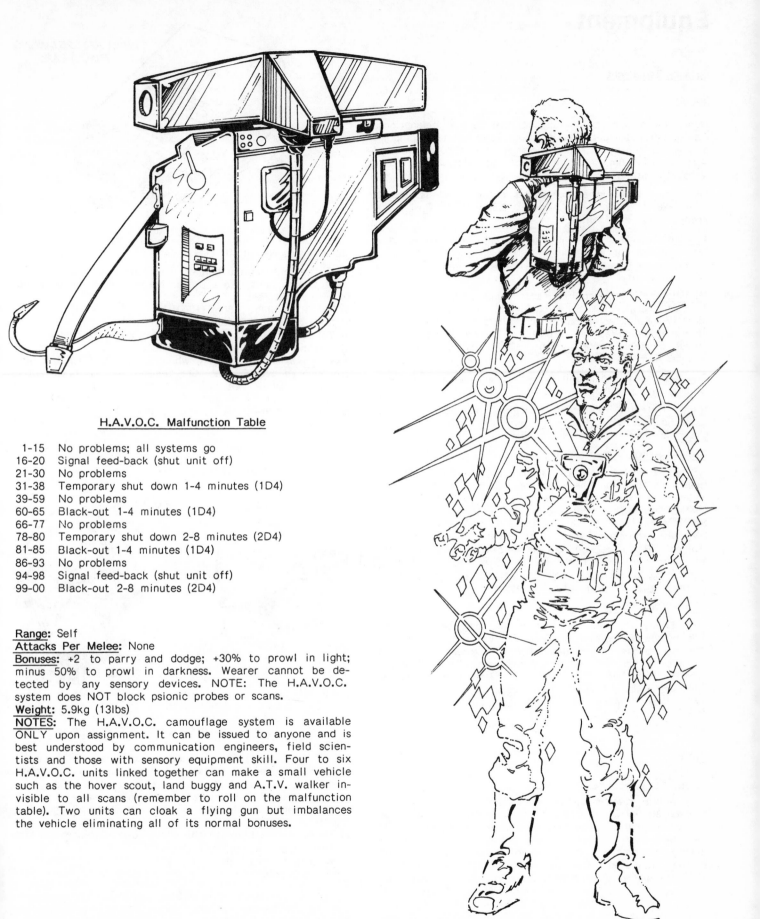

H.A.V.O.C. Malfunction Table

1-15	No problems; all systems go
16-20	Signal feed-back (shut unit off)
21-30	No problems
31-38	Temporary shut down 1-4 minutes (1D4)
39-59	No problems
60-65	Black-out 1-4 minutes (1D4)
66-77	No problems
78-80	Temporary shut down 2-8 minutes (2D4)
81-85	Black-out 1-4 minutes (1D4)
86-93	No problems
94-98	Signal feed-back (shut unit off)
99-00	Black-out 2-8 minutes (2D4)

Range: Self
Attacks Per Melee: None
Bonuses: +2 to parry and dodge; +30% to prowl in light; minus 50% to prowl in darkness. Wearer cannot be detected by any sensory devices. NOTE: The H.A.V.O.C. system does NOT block psionic probes or scans.
Weight: 5.9kg (13lbs)
NOTES: The H.A.V.O.C. camouflage system is available ONLY upon assignment. It can be issued to anyone and is best understood by communication engineers, field scientists and those with sensory equipment skill. Four to six H.A.V.O.C. units linked together can make a small vehicle such as the hover scout, land buggy and A.T.V. walker invisible to all scans (remember to roll on the malfunction table). Two units can cloak a flying gun but imbalances the vehicle eliminating all of its normal bonuses.

Equipment

Sensory Equipment

Sensors

Heat: Special sensors pick-up and measure heat emanations. Can monitor temperature or made directional to pinpoint a specific heat point/target. Range: 76m (250ft); field of detection is 7.6m (25ft). Portable/hand held; weight: 3.6kg (8lbs). Costs: 1200 credits. Poor availability.

Dosimeter: Picks-up and measures radiation levels. Range: 6.1m (20ft). Hand held; weight: 0.5kg (1lb). Costs: 200 credits. Wide availability.

Motion: Detects movement and pinpoints location. Requires sensor placement and monitor screen. Range: 27.4m (60ft). Portable; total weight: 6.8kg (15lbs). Costs: 400 credits. Fair availability.

Mini-Radar/Sonar: Requires radar signal unit and monitor. Trained operators (sensory equipment skill) can positively identify readings/objects, pinpoint location, estimate rate of travel and direction at 65% proficiency. Range: 8km (5 miles). Portable; total weight: 8.2kg (18lbs). Costs: 2500 credits. Fair availability.

Standard Radar/Sonar Unit (large): Range: 80km (50 miles); weight: 117kg (260lbs). Costs: 16,000 credits.

Radar Detector (portable): Indicates the use/presence of radar in the area. Range of detection: 1.6km (1 mile). Costs: 200 credits. Poor availability.

Ground Sensor System

Uses seismic and laser sensors to detect vehicles, men their direction and their numbers. A good communication engineer can make such projections with 75% accuracy. The control unit with digital display, computer mount and monitor is the center of this sensor web or fence. Up to 22 transmitter/receiver sensor units can be linked to the control unit. Range between transmitters is 240 meters (800ft) and can register activity up to 16km (10 miles) away. Cost: 18,500 credits. Poor availability, generally limited to the military and scientific research.

Micro-Wave Fence

Transmitter and receiver sensor posts emit an invisible microwave curtain or fence that will light up and send a signal to the control unit when an intruder breaches its curtain. Range between transmitter posts is 150 meters (500ft). Posts are 2 meters high (7ft). Can effectively cover a 22km (14 mile) area. Costs: 20,000 credits. Poor availability, primarily used for military purposes.

Optics

Infra-Red Distancing Binoculars

A high-powered optical enhancement device with infra red adjustments, cross hair indicator lines, and digital read out of estimated distance and rate of travel. Range: 3km (2 miles). The I.D. binoculars enjoy extreme popularity among the colonists, being used for field work, exploration, recreation and are standard issue for the military. Costs: 1200 credits; wide availability.

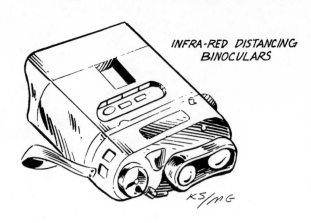

INFRA-RED DISTANCING BINOCULARS

Multi-Optics Helmet (M.O.H.)

The multi-optics helmet is a special optical enhancement system built into a protective helmet. It includes the following features:
1) **Targeting Sight:** 480m (1600ft)
2) **Infra-red Optic System:** 480m (1600ft)
3) **Telescopic Monocular Lens:** range: 3km (2 miles)
4) **Thermo-imager:** range: 480m (1600ft)
Special bonus: +1 to strike when optics and targeting sight are engaged. NOTE that the thermo imager is effective against invisible foes and night combat. Thus, the usual penalties against invisible opponents or night limitations do not apply when the M.O.H. is used. Costs: 2900 credits, good availability.

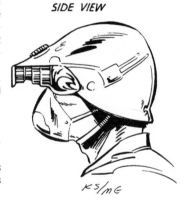

MULTI-OPTICS HELMET

SIDE VIEW   FRONT VIEW

Optics Band

The optics band is a head band type optical system most often used in research, micro-repairs and scientific study. Its range is limited as it is designed for close work not long distance or combat surveillance. Features include:
1) **Infra-red and Ultra-violet optic system:** Range: 90m (200ft) maximum.
2) **Magnification Lens (to the 400th power):** Range: 2m (7ft)
3) **Night sight:** Range: 90m (200ft)
4) **Adjustable color filters.**
Costs: 800 credits

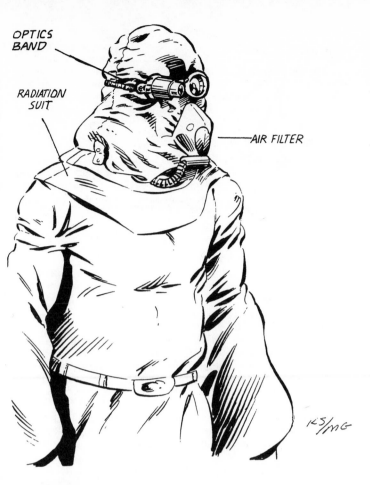

OPTICS BAND

RADIATION SUIT

AIR FILTER

Goggles and Binoculars

Infra-red Optic Systems
Range: 360m (1200ft)
This type of optical enhancement device relies on a source of infra-red light, usually a pencil thin beam of light projected from the goggle or binoculars to illuminate its targets. The narrowness of the beam severely limits the scope of one's view to a small area of about two square meters (7ft). This can make surveying a large area a problem. Another drawback is that the infra-red light beam is clearly visible to another infra-red optic system, giving away the operator's position. These drawbacks are inherent to ALL infra-red systems. Costs: about 1000 credits; fair availability.

Thermo-imager
Range: 480m (1600ft)
Basically an optical heat sensor, it converts the infra-red radiation of warm objects into a visible image. These devices allow its operator to see in darkness, shadows and through smoke. Battery powered and electrically cooled. A typical running life is 16 hours. Costs: about 1400 credits; poor availability.

Ultra-violet Systems
Range
: 120m (400ft)
Enables its wearer to see into the ultra-violet range of light radiation. It's usually integrated into a larger optics package rather than used alone. Costs: 500 credits.

Night-sight
Range: 480m (1600ft)
A night vision optics system is an image intensifier, meaning that it is a passive system that does not emit any light of its own, but electronically amplifies existing ambient light to provide a visible picture. Costs: 1400 credits; poor availability.

Pocket Night Viewer
Range: 240m (800ft)

This is a mini night sight, usually a monocular style, easily concealed and portable. Commonly used for planet exploration. Costs: 800 credits; poor availability.

Conventional Binoculars
Range: 1.6km (1 mile)
Magnification through a series of lenses. Costs: 700 credits; fair availability.

Surveillance Equipment

Remote Flying Camera

The remote flying camera or "whirly eye" as it's more commonly referred to; is a small flying video camera. The housing device is essentially a miniature helicopter with a rotating video camera in the nose. The device can be operated by radio control, using the video image to guide it, or it can be set on "drone probe"; a sort of automatic pilot. Sensors prevent it from flying into walls or objects when on drone probe. The camera, located in the nose, can rotate a full 360 degrees with two normal lenses one telescopic lens in the center, and a sensor eye. The video camera directly broadcasts its transmissions to a monitoring unit up to a distance of 480m (1600ft). The monitor can be a simple hand held mini-unit or a large viewing screen or multiple screen unit. When a large monitoring unit is used the transmissions can be recorded and all three cameras can broadcast simultaneously. Camera lens range: 60m (200ft) or 240m (800ft) with the telescopic lens.
Cost: 225 credits for the remote flying camera and 150 credits for the hand held mini-monitor; 200 credits for one laser unit. Size: .5m (approximately 1½ft) long; weight: 1.4kg (3lbs).
NOTE: the helicopter blades have a special whisper mode which renders it nearly silent.

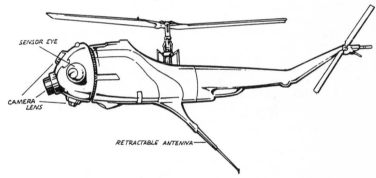

SENSOR EYE

CAMERA LENS

RETRACTABLE ANTENNA

Keyhole or Tube Microphones

A microphone (mic) with a long hollow tube which can be flexible or stiff, allowing it to be placed in cracks, mounted in walls or placed in similar small "keyhole" type crevices. Picks up sounds up to 10m (34ft) away and transmits up to 300m (1000ft). Costs: 150 credits; fair availability.

Video Wall Mount

This small remote video camera is only about the size of a man's palm (5 inches in diameter), thus it's easily concealed. The camera is backed with a powerful suction device that will adhere to any smooth surface whether it be a wall, table, appliance, vehicle and so on. The video wall mount can broadcast continually for 72 hours or by remote or preprogrammed regulated intervals. The lens has limited mobility, able to rotate in about a 90 degree radius. It's audio capacity has twice the duration of its video transmission and able to pick-up sounds up to six meters (20ft) away with crystal clarity. The monitor can be the mini-hand held screen or any variety of larger or multi-unit monitors. Costs: 200 credits; fair availability through the conventional market, but a hot commodity at 300 credits on the black market. Hand held monitor costs 150 credits.

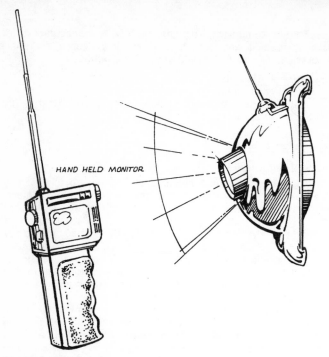

HAND HELD MONITOR

Contact Microphone

Translates vibrations into sound, but requires a sounding board such as a wall, window, large object etc. Can be as small as a tie tack. Picks up sounds up to 10 meters away and transmits up to 300m (1000ft). Costs: 170 credits fair availability.

Wireless Microphone

This compact mic is about the size and thickness of a box of matches. It can pick-up sounds up to 4m (14ft) away and broadcast up to 90m (300ft) away. Costs: 250 credits; poor availability.

Tracer Bug

This is a tiny device about the size of a checker which has a sticky or magnetic side that can be attached to a vehicle, Mechanoid or slipped into a person's pocket, back pack, briefcase, etc. It can transmit a signal that can be followed up to 12km (8 miles) away. Battery powered it has a limited life of 72 hours of constant transmission. Costs: 140 credits; fair availability.

Pocket Scrambler

The scrambler will distort or "scramble" out going radio signals, preventing interception and interpretation by the enemy. Costs: 300 credits; good availability.
NOTE: Other more conventional video systems, cameras lenses and optics are also effective tools for surveillance.

Ultra-violet Signaler

The signaler is a small strip of ultra-violet sensors and another transmitter strip that can be adhered to a doorway, walls and so on, to create a beam of invisible light blocking that area. When the beam is broken by an intruder or vehicle, etc. it will send a silent signal to a monitoring device and/or trigger a video unit. Costs: 900 credits; fair availability.

Motion Detector Signaler

This device is virtually identical in purpose and use as the ultra-violet signaler except that it does not emit any vibrations in the air. Costs: 900 credits; poor availability.

Communication Equipment

Communications equipment is fairly basic in regards to characters use and needs. Various surveillance and video systems might be added on depending on the circumstances and players ingenuity.

Field Radio

A back-pack style radio transmitter and receiver with wide band, long range capabilities, frequency equalizer, field strength detector and scrambler. Range: 96km (60 miles). Weight: 7kg (about 16lbs). Costs: 600 credits; good availability.

Hand Held Communicator

Basically an enhanced walkie-talkie, it is a basic instrument issued to all military personal and field operatives. Was also used by the public in recreation. Costs per single unit 150 credits; excellent availability (common). Weight: 170 grams (6 ounces). Range: 4.8km (3 miles).

Special Equipment

Portable Bio-Scan

The bio-scan is an impressive biological monitoring device with a multitude of functions. Sensors are attached to the skin and body which sends information to the computer display screen and/or to be recorded.
1) **Basic bio mode** indicates and records such basic body functions as body temperature, heart beat/rate, blood pressure, breathing and glandular changes in the skin, including sweating.
2) **Stress evaluator** operates much like a polygraph machine recording stress and anxiety, without attaching sensors, by monitoring the voice quality of its subject. A communication engineer O.C.C. or field scientist O.C.C. (and only those two O.C.C.'s) can use the device as a "lie detector", but the information is often difficult to read and open to interpretation. Even a positive reading can not be declared absolute evidence of a falsehood. Chance of proper reading as a lie detector is 25% plus 5% per level of experience.
3) **Toxic analyzer** can analyze any liquid (water, blood, etc.) and be able to identify 380 toxins dangerous to humans. Solid items such as fruits and vegetables must be pulped or squeezed in order to be analyzed.
4) **Dosimeter** is used to measure radiation. Costs: 5000 credits; poor availability, since it's generally reserved exclusively for field expeditions of a scientific or military nature. Weight of this unit is 9kg (20lbs).

Portable Laboratory
This is another impressive portable unit that can perform several functions.
1) **Microscope** in a specially padded housing.
2) **Dozen specimen slides** and another dozen specimen trays for storage and transportation of item(s) for further analysis. A variety of vials, jars and test tubes.
3) **Incubation chamber** that is about the size of a VCR (1½ X 1ft X 8 inches deep).
4) **Four burners.**
5) **Instrument tray** with a variety of common tools such as scalpels, tweezers, pins, medical laser lance (20 charges) tape, needles, calculator, etc.
6) **Refrigeration chamber** which is about half the size of the incubation chamber.
7) **Isolation chamber** is a special, air tight sealable compartment about the size of the incubation chamber.
8) **Chemical cabinet** which holds several dozens chemicals commonly needed in the analysis of chemical structures.
9) **Centrifuge Device.**
10) **Dosimeter**
11) **Tape recorder.**
12) **Mini-computer**
13) **Mini-still camera**, 35mm, 32 photo capacity
14) **Toxic analyzer**, identical to the one used in the "portable bio-scan". Costs: 12,000 credits; poor availability. Weight of the whole unit is 26kg (58lbs).

Portable Scan Dihilator

The portable scan dihilator is a uniquely comprehensive sensory device with FULL scanning capabilities.

1) **Radar/Sonar:** Range is limited to an 8km (5 mile) area. A trained operator (sensory equipment skill) can positively identify readings as specific objects or vehicles, pinpoint location and estimate rate of travel and direction at 65% proficiency.

2) **Sensors** include dosimeter, radar detector, heat, infrared, ultra-violet, micro-wave, and energy sensitive instruments all of which identify, locate source, and record.

3) **Long range wide band radio** with scrambler. Range: 64km (40 mile) radius.

4) **Detachable short range** (hand held) communicator. Range: 4,8km (3 miles).

5) **Video camera** (mini) with both wide and narrow angle lens. Audio-visual recorder on metal discs with digital meter, lens filters, telescopic lens (480m) and tripod included. Capable of radio telemetry when boosted by long range radio. Costs about 4200 credits. Fair availability.

Body Armor

A limited variety of body armor is available L.B.A. and E.B.A. are usually assigned to characters and are NOT available on the commercial market. Such armor purchased on the black market is illegal leading to the confiscation of the armor and a 5000 credit fine.

Rover armor must be traded for to get. The number of credits listed is to provide an idea of the value of the item(s) needed for the trade. This may vary 40% up or down depending on the particular rover and circumstances. ALL are full suits except the web vest.

Cost	Armor Type	A.R.	S.D.C.	Weight
100	Rover Padded	6	12	3.6kg
170	Rover Soft Leather	8	28	4.5kg
240	Rover Hard Leather	10	30	5.4kg
300	Space Suit	6	12	3.6kg
300	Web Vest	9	30	5.4kg
1000*	L.B.A.	12	72	6.8kg
2600*	E.B.A.	15	150	13kg

*Black market price.

Miscellaneous Equipment

Field	Cost
Sunglasses	15 credits (cr)
Tinted protective goggles	25cr
Gloves	10cr
Flashlight	25cr
Handcuffs	25cr
Night stick (1-6 damage)	10cr
Leather jacket	200cr
Utility belt	20cr
Back pack (small)	30cr
Back pack (large)	50cr
Hiking boots	50cr
Coveralls	20cr
Small knife (1-4 damage)	20cr
Hat - baseball type	10cr
Hard hat	40cr
Canteen (1 quart)	15cr
Compass	30cr
Wrist watch	50cr

Video/Photo Equipment

35mm Camera	250cr
35 Extra Lens	80cr
Flash	50cr
Film: 36 exposure	3cr
Video system (complete)	2000cr
Video recorder only	700cr
Video surveillance - camera	600cr
Tape recorder (portable)	125cr

Standard Issue of Field Equipment

Signal Flares (two rocket type)
Binoculars
Knife
Hand held short range communicator (range: 4.8km/3 miles)
Gas mask or air filter
Protective goggles
Back pack
Canteen
Food ration and water, two week supply
First aid kit

Conditional Additions Field Equipment

Grappling hook
Nylon cord (suitable for climbing)
SLR spike launch rod
Detection Equipment (conventional)
Camera or video system
SB-14 simple blaster
Rosenstein Land Buggy or . . .
Hover Scout or . . .
A.T.V. Walker
NOTE: The portable scan dihilator is always available to the communications engineer O.C.C. while the portable laboratory and bio-scan are available to the field/scientist.

GUSTOVICH

Vehicles

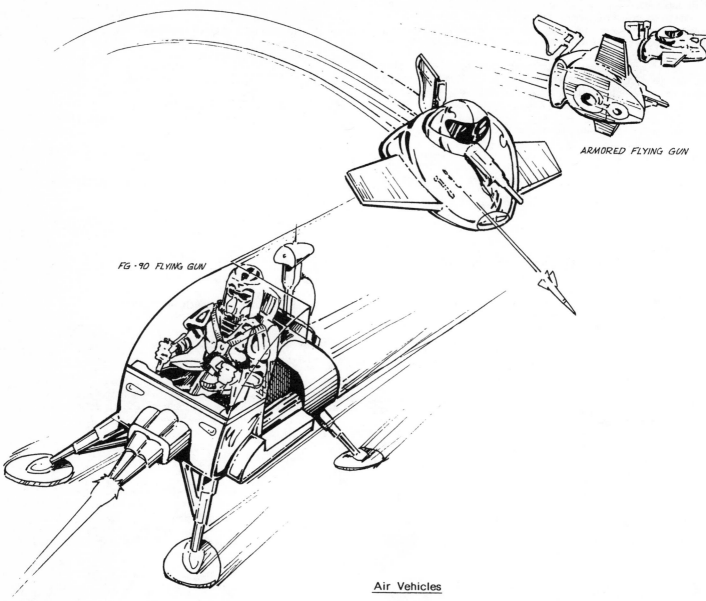

ARMORED FLYING GUN

FG-90 FLYING GUN

Air Vehicles

FG-90 Flying Gun
AFG-66 Armored Flying Gun
HS-180 Hover Scout
AHS-180 Assault Hover Scout
MHT-180 Modified Hover Transport
Hover Jet Fighter
Dreadnought
Orbital Shuttle

Ground Vehicles

A.T.V. Walker
Ground Armor Missile Launcher
MLR-120 Modified Land Rover
Hover Plasma Tank
Rosenstein Land Buggy

See Ancient Alien devices and vehicles as well.

NOTE: Unless otherwise stated, vehicles are not generally available for purchase by private citizens.

Air Vehicles

FG-90 Flying Gun

This one man air vehicle is designed as a limited range assault weapon specifically for the E.B.A. division. However, it may also be assigned to the L.B.A. division or special field operatives. The FG-90 is a dynamic, extremely, maneuverable war machine. It is equipped with radar laser targeting and directional mid-range radio. Availability moderate; manufactured at the Kucharski colony.

Vital Statistics

Weapons: Laser cannon front mount
    Range: 1400 meters (4600ft)
    Damage: 6-36+4 (6D6+4)
    Attacks Per Melee: Two
    Energy Capacity: 20 charges
Equipment: Radar: 20km (13 miles)
    Directional Radio: 25km (16 miles)
Function: Assault and Defense
Speed: 96kmph (60mph), hover; **Total flight time possible:** 10 hours.
Bonuses: +4 to dodge, W.P. Heavy Weapons skill bonuses DO apply.
A.R.: 9

S.D.C.: 110
Size: 1.8 meters (6ft) long, 1.3 meters (4½ft) tall, 1.2 meters (4ft) wide.
Weight: 54kg (120lbs)
NOTE: The piloting of the FG-90 and/or AFG-66 is a separate skill ability "Pilot Flying-Gun".

ANGLE OF FIRE 45°
LASER CANNON

MISSILE TRACKS

AFG-66 Armored Flying Gun

The armored flying gun is a heavily modified one man assault vehicle with hover and jet propulsion capabilities. In addition, it is armed with four heat seeking missiles.

Vital Statistics
Weapons: Laser cannon with a 45 degree angle adjustment.
  Range: 1400 meters
  Damage: 6-36+4
  Attacks Per Melee: Two

  Mini-heat seeker missiles (4)
  Range: 10km (6 miles)
  Speed: 1800kmph
  Damage: 25 points
  Attacks Per Melee: Total of four; once all four missiles are fired the AFG-6 is without a missile offense.
  A.R.: 8   S.D.C.: 25 each
  Bonuses: +4 to strike
Equipment: Radar 20km (13 miles)
  Directional Radio 25km (16 miles)
  Hover jets
  Rear booster jets
Function: Assault and Defense
Speed: 64kmph (40mph) on standard hover jets; up to 643kmph (400mph) with rear booster jets. Note: booster jet limited to 2 hours fuel capacity. **Total Flight Time** possible is six hours.
Bonuses: +2 to dodge (less maneuverable than the FG-90) W.P. Heavy Weapons skill bonuses applicable.
A.R.: 12
S.D.C.: 210 body; 110 laser cannon (only)
Size: 2.2 meters (7½ft) long
Weight: 120kg (240lbs)

HS-180 Hover Scout

The HS-180 Hover scout is a highly maneuverable vehicle that serves a multitude of purposes from reconnaissance to transportation. It is often assigned to field researchers, military type operations and special operatives. The hover scout is clearly the most popular and widely available vehicle next to the Rosenstein Land buggy. It seats a pilot and four passengers comfortably although four others could be squeezed in if absolutely necessary. Maximum weight allowance is 1800kg (3600lbs); reduce the scout's speed 25kmph for every 150kg (300lbs) beyond the maximum weight allowance.

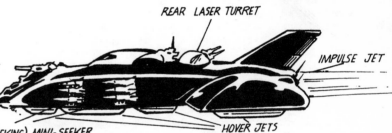

SCOUT

HOVER JETS

LANDING GEAR

Vital Statistics
Weapons: None are standard, although all have a rear weapons mount for the placement of any rifle. A laser cannon can also be mounted, but these are limited exclusively to military use.
  Laser Cannon
  Range: 1400 meters (4600ft)
  Damage: 6-36+4
  Attacks Per Melee: Two
  Energy Capacity: 20 charges
Equipment: Radar: 40km (28 miles) range.
  Wide Band Radio: 64km (40 miles)
Function: Transport/Reconnaissance
Speed: 180kmph (120mph), hover; **Total Flight Time** is 12 hours (2160km)
Bonuses: +2 to dodge
A.R.: 10
S.D.C.: 100
Size: 64 meters (22ft) long, 1.8 meters (6ft) wide, 1.5 meters (5ft) tall
Weight: 1000kg (2000lbs)
NOTE: The hover scout is extremely quiet. Maximum altitude is a modest 60 meters (200ft). Cost: 6000 credits; good availability.

REAR LASER TURRET

IMPULSE JET

HOVER JETS

(HEAT SEEKING) MINI-SEEKER
MISSLES WITH FUSION BLOCK WARHEADS · 6 EACH SIDE

AHS-180 Assault Hover Scout

The AHS-180 is a sturdy, reinforced, armored body casting built upon the exact basic frame as the normal hover scout. In addition to the armor, the assault hover scout is equipped with a small, front particle beam gun, rear laser turret, a battery of mini-seeker missiles and a jet propulsion unit for greater speed. The assault hover scout is limited to military operations and special operations.

Some major changes besides the armaments is that the vehicle can now only seat a pilot, laser turret gunner and one passenger. The addition of the jets and weapons has taken up much room.

The weapons' energy source is a total of 80 charges. This means that ALL weapons draw from the same source, much like the balrog destroyer. Consequently, players must be careful to distribute the energy charges where they will be most effective. Once all the energy charges are used up no weapons can be fired or missiles launched. If there is no energy to launch the mini-seeker missiles they can be manually dropped like bombs, however this is extremely dangerous as they each house type one fusion blocks and being caught in such a blast(s) could have deadly consequences.

Vital Statistics
Weapons: Particle Beam Gun (front)
  Range: 1600 meters (4620ft)
  Damage: Standard
  Attacks Per Melee: Two
  Energy Cost: 4 charges equal to one blast

  Duo-Laser Turret
  Range: 1800 meters (5280ft)
  Damage: 6-36 X 2 (6D6X2)
  Attacks Per Melee: One

Energy Cost: 3 charges equal one blast
Mini-Seeker (heat) Missiles
Range: 10km
Damage: same as type one fusion block. Note: 20% chance of not detonating.
Speed: 804kmph (500mph)
Number Launched Per Melee: 1-4; Total payload is 12 missiles.
Energy Cost: 2 charges each
Bonuses: +2 to strike
Note: All weapons can be fired in the same melee if applicable.
Equipment: Radar: 40km (26 miles)
        Wide Band Radio: 64km (40 miles)
Function: Assault and Defense
Speed: 320kmph (200mph) with booster jets; 160kmph (100 mph) on standard hover jets, hover. Note: Booster jets limited to a 2 hour fuel capacity. Total flight time possible is 8 hours using standard hover jets. 1286km (800 miles) or six hours, two of which with booster jets 1280 km (800 miles).
Bonuses: +2 to dodge
A.R.: 10
S.D.C.: Vehicle's body 280, particle beam front gun 100, laser turret 150, seeker missiles 30 S.D.C. each. If the missile loses all S.D.C. it explodes; if one explodes it will detonate all the others. Thus, it "may" be prudent to launch the majority of missiles early in combat.
Weight: 2000kg (4000lbs)
NOTE: Maximum altitude is 60 meters (200ft). Characters with a W.P. Heavy Weapon skill can apply those skill bonuses to the AHS-180's guns potential to strike.

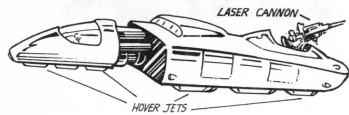

MHT-180 MODIFIED HOVER TRANSPORT

LASER CANNON

HOVER JETS

MHT-180 Modified Hover Transport

The MHT-180 is still used for the transportation of supplies and personnel. The only modifications are a reinforced hull and rotating laser cannon which can be fired by remote control or manually. Requires a pilot and co-pilot. Pilot's cabin can hold a total of four; the cargo area can hold 40 people and/or a maximum weight of 51,800 kilograms (25,900lbs). Moderate availability.

The "UN"-modified hover transport (HT-180) is identical in every way minus the laser turret and additional armor. A.R.: 10, S.D.C. 110.

Vital Statistics
Weapons: Laser Cannon (rapid fire)
        Range: 1800 meters (5280ft)
        Damage: 6-36+6
        Attacks Per Melee: Four
        Energy Capacity: 30 charges (costs one per blast)
Equipment: Radar: 20km (13 miles)
        Wide Band Radio: 36km (16 miles)
Function: Transport
Speed: 180kmph (120mph)
A.R.: 10
S.D.C.: 220
Size: 10.7 meters (35ft) long, 2.7 meters (9ft) tall, 4.6 meters (15ft) wide.
Weight: 10 metric tons
NOTES: Maximum altitude 30 meters (100ft).

Hover Jet Fighter

The hover jet fighter is one of the few actual war vehicles the colonists had before the Mechanoids' appearance. Since the Mechanoids' initial attack the colonies have manufactured a few thousand fighters, but even these powerful weapons have proven to be insufficient in stopping the dreaded aliens.

The hover jet fighter is a small vehicle seating a pilot, co-pilot and communications engineer in the cock pit. One additional person can also fit comfortably in the cockpit. The cargo bay is extremely limited, but can hold four tiger or six conventional I.L.R.M.s, or a dozen people, or cargo. The I.L.R.M. (intelligent missiles) can be launched by opening the cargo bay doors in the floor. Unfortunately, this means that all I.L.R.M.s must be released simultaneously, but they can be told to fly along near the jet until a specific target is indicated or they can all let loose to search out and destroy mechanoids as they determine.

Particle beam turrets are mounted under each wing. Both are capable of 360 degree rotation. No other weapons are available (other than the I.L.R.M. in the cargo bay), but the assignment of I.L.R.M.s are NOT standard, usually reserved for major confrontations.

The hover jet is quite versatile and maneuverable. Equipped with jet propulsion and conventional hover capabilities it is able to perform vertical and horizontal lift-offs, travel at a wide range of speeds, hover suspended in mid-air and fly as low to the ground as 30 meters (100 feet).

Vital Statistics
Weapons: Two Particle Beam Turrets
        Range: 2200 meters (7260ft)
        Damage: Standard
        Attacks Per Melee: Two per each turret for a total of four.
        Energy Capacity: 24 per each turret for a total of 48 P-beam blasts.
        Optional Weapon Possibility: Use of Intelligent Limited Range Missiles (I.L.R.M.) see experimental weapons for details.
Equipment: Radar: 48km (40 miles)
        Long Range Directional Radio: 160km (100 miles).
        Laser Targeting
        Cockpit ejection and parachute system
        Spotlights, 90 degree rotation, Range: 30 meters
Function: Assault and Defense
Speed: Jet propulsion 1800kmph; in hover mode up to 180 kmph (120mph), stationary hover above the ground. Total Flight Time possible is 5 hours.
Bonuses: +2 to dodge, +1 to strike, W.P. Heavy Weapon skill bonuses apply if the P-beam turrets are manually operated instead of robot remote
A.R.: 10
S.D.C.: 180
Size: Overall length is 8.4 meters (27ft); cargo bay is 4.6 meters long (15ft), 1.5 meters (5ft) wide and 2.1 meters tall (7ft).
Weight: 18 metric tons

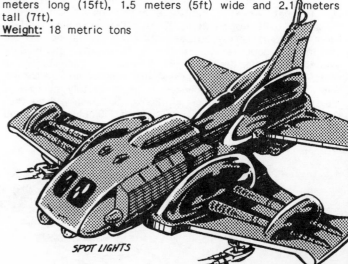

SPOT LIGHTS

ROBOT PARTICLE BEAM TURRET

Dreadnought

The dreadnought is a reconstructed orbital shuttle with ground hover capabilities. The cargo bay has been refitted with a particle beam turret main gun and two smaller particle beam turrets. The vehicle is further supplemented by eight I.L.R.M.s and forward laser guns.

Although the instrument of incredible destructive powers, these war machines have proven to be too slow and ponderous than to provide anything more than ground support. Consequently, the manufacturing of the dreadnoughts has been suspended in favor of other, much easier vehicles to produce. The few dozen that do exist will be reserved for the final flight/assault on the Mechanoid mothership.

Vital Statistics

Weapons: Main Particle Beam Cannon
Range: 3200 meters (10,500ft)
Damage: 7-70 (+25 if a direct hit)
Attacks Per Melee: Two
Bonuses: +1 to strike
Energy Capacity: 20 blasts

Secondary P-Beam Turrets (2)
Range: 2700 meters (7260ft)
Damage: Standard
Attacks Per Melee: Two per each turret for a total of four attacks.
Energy Capacity: 30 charges/blasts per each turret (60 total)

Forward Laser Cannon
Range: 2200 meters (7260ft)
Damage: 6-36
Attacks Per Melee: Two
Energy Capacity: 30 blasts

8 I.L.R.M. are also part of the weapon arsenal.
NOTE: Total possible number of attacks per melee, excluding I.L.R.M.s, is eight.

Equipment: Radar: 64km (40 miles)
Long Range Radio: 160km (100 miles)
Designed to withstand the rigors of space flight and reentry.

Function: Assault
Speed: On the ground via hover jets, 80kmph (50 miles), in space 210kmph.
A.R.: 11
S.D.C.: 460 on the body, 250 main turret, 150 for the two secondary turrets.
Size: Same as orbital shuttle.
Weight: 84,774kg (42,440lbs)

Orbital Shuttle

This is your standard freight and satellite orbital shuttle of which its original purpose was to rendezvous with the space station Alpha Q, supply ships, satellite repair and planet mapping. The shuttles, as is, are useless against the Mechanoids. As things now stand, the shuttle and other space-worthy vessels will carry a small portion of the colonists to invade the Mechanoid mothership. There is nowhere else to evacuate to.

Vital Statistics

Weapons: None
Equipment: Radar: 64km (40 miles)
Long Range Radio: 100 miles
Designed to withstand the rigors of space and reentry.

Function: Transport and Research
Speed: Varies, about 200kmph
A.R.: 11
S.D.C.: 400
Weight: 78,400kg (39,200lbs)

GROUND VEHICLES

A.T.V. Walker

The A.T.V. Walker is an all-terrain-vehicle commonly used in planetary exploration expeditions, underwater research and occasionally for repairs in outer space. Because of its use as an environmental vehicle, especially in deep sea exploration, the A.T.V. Walker is heavily armored and designed to withstand the rigors of space and the pressure of ocean depths.

Despite its toughness the A.T.V. Walker is of limited value as a combat vehicle. Weapons are restricted to a laser-top mounted gun and/or a mini-laser mounted on the front underside in place of the robot arm. Most crippling is its sluggish speed of 64km per hour (40mph). This lack of speed makes it an easy target for wasps or even brutes, as well as making for a tediously long journey when traveling great distances. Of course, the A.T.V. Walkers can be transported via land rover, hover-transport or orbital shuttle, but only a handful can be hauled per vehicle.

However, the A.T.V Walker has proven to be an excellent defense weapon and short range scout for the elimination of weavels, skimmers and tunnel crawlers. It is also ideal for the defense and exploration of the ancient tunnels which honeycomb Gideon-E.

Vital Statistics

Size: 3 meters tall when standing erect, 3.2 meters long (10ft tall, 12ft long). Seats a maximum of four with a small cargo bin.
Weight: 589.68kg (1300lbs)
A.R.: 14
S.D.C.: 425 body; specific possible targets: 200 S.D.C. per each leg, 100 S.D.C. laser top mount, 50 S.D.C. mechanical arm.
Weapons: Laser Top Mount: 3 attacks per melee, 6-36 damage per blast. Range is 1400 meters (4600ft). The laser top mount can be operated manually (add W.P. bonuses if operator has a W.P. laser rifle or W.P. heavy weapons) or automatic computer tracking (+1 to strike).
A Mini-Laser can be mounted on the undercarriage in place of the mechanical arm. Two attacks per melee doing 3-18 damage; range is 900 meters.
The Mechanical Arm is not intended to be used as a weapon, but for picking things up and grasping. Mechanical arm's strength is equal to a P.S. 20 and able to lift up to 113.4kg (250lbs), with a 3 meter reach.
Speed: 64kmph (40mph)
NOTES:
Spotlight: 180° rotation, beam range 90 meters (200ft), 7.6 meter diameter (25ft).
Fuel Capacity: 1939km (1200 miles)
Communication wide band and directional radio; range 80km.
Sensors: Dosimeter, exterior thermometer (heat/cold), radar/sonar; range 9.5km (6 miles)
Underwater Capabilities: Flotation and ballast device, water sealed, environmental cabin with life support and 10 hour emergency oxygen supply, hyperbaric chamber.
Maximum Crush Depth: can survive deep sea pressure equal to 3.2km (2 miles)
Environmental Cabin: Computer controlled life support system with manual override, internal cooling and temperature control, humidifier, air circulation; heat, cold and electrically insulated, and radiation shielded. Can survive under water or in a non-oxygen environment for six days plus 10 hour emergency oxygen supply. After that time the air becomes too foul to support life.
On board computer for computations and data file.
Additional equipment can be added. These include the laser mount, video or still cameras, portable laboratory, S.C.U.B.A or Deep sea equipment (limited to two suits), special optics, additional sensors and computers.

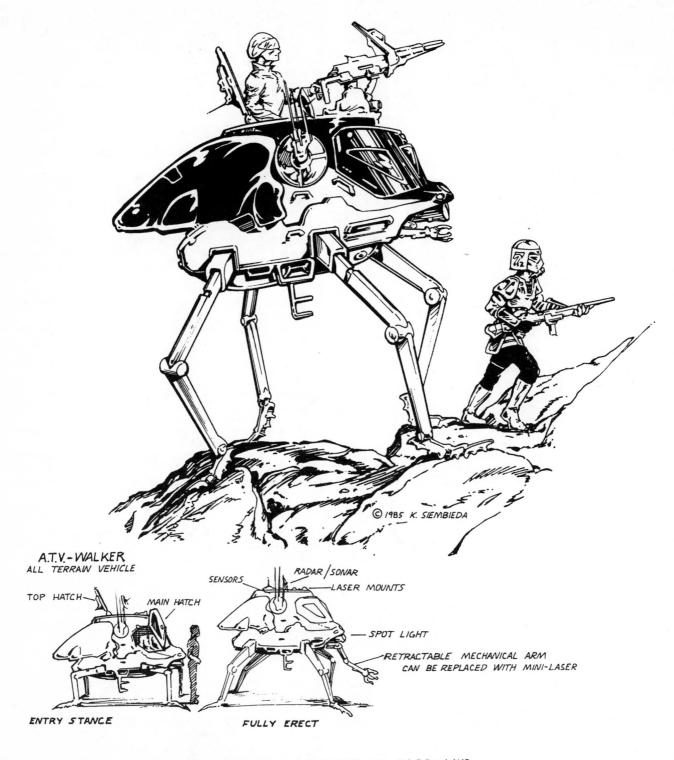

© 1985 K. SIEMBIEDA

A.T.V.-WALKER
ALL TERRAIN VEHICLE

TOP HATCH

MAIN HATCH

SENSORS

RADAR/SONAR

LASER MOUNTS

SPOT LIGHT

RETRACTABLE MECHANICAL ARM
CAN BE REPLACED WITH MINI-LASER

ENTRY STANCE

FULLY ERECT

THE A.T.V.-WALKER CAN BE USED IN SPACE   UNDER-WATER AND ON DRY LAND.
SEATS A MAXIMUM OF FOUR.
MAXIMUM SPEED IS 64 kmph OR 40 mph.
HEAVILY ARMORED ENVIRNMENTAL CABIN.

Ground Armor Missile Launcher

The missile launcher is another modification of the land rover but much more drastic than the modified land rover whose description follows this one. The missile launcher is no longer capable of transporting any kind of cargo or personnel, but is now a rolling arsenal.

Directly behind the cab are the missile launch tubes. A portion of the ceiling rises up providing an armored shield for the now revealed missile tube. A retractable missile tracking system is also concealed in this area. In the rear is a particle beam turret and radar and tracking system to monitor the approaching enemy. This tracking system is a complete sensor scanning system including, radar, microwave, heat, infra-red, ultra-violet and radiation.

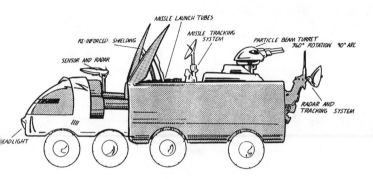

RE-INFORCED SHIELDING
SENSOR AND RADAR
HEADLIGHT
MISSILE LAUNCH TUBES
MISSILE TRACKING SYSTEM
PARTICLE BEAM TURRET 360° ROTATION 90° ARC
RADAR AND TRACKING SYSTEM

Vital Statistics
Weapons: Particle Beam Turret
>Range: 1600 meters (5300ft)
>Damage: Standard
>Attacks Per Melee: Two in addition to missile attacks.
>Energy Capacity: 20 blasts
>Note: Turret can rotate a full 360° and a 90° arc.

The Missile Bank
>Type: Anti-aircraft/heat seeking
>Payload: 18
>Rate of Fire: up to 6 per melee
>Range: 50km (32 miles)
>Speed: 1500kmph
>Bonuses: +2 to strike
>Damage: 6-36+4 each (6D6+4)
>
>Type: Anti-personnel (fragmentary)
>Payload: 6
>Rate of Fire: up to 6 per melee
>Range: 2km (1 mile)
>Speed: 150kmph
>Bonuses: +2 to strike ground target
>Damage: affects a 10 meter area (33ft) doing 5-30 (5D6) points of damage to everything in the blast radius.
>
>Type: I.L.R.M. (6) see description under experimental weapons.
>Type: Tiger I.L.R.M. (4) see description under experimental weapons.
>Note: a TOTAL of six missiles in any combination can be launched each melee.

Equipment: Forward sensor and radar; range 64km (40 miles)
>Missile Tracking System: tracks and directs missiles, range: 64km.
>Rear Radar and Tracking System with full sensory scanning capabilities, range: 25km (16 miles).
>Wide Band Long Range Radio with booster and scrambler; 482km (360 miles)

Function: Assault
Speed: 144kmph (90mph), fuel capacity is 2000km
A.R.: 10
S.D.C.: Driver's cabin (seats four) 200, Body 250, shielding

for missiles 150, missile tubes 200 (A.R. 14), p-beam turret 150, tracking systems 50, tires 40.
Size: 10 meters (33ft) long, 3.9 meters (13ft) tall.
Weight: 14 metric tons
NOTES: If all the missile launch tubes' S.D.C. are depleted the entire payload of missiles will detonate. Without sensors or tracking, missiles are -2 to strike. No cargo hold.

MLR-120 Modified Land Rover

The MLR-20 is a land rover transport/cargo vehicle modified with two particle beam weapons facing the front and rear. Both P-beam weapons are limited to a 45° rotation and arc.

The cargo bay can be used to transport ground troops, personnel or heavy equipment. Up to 56 people can be situated comfortably with twice as many in a tight squeeze. Maximum weight allowance: 60 metric tons.

Fusion powered, the MLR-120 can drive up to a maximum of 40,000km without refueling. To prevent over heating of the engine/power unit the MLR-120 must rest and cool six hours for every 6 days of constant use.
NOTE: the same applies to the Ground Armor Missile Launcher.

Moderate availability. Manufactured at Kucharski and Stelvenson. Not available to civilian personnel.

The "unmodified" Land Rover is identical to the MLR-120 minus the particle beam weapons. This is a common cargo vehicle with wide availability. Cost is about 36,000 credits for private use.

Vital Statistics
Weapons: Particle Beam Mounts (2)
>Range: 1600 meters (5300ft)
>Damage: Standard
>Attacks Per Melee: Two per each weapon for a total of 4.
>Energy Capacity: 30 charges/blasts each (total 60)
>NOTE: W.P. Heavy Weapon skill bonuses are applicable to the P-beams.

Equipment: Radar and Sensor disc (front): 64km (40 miles)
>Wide Band Radio with booster and scrambler; 482km (300 miles)

Function: Transport
Speed: 120kmph (80mph), able to cover rough terrain, fuel capacity: 2000km.
A.R.: 10
S.D.C.: Driver's cabin 100, cargo body 200, P-beam weapon mounts 100 each, tires 40.
Size: 10 meters (33ft) long, 3.9 meters (13ft) tall, cargo bay 7.3 meters (24ft) long.
Weight: 10 metric tons.

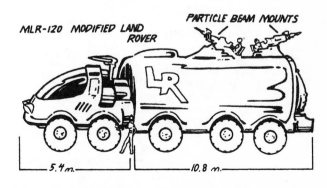

MLR-120 MODIFIED LAND ROVER
PARTICLE BEAM MOUNTS
LR
5.4 m.
10.8 m.

Hover Plasma Tank

This heavy duty offensive weapon vehicle is the only unmodified ground assault vehicle, other than the balrog destroyer. Normally the hover plasma tank is used as a major back up defense weapon against potential hostile forces. Their presence is fairly abundant at the Gideon colony and Orz, the latter is the sole manufacturer. Distribution to other locations is poor.

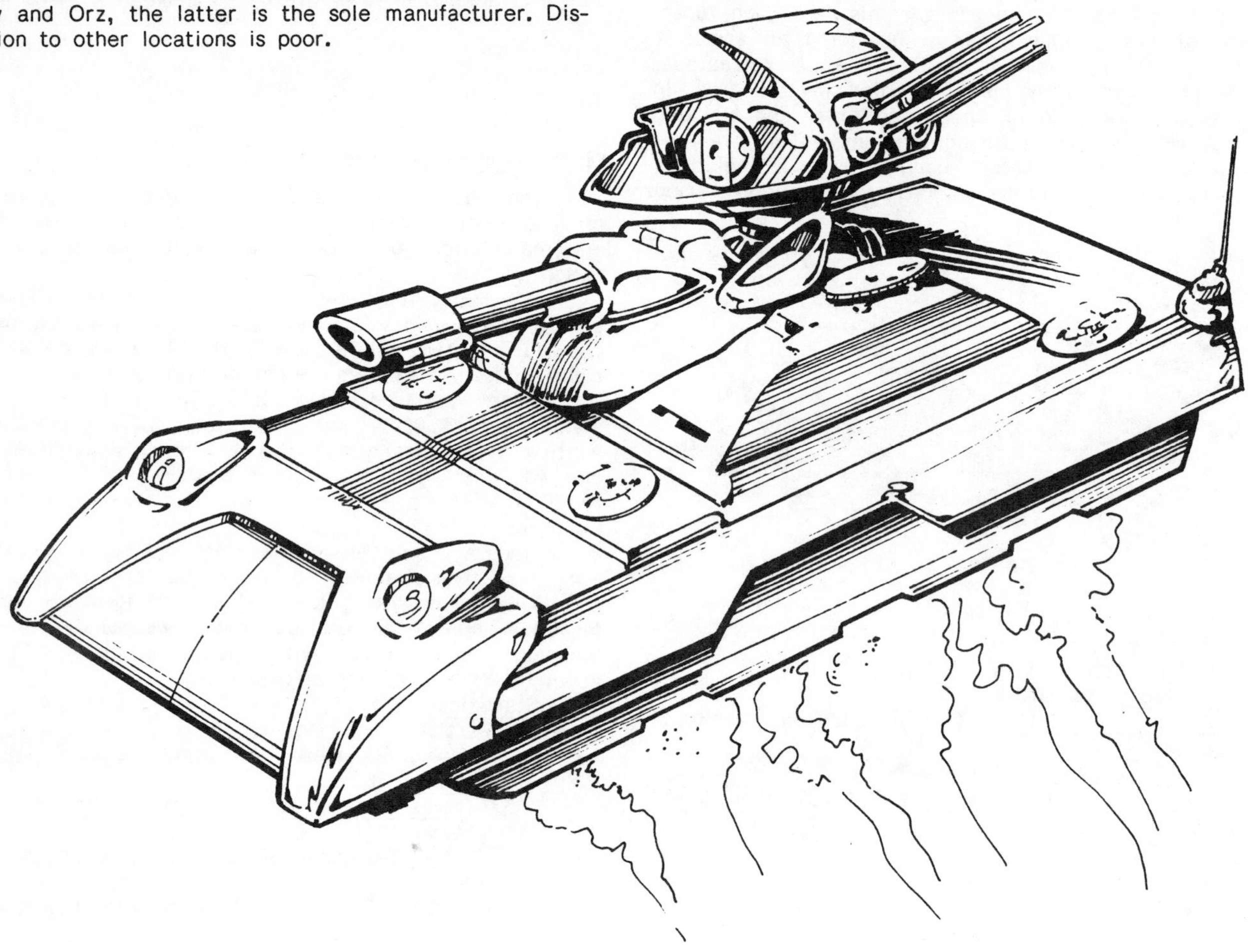

Vital Statistics

Weapons: Plasma Cannon
    Range: 3000 meters (9900ft)
    Damage: 8-80+10 (8D10+10)
    Attacks Per Melee: Four
    Bonuses: +2 to strike
    Energy Capacity: 28 plasma blasts

    Particle Beam Turret
    Range: 2200 meters (7260ft)
    Damage: Standard X 4; all four guns fire simultaneously.
    Attacks Per Melee: Two
    Bonus: +3 to strike
    Energy Capacity: 68 (one charge fires all four guns simultaneously).
    NOTES: 360° rotation, 65° arc.

Equipment: Laser Controlled Range Finder, digital, solid state.
    Ballistic Computers
    Radar and full sensory scanner, range: 64km (40 miles).
    Wide Band, Long Range Radio with booster and scrambler; range: 482km (300 miles).

Special Optical Enhancements: thermo imager, ultra-violet, infra-red, night sight and tele-scopic. Range: 650 meters (2150ft).
On Board Computer
Special Air Filtration, circulation and cooling system.
Emergency Oxygen supply; 2 hours
Medical Kit
Four Food Ration Packs
Two Rocket Signal Flares
20 gallons of purified drinking water

Function: Assault and Defense
Speed: 144kmph (90mph), maximum hover height: 4 meters (15ft)
A.R.: 14
S.D.C.: Tank body 610, plasma cannon 250, P-beam turret 400.
Size: 6 meters (20ft) long, 2.4 meters (8ft) wide, 3.2 meters (12ft) tall.
Weight: 18 metric tons.
NOTES: Spotlights have a 26 meter (85ft) range. The four access hatches seal air tight. The interior cabin is radiation shielded.

Rosenstein Land Buggy

The land buggy is the standard, personnel, all purpose-type vehicle and more common than any other. It is extremely mobile and suitable to rough and/or sandy terrains. It is constructed of light weight metal alloys and has a tinted, unbreakable polystructural windshield.

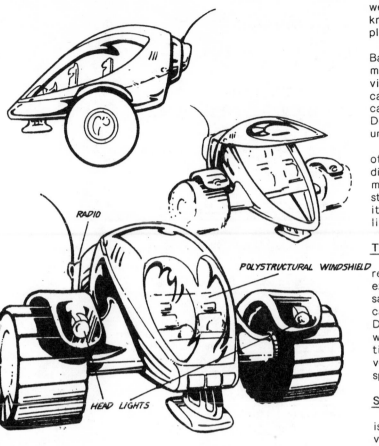

RADIO

POLYSTRUCTURAL WINDSHIELD

HEAD LIGHTS

Vital Statistics
Weapons: None
Equipment: Infra-red laser distancing optics system.
Short Range Wide Band Radio, 25km (16 miles)
Storage Compartment: 2.4 meters X 2.4 meters.
Function: Transportation
Speed: 150kmph (100 mph)
Bonuses: +2 to dodge
A.R.: 10
S.D.C.: 120
Size: 2.1 meters (7ft) long, 3 meters (10ft) wide from wheel to wheel.
Weight: One metric ton.
NOTES: Seats four comfortably.

Balrog Destroyer

During one of the shake-ups to accommodate the many refugees from surrounding colonies, the Gideon colony made a startling discovery. In 21 interstellar packing crates labeled "Agricultural Irrigation Pumper", they found the most highly-advanced fighting machine designed by Earth: the Balrog Destroyer. How these lethal machines were mislabeled and shipped to the Gideon colony is unknown, but is believed to be the result of a bungled interplanetary smuggling operation.

The giant (approximately the length of a city block) Balrog Destroyer is the absolute latest in sentient automation on Earth. Designed specifically for war zone environments too hostile to support human life or more delicate devices, the Balrog is a completely independent force capable of individual thought, analysis, and action. Balrog Destroyers even have personalities, opinions, and character unique to each specific unit.

These sentient machines are frighteningly reminiscent of Mechanoids, but though endowed (programmed) with individual human-like characteristics, thoughts, and decision-making capabilities, they are just machines. Balrog Destroyers are tools created by mankind to aid and protect it. Their prime directive is to protect and preserve human life at all cost.

The Hover Droids

Each Balrog Destroyer has two Hover Droids (often referred to as Scitz and Fritz), which are simply sensory extensions of the Balrog. Although each Droid possesses the same memories and attitudes of its Balrog, they are also capable of independent thoughts and actions. The Hover Droids are primarily used for maintenance, simple repair work, and scouting (directly sending and receiving information to "its" Balrog and/or human allies). Hover Droids are very seldom used in battle. See: **Balrog: Rear section** for specific details of abilities.

Sensor Clusters

Among the various missiles in the Balrog's armory is the Sensor Cluster. This is an information gathering device that will probe, record, and continue to relay data to the Balrog until it is destroyed, turned off or runs down (it can transmit for a maximum period of 320 hours). The maximum transmission range is 50km. Among the Cluster's scanning abilities are radar and sonar (50km range).

Critical Points

The Balrog Destroyer has **three critical points** which can destroy or immobilize it; missile storage/rear section; main fusion reactor/midsection; and sentient computer/forward section.

The missiles stored in the rear section become vulnerable after all the missile launch tubes are destroyed (total S.D.C. 1120) or the body casing destroyed (S.D.C. 480). If the missile storage is set off, the Balrog takes the following damage: 30 points for each anti-aircraft missile, 10 for each anti-personnel, 60 for each anti-tank, 10 for each Sensor Cluster, 300 for each fusion, 110 for each I.L.R.M. Half of the total damage should be applied to the mid-section and the remaining half specifically to the weapons turret on the mid-section. Speed factor is reduced by 3/4, assume the rear section is totally atomized.

The fusion reactor is located in the mid-section and powers both the hover jets and weapons. If the reactor is destroyed (150 S.D.C.) the Balrog is destroyed in a massive nuclear explosion; center of explosion affects a 200-meter radius, doing 10,000 points of damage. Of course the mid-section with its 550 S.D.C. must be penetrated first.

The sentient computer is housed in the forward section of the Balrog Destroyer. If it is "damaged", all weapon systems, communications, speed factor and analysis are reduced by half. If destroyed, the entire Balrog is completely immobilized (S.D.C. 75 for the actual computer).

More On Armor And S.D.C.

You'll notice that most of the other parts, such as hover jets and weapons, are given their own S.D.C. because individual components are likely to be targets of attack. These individual component's S.D.C. are in addition to the section's body housing S.D.C. (Example: mid-section 550 S.D.C. "plus" individual components like the actual turret, plasma cannon, lasers, etc.) ALL structures have an armor rating of 14 unless otherwise stated.

Energy Points (120 per melee round)

Weapons and Attacks: The Balrog Destroyer can expend only so much energy per melee round, thus, it can only provide **120 points of energy** to its weapons each melee. For this reason, each weapon type is given an energy point rating, indicating how much energy is needed to activate each particular device for one melee round. The 120 energy points can be distributed in any combination, but can never exceed the 120 maximum.

NOTE: Only eleven Balrog Destroyers remain. See chronology of dissection of Gideon E.

The Balrog Destroyer: A.R.: 14; Speed factor 0-85kmph.
Can lift 3 meters maximum off the ground, I.Q. equivalent 13.

Forward Section: A.R.: 14; S.D.C.: 620
Weapons:
Main Particle Beam
Attacks Per Melee: 4
Range: 2200 meters (7300ft)
Damage: 7-70+25
Bonuses: +1 to hit
S.D.C.: 150; A.R.: 14
Energy Points: 60

Secondary Particle Beam
Attacks Per Melee: 2
Range: 1800 meters (5900ft)
Damage: 5-50+25
Bonuses: +2 to hit
S.D.C.: 80; A.R.: 14
Energy Points: 30

Ram Prow
Affects a 60X60 meter area per melee
Damage: 10-50+50 (the Balrog takes 1 S.D.C. damage for every 5 points of damage inflicted)
S.D.C.: 440; A.R.: 14
Energy Points: None

Hover Jets
Forward Module Total: 6
S.D.C.: 25 each; A.R.: 14

Sentient Computer
S.D.C.: 75; A.R.: 9

Mid-Section: A.R.: 14; S.D.C.: 550
Weapons:
Main Weapon Turret
Body Housing S.D.C.: 220, capable of 360 degree rotation.
A.R.: 14

Plasma Cannon
Attacks Per Melee: 2
Range: 3600 meters (12,200ft)
Damage: 4-24X10 (+100)
Bonuses: None
S.D.C.: 210; A.R.: 14
Energy Points: 50

Mini Laser Cannon
Attacks Per Melee: 2
Range: 2200 meters (7500ft)
Damage: 6-36+20
Bonuses: +3 to hit
S.D.C.: 80; A.R.: 10
Energy Points: 20

Secondary Laser Banks
Total Number of Lasers: 5
Attacks Per Melee: One each
Range: 1800 meters (5900ft)
Damage: 6-36+6
Bonuses: +2 to hit
S.D.C.: 50 each; A.R.: 10
Energy Points: 10 each

Bi-Laser Turrets (Right or Left)
Attacks Per Melee: 4
Damage: 4-24+6 (each blast; total four)
Range: 1400 meters (4700ft)
S.D.C.: 40; A.R.: 10
360 degree rotation.
Energy Points: 20 (each for right or left)

Tri-Laser Turrets (right or left)
Attacks Per Melee: 6
Range: 1400 meters (4700ft)
Damage: 4-24+6 (each blast; total six)
S.D.C.: 50; A.R.: 10
360 degree rotation
Energy Points: 30 each

Hover Jets: Mid-Section Module
Total: 10; A.R.: 14

Right: 2	S.D.C.: 50 each
Mid: 6	S.D.C.: 25 each
Left: 2	S.D.C.: 50 each

Rear Section: A.R.: 14; S.D.C.: 480
Weapons:
Missile Bank
ALL missiles A.R.: 10; S.D.C.: 20
Attacks Per Melee: 12 (maximum number of missiles fired)
Energy Points: 10 for each missile fired.

Anti-Aircraft (heat seeking)
Range: 50km
Damage: 6-30
Bonuses: +2 to hit
Speed Factor: 1500kmph
Total Number Stored: 16

Anti-Personnel (fragmentary)
Area Affected: 10 meter radius
Range: 2km (1½ miles)
Damage: 5-30
Speed Factor: 150kmph
Total Number Stored: 16

Anti-Tank (armor piercing)
Range: 2km (1½ miles)
Damage: 8-80
Speed Factor: 250kmph
Total Number Stored: 16

Fusion Bomb
Range: 16km (10 miles)
Damage: 300 points (blast center/radius 30 meters); 100 damage from secondary blast radius 30 meters beyond blast center.
Total Number Stored: 4

Sensor Cluster
Range: 50km (31 miles)
Damage: None
S.D.C.: 20; A.R.: 10
Total Number Stored: 4

I.L.R.M.
Total Stored: 2

Missile Launch Tubes
S.D.C.: 70 each; A.R.: 14
Total: 16

Two Hover Droids
S.D.C.: 50; A.R.: 9
Bonuses: +3 to dodge

Full sensory and communications capabilities/radar 20km (13 miles) radius. Weapons: laser lance, 2 attacks per melee. Adjustable damage capability; 2-12 or 4-24; +2 to hit; (total charges of laser lance: 40 at full power).
Speed Factor: 180kmph

Hover Jets
S.D.C.: 25 each
Rear Module Total: 4
NOTE: At least one jet in each main section (forward, mid and rear) must be operational to maintain movement. (Although reduced to a speed factor of 10kmph).

Rear Section
1. Hover Droid
2. Missile Launch Tubes
3. Missile Storage Section

Mid-Section
4. High Power Search Light
5. Main Weapon Turret/360° Rotation

Mid-Section
4. High Power Search Light
5. Main Weapon Turret/360° Rotation
6. Plasma Cannon
7. Secondary Laser Banks
8. Main Laser Cannon
9. Tri-Laser Turret/360° Rotation
10. Bi-Laser Turret/360° Rotation

Forward Section
11. Main Particle Beam/360° Rotation
12. Secondary Particle Beam/360° Rotation
13. Ram Prow
14. Additional Shielding
15. Wasps
16. E.B.A.
17. PR-10 Particle Beam Rifle

SENSOR CLUSTER

Balrog Destroyer Hit Location Chart

This chart is provided so players can keep easy score of this complex machine. Of course photocopies of this chart can be made.

Section	Specific Target	A.R.	S.D.C.	Damage Sustained (S.D.C. Lost)
Forward	Body Housing	14	620	
	Sentient Computer (with the body housing)	9	75	
	Main P-Beam	14	150	
	Secondary P-Beam	14	80	
	Ram Prow	14	440	
	Hover Jets	14	25	
Mid	Body Housing	14	550	
	Main Weapon Turret	14	220	
	Plasma Cannon	14	210	
	Main Laser Cannon	10	80	
	Secondary Laser Bank	10	250 (50 each)	
	Bi-Laser Turrets (2)	10	40	
	Tri-Laser Turrets (2)	10	50	
	Fusion Reactor (within housing)	9	550	
	Hover Jets: Right(2)	14	50 each	
	Mid (6)	14	25 each	
	Left (2)	14	50 each	
Rear	Body Housing	14	480	
	Missile Launch Tubes	14	1120	
	Missiles (within launch tubes)	10	20 each	
	Sensor Clusters (4)	10	20 each	
	Hover Droids (2): Scitz	9	50	
	Fritz	9	50	

KEVIN SIEMBIEDA

THE MECHANOIDS

THE NIGHTMARE BEGINS

The Mechanoids are an ancient race of creatures renowned for their unrivaled technology, power and evil. Their cruelty quickly became a thing of legend as they swept the universe, hunting out and exterminating entire worlds. The Mechanoids are a race of merciless, megalomaniacs with but three all consuming purposes: **expansion, knowledge** and **the termination of all human life.** If the Mechanoids' powers rival the gods then they are mad gods; god-beings without mercy, justice or compassion. A malevolent force consumed in utter hatred and contempt for all living things. A devouring madness that makes them view humanity, its cousins, and its allies as all being a part of a hideous, malignant cancer that must be terminated. Total genocide of all humanoid life and its sympathizers wherever it's found.

Ironically, the Mechanoid's ancestry is rooted in human (humanoid) origin. A people whose only true flaw was their insatiable quest for knowledge, irregardless of the cost. It would be their genetic reconstruction experiments to create a superior breed of man that would spawn the Mechanoids. Originally designed to better withstand the rigors of space exploration, the frail human creatures were genetically reconstructed and reinforced with advanced robotics; creating the ultimate cyborg. The experiments were perhaps too successful, for it created a new type of creature, a creature too far removed from the realm of humanity. The new life form soon proved to be superior to its creators in every way and although these quasi-mechanoids were both loyal and benevolent their presence instilled only suspicion and hatred among their human creators. Eventually the paranoia provoked the humans to destroy that which they had created. However, the new life fled; wracked in confusion and sorrow.

In a futile attempt to appease their creators, the new life gathered great knowledge from every corner of their galaxy. They achieved in a few brief centuries what man could not have attained in a thousand. During that time they also made great strides in improving both their genetic and robotic structure. When they returned home the new life appeared even more alien than before their departure and were greeted with horrendous animosity. The agony of rejection, the fear, the hatred, were all magnified by the mechanoid's empathic nature and forever ingrained within the racial memory that would corrupt every mechaoid to come. Eventually the humans and the new life (mechanoids) clashed in a long and bloody battle that saw the mechanoid rise triumphant over the ashes of its creators. Human-kind had created them, deserted them, and tried to destroy them; yet it was they who proved superior. No longer would they tolerate such degradation at the hands of inferiors. The new life had been instilled with a bloodlust that would never be sated. The Mechanoid nightmare had begun.

The "insane" hatred for humanoid life is likely to be a genetic weakness, perpetuated by continual cloning of the same flawed DNA structure, and stimulated and exaggerated by racial memory and psionic empathy passed on from generation to generation.

Until the Mechanoids' attack on the Gideon-E research colonies, neither the Earth humans nor their allies in the Intergalactic Federation (I.F.) had known of their existence. Indeed, the entire Gideon-E incident is pure chance, for the Mechanoids were merely on a routine mining expedition to replenish the mothership's resources. Finding humans is just an extra bonus providing some welcomed entertainment and relaxation. It's for the sake of satisfying their maniacal pleasures that they have established so many temporary bases and allowed the humans to live.

THE MECHANOID BRUTE ORGANISM

bine both.

It's important to note that only the four members of the Mechanoids' upper caste, the freedom thinkers, Overlord, Oracle, Brain and Runner can initiate new ideas and programs. Only they have the freedom to satisfy their insane hatred in the most gruesome manners. They are the organizers, the directors of their people. As free thinkers only they are even capable of truly independent thoughts and concepts. ALL the others, from the brute and mantis to the exterminator and tunnel crawler, are simply clever creatures programmed to fulfill a need. While they experience the same emotional and psychological traumas/hatred they express it in a much more direct, usually destructive way. A brute, wasp or exterminator, for example, might toy with a human like a cat would a mouse and/or kill the person slowly. Their idea of torture would be ripping a person apart limb by limb. Games to crush a person's will or mind; or delicate physical experimentations are too subtle for them; these are the methods of the runner or brain. A word of caution. It is folly to underestimate the intelligence or cunning of the lesser Mechanoids, especially the wasp, which is a tactical and strategic master.

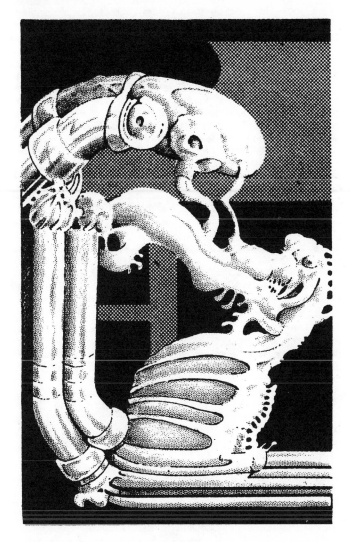

Mechanoid Reaction To Humans

Mechanoids are easily provoked by humans' strength, ingenuity, and arrogance. This may stimulate any number of reactions including mindless aggression, berserker rage, suicidal revenge, or methodical jack-the-ripper-type slaughter. Personality disorders, fetishism, phobias and schizophrenia add to the cacophony of screaming emotions inside a Mechanoid. Although they may appear to be calm, calculating creatures the Mechanoids are driven by burning hatred, anger and frustration when it comes to humanoids. The tortured aliens crave revenge against ALL humanoid life for they see humans as the ultimate evil and cause of eons of mental/emotional pain. Consequently, their cruelty toward humanoids is without parallel. Humanoids are subjected to all types of sadistic torture at the hands of the Mechanoids. Hideous experiments, biopsies on the living, degradation and mental and physical torture of all kinds are typical of these insane creatures. Of course each individual Mechanoid has his own unique style and approach. Some prefer mind games, others straight forward physical torture while others com-

A CUT-AWAY REVEALING THE THE MECHANOID ORGANISM.

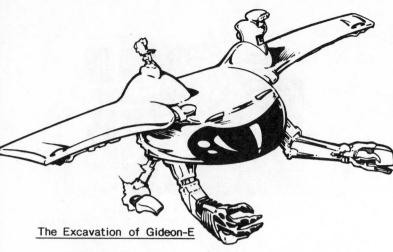

The Excavation of Gideon-E

The Mechanoids' excavation of a planet is a spectacle beyond man's comprehension. Within a short three month period they will quite literally consume an Earth size planet. Usually planets or moons with a molten core are selected so that the Mechanoids can convert the fiery center into an energy crystal to power the gargantuan mothership. The cyborgs are careful to choose only worlds that are barren or inhabited by humanoids or humanoid sympathizers. Planets occupied by humanoid life are top priority targets.

After an appropriate planet has been selected temporary ground bases are established for a quick planet wide reconnaissance and to direct the planet's consumption. Defoliation is next (if needed) followed by the locating of and quick devastating, strip mining of fossil fuels and major mineral deposits. The crude ores are transported to the Mechanoid mothership where they are processed, purified and stored. Those raw materials will be used in the construction and repairs of robots, vehicles and the ship itself during the mothership's centuries long sojourn through space. Shortly after the bulk of the mineral resources have been plundered the **diggers** begin to slice the planet's crust from pole to pole in one long continuous line just as we might slice an orange to decorate a dessert. During this time the world's waters are also siphoned away to be stored and purified on the mothership.

When the diggers have completed carving kilometers deep trenches in the planet's crust, and the bulk of useful minerals and waters have been mined, the planet is ready for its final stages of transformation. Immediately after excavation of the Mechanoid bases a series of powerful explosive charges are activated by the automated bridge forts, shattering the planet's surface, hurling them into space. A large percentage of these chunks will be gathered by the Mechanoid haulers and placed in the mothership.

The fiery molten planet's core is now exposed and ready to be converted into what the Mechanoid's call a "power crystal". The core is subjected to a series of energy and dimensional (space/time) warping conditions which alters its atomic structure. Unfortunately, the process is unreliable; thus only one out of every twenty attempts are successful. However, it is well worth the time and effort, for one Earth-size planet will create a power crystal no larger than the size of a two story house and capable of powering the Mechanoid mothership for a hundred years.

The entire planet consumption process for an Earth-size planet takes approximately three months, while the crystal conversion requires an additional two to three weeks.

NOTE: The colonists of Gideon-E are not completely aware of the Mechanoid's intentions nor the procedures just previously outlined. The humans are aware that this is some sort of mining operation, the Mechanoid's intend to destroy Gideon-E and time is running desperately short!

THE MECHANOIDS

In many insect societies, entire groups within that society serve a specific function to preserve that society. In much the same way, specific types of Mechanoids serve a particular function(s) within their society. Whatever that function may be, it is their life's purpose. They simply perform their function; rest, eat - and continue to perform their function until they are no longer able.

There is little need for recreation or diversions, because there is no dissension, fears, questions, or longings of purpose or self-expression. Each Mechanoid type has been physically and mentally designed, conditioned and bred to perform its particular function within its world. Each is part of the whole and must serve the whole as it was designed to do. Without question. Without thought. The whole must continue. The whole is life. All this is ingrained within their very genetic structure, cloned and continued for thousands of years. Only a genetic error or mutation can disturb the balance. Such mutations, when discovered, are destroyed immediately.

The following descriptions are listed in the order of the Mechanoid caste society, from the lowest to the highest. Robots are not included.

The Cargo Haulers are among the drones of the Mechanoid society. They are capable of little independent thought. Their function is simple: to sort, gather, and store. These simple-minded workers will ignore any other activity (battles, humans, etc.) and continue to work, unless otherwise directed. Haulers obey the Black Widow, Brutes, Mantis, Runner, Brain, Oracle and Overlord.

They possess all Level One psionics and limited telepathy. I.S.P.: 190, Third Level proficiency.

Hit Points: Type I: 230; Type II: 120; Type III: 60.

The Digger is another drone designed for massive excavation and dissection of planets. When it has no target, it slips into a psionically-induced state of suspended animation, slowing body functions to almost nothing. It is awakened telepathically when needed by a Mantis or Brain. The living organism itself is genetically structured to feed off nuclear radiation. Consequently, the Digger must have a heavily radioactive environment to survive. Although it can, and does, feed off the radiation from its continual hydrogen fusion chamber. Obeys Mantis, Brain, Oracle and Overlord.

It has all Level One and Two psionics. I.S.P.: 870; Fifth Level proficiency.

Hit Points: 720

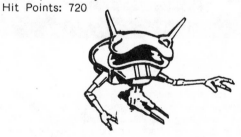

The Seeker Pod is a living blood hound. Its sole function is to locate any creatures which have been classified for extermination, notification of location to its masters and help terminate the creature(s). These Mechanoids are fairly intelligent in that they are not easily duped or confused. However, they have no knowledge of science of skills, other than tracking and extermination. Seeker Pods are specially designed to aid and obey the Exterminator, but will also obey any other Mechanoid above its own rank (especially the Tunnel Crawler, Brute and Wasp).

It has all Level One psionics, as well as limited telepathy, empathy and mind block. I.S.P.: 75; Third Level proficiency.

Hit Points: 10

Mechanoid Digger

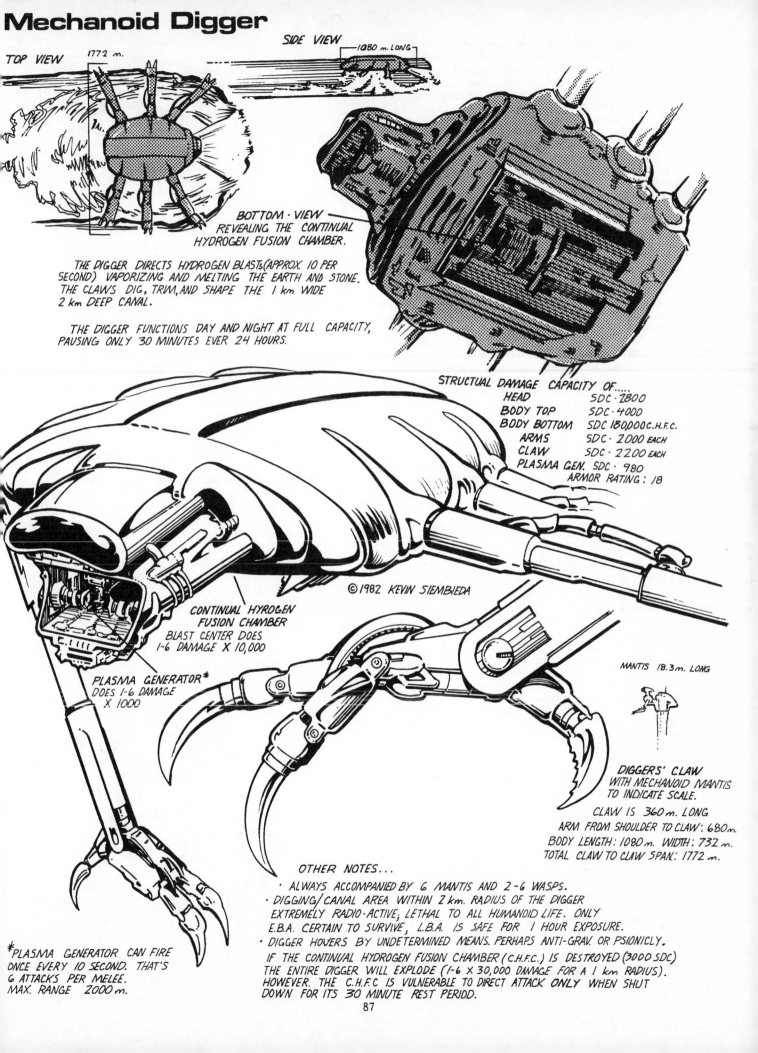

TOP VIEW

1772 m.

SIDE VIEW

1080 m. LONG

BOTTOM · VIEW
REVEALING THE CONTINUAL
HYDROGEN FUSION CHAMBER.

THE DIGGER DIRECTS HYDROGEN BLASTs (APPROX. 10 PER SECOND) VAPORIZING AND MELTING THE EARTH AND STONE. THE CLAWS DIG, TRIM, AND SHAPE THE 1 km WIDE 2 km DEEP CANAL.

THE DIGGER FUNCTIONS DAY AND NIGHT AT FULL CAPACITY, PAUSING ONLY 30 MINUTES EVER 24 HOURS.

STRUCTURAL DAMAGE CAPACITY OF.....

HEAD	SDC· 1800
BODY TOP	SDC· 4000
BODY BOTTOM	SDC 180,000 C.H.F.C.
ARMS	SDC· 2000 EACH
CLAW	SDC· 2200 EACH
PLASMA GEN.	SDC· 980
ARMOR RATING:	18

CONTINUAL HYROGEN
FUSION CHAMBER
BLAST CENTER DOES
1-6 DAMAGE X 10,000

© 1982 KEVIN SIEMBIEDA

PLASMA GENERATOR*
DOES 1-6 DAMAGE
X 1000

MANTIS 18.3 m. LONG

DIGGERS' CLAW
WITH MECHANOID MANTIS
TO INDICATE SCALE.

CLAW IS 360 m. LONG
ARM FROM SHOULDER TO CLAW: 680 m.
BODY LENGTH: 1080 m. WIDTH: 732 m.
TOTAL CLAW TO CLAW SPAN: 1772 m.

OTHER NOTES...

· ALWAYS ACCOMPANIED BY 6 MANTIS AND 2-6 WASPS.
· DIGGING/CANAL AREA WITHIN 2 km. RADIUS OF THE DIGGER EXTREMELY RADIO-ACTIVE; LETHAL TO ALL HUMANOID LIFE. ONLY E.B.A. CERTAIN TO SURVIVE, L.B.A. IS SAFE FOR 1 HOUR EXPOSURE.
· DIGGER HOVERS BY UNDETERMINED MEANS. PERHAPS ANTI-GRAV. OR PSIONICLY.

IF THE CONTINUAL HYDROGEN FUSION CHAMBER (C.H.F.C.) IS DESTROYED (3000 SDC) THE ENTIRE DIGGER WILL EXPLODE (1-6 X 30,000 DAMAGE FOR A 1 km RADIUS). HOWEVER, THE C.H.F.C IS VULNERABLE TO DIRECT ATTACK ONLY WHEN SHUT DOWN FOR ITS 30 MINUTE REST PERIOD.

*PLASMA GENERATOR CAN FIRE ONCE EVERY 10 SECOND. THAT'S 6 ATTACKS PER MELEE. MAX. RANGE 2000 m.

The Exterminator is a born predator which delights in the hunt and destruction of other living creatures (including rogue Mechanoids). It is designed for pest control in the mothership's pipelines, nothing more. Consequently, they are constantly roaming through the ship's labyrinth of pipes and tunnels in search of prey. The exterminator is a very treacherous and crafty hunter who enjoys tricks traps, ambushes, and cat-and-mouse games. They are fairly intelligent and master hunters, although they have no knowledge of science or other skills. They may command up to 6 robots or 1-4 Seeker Pods and are often accompanied by Tunnel Crawlers or other exterminators. It obeys any Mechanoid above its rank.

It has all Level One psionics plus empathy, mind block, night vision, levitate, limited telekinesis and extended telepathy. I.S.P.: 120, Sixth Level proficiency.

Hot Points: 50

The Tunnel Crawler is designed exclusively for pest control. This sadistic exterminator is a free agent, able to go wherever it pleases. Although its attacks are limited to close range confrontations, its heavy environmental body armor provides more than adequate protection. They are also able to release a toxic nerve gas which lingers for about 2 hours. These loners of the Mechanoid race are often accompanied by no more than a few robots. Tunnel Crawlers obey Runners, Brains and Overlords.

Its psionic abilities include presence sense, see aura detect psionics, levitate, night vision, mind block, limited telekinesis and extended telepathy. I.S.P. 120; Sixth Level proficiency.

Hit Points: 43

The Black Widow is quite intelligent, commanding an army of robots, transport ships, cargo freighters and haulers. The Black Widow is the co-ordinator of salvage and storage operations. She answers to the Mantis, Runner, Brain, Oracle and Overlord. They are most often found on the ship's exteriors and storage areas (Levels 1-3).

They possess all Level One and Two psionics. I.S.P.: 500; Eighth Level proficiency.

Hit Points: 218

The Brutes, although a bit of a predator used in both offensive and defensive actions, they are often found assisting in construction, repairs and robot supervision. Brutes are the Mechanoids' robotics experts and are responsible for their construction, maintenance and direction.

These intelligent, but cruel Mechanoids can be found anywhere on the ship (usually accompanied by a handful of robots).

Their psionic abilities include all Level One plus bio-regeneration, mind block, levitation, limited telekinesis and extended telepathy. (Note: these are somewhat increased abilities than those listed in the original Mechanoid Invasion Book). I.S.P.: 500; Eighth Level proficiency.

Hit Points: 45

The Wasp is the most intelligent and deadly of the Mechanoid predators. These fast-thinking strategists are the very heart of the Mechanoid assault and defense network. Daring and flamboyant, they thrive relentlessly in battle fighting, and are without mercy or conscience. Encased in a powerful environmental body shell, they are able to withstand both the rigors of space and heavy assault while maintaining high maneuverability, speed and strike potential. The Wasp is legendary for its ability to maneuver with unerring accuracy while flying at top speed (1500kmph), and/or under under adverse conditions. A unique coupling of technology and psionics makes this possible. It is this science which allows the Wasp to go from 1500kmph to a dead stop instantly. They obey all Mechanoids above their rank.

Wasps possess all Level One and Two psionics. I.S.P.: 313; Tenth Level proficiency.

Hit Points: 56

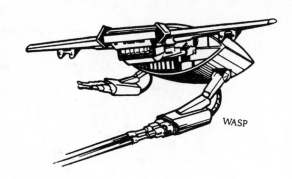

WASP

The Battle Cruiser is an actual Mechanoid organism, and is the last of the Mechanoid predators contained on the mothership. They are deployed against major threats to the mothership and planet assaults.

The Battle Cruiser obeys the Brain, Oracle, and Overlord. It has not been deployed against the populace of Gideon-E.

They possess all Level One and Two psionic abilities. I.S.P.: 440; Tenth Level proficiency.

Hit Points: 390.

The Octopus is a mechanical wonder continually involved in construction, electronics, mechanics, repairs and even surgery and genetics. Having 3 separate brain sacs it can perform 3 separate actions simultaneously; or concentrate its efforts on one problem with maximum efficiency. Although very intelligent, its role is to act as a submissive (though brilliant) assistant to the Mantis, Runner, Brain, Oracle and Overlord. It is instilled with very little drive or ambition, leaving those ranking above it to deal with experimentation and research, while it handles the mundane day-to-day regimen of the ship.

It possesses all Level One and Two psionic abilities. I.S.P.: 1000; Tenth Level proficiency.

Hit Points: 130

The Mantis is a specialist in engineering and mining operations. It selects planets for mining, directs planet dissection, analyzes minerals, etc. When not actively involved in excavation, it plans and supervises construction, energy consumption, metallurgy, research and development. Mantises can be found throughout the ship. They obey the Runner, Brain, Oracle and Overlord.

Its psionic abilities are limited to presence sense, see aura, resist fatigue, extended telepathy, and extended telekinesis. I.S.P.: 570. Tenth level proficiency.

Hit Points: 50

MANTIS

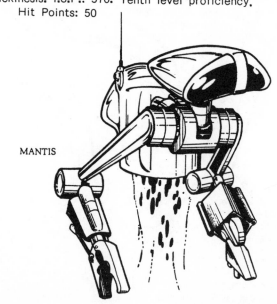

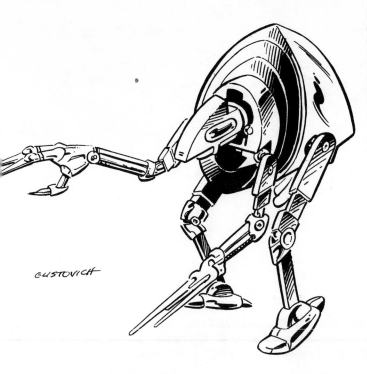

GUSTOVICH

The Runner is the Mechanoid jack-of-all-trades. All Runners have a rudimentary knowledge of physics, genetics biology, surgery, electronics, navigation, mechanics, robotics and communication. The typical Runner is an expert in two of these areas. Runners are among the few free thinkers in the Mechanoid society. This allows them access to ship computers/brain pools, experimental/research centers and free time. (Note: Only the Runner, Brain, Oracle and Overlord can tap into ship computers/brain pools).

Possessed by an insane hatred of humanoid life, they often spend free time conducting hideous biological and genetic experiments on them. (It was such experimentation that created the mutants). Runners also enjoy pipeline hunting expeditions.

They possess all Level One and Two psionics plus extended telepathy. I.S.P.: 690; Twelfth Level proficiency.

Hit Points: 44.

The Brain oversees all planetary and mining operations, planet assault, navigation and ship operations. They function as a million little generals, directing and observing a vast army of Mechanoids and robots. If the Brains have a specialized function, it is a pilot. Only the Brain can pilot the spider fortress, transport and freighter vessels.

Brains, like the Runner, can tap into the computer decks and brain pools, selecting any information needed. Unlike the Runner, which often works under the Brain's direction, the Brain is capable of assimilating extraordinary amounts of data and retains it (total recall) for 72 hours.

Being free thinkers, they have full run of the ship and generous amounts of free time for experimentation and personal expression.

They possess the full range of Level One and Two psionics plus extended telepathy, extended telekinesis, see the invisible, and bio-manipulation. I.S.P.: 2000; Thirteenth Level proficiency.

Hit Points: 35.

The Oracle is perhaps the most enigmatic of all the Mechanoids. Its prime function is that of a systems analyst, observing and improving upon ship operations and equipment. Its brain capacity and psionic abilities surpass even the Overlord's and the Mechanoid Brain's in both size and ability, making it a virtual living computer. It too can tap directly into the computer/brain pools, but

is the "only" Mechanoid that is able to block its thoughts or break contact with the computer on its own. This has been a matter for concern among some Mechanoids, who fear that the Oracle has mutated into something beyond its original purpose. The Runners harbor the greatest concern, especially in light of the Oracle's philosophical and non-aggressive outlook toward intelligent humanoid life forms. The Overlords, though concerned, simply watch with suspicion, waiting for some transgression.

While deprived of physical limbs or weapons, the Oracle is far from helpless, possessing all known psionic abilities. It is answerable only to the Overlord and Brain.

Possesses ALL known psionics. I.S.P.: 4200; Thirteenth Level proficiency.

Hit Points: 90

The Overlords are the prime movers and masters of the ship. ALL Mechanoids must answer to them, including the other free-thinkers. None may defy them. They tend to be cold, analytical thinkers (second only to the Oracle), constantly in touch with all major ship operations, applying their quick, methodical logic to any crisis. They are also excellent strategists (only the Wasp is its equal), and adept in navigation, engineering physics, genetics, cloning and biology. Most importantly, they alone hold the secret of the power crystal conversion (some believe the Oracle also holds the secret) and they alone can merge/link directly with the **Master Computer Brain**.

They possess all Level 1-3 psionics. I.S.P.: 2900; Twentieth Level proficiency.

Hit Points: 90.

Mechanoid Technology

The Mechanoids are considerably more advanced than the humans as the mammoth mothership, spider fortress and the Mechanoids themselves would indicate. With the exception of a few droids like the runt and thinman ALL machines, weapons and vehicles are integrated with living organisms. Their entire technology is based upon cybernetics, robotics, and psionics. This makes it quite impossible for a human, unless psionic, to use any Mechanoid device. For example: there are no "external" buttons, knobs, switches, levers or instrumentation. Everything is internal.

In one play test adventure my players jumped into a mechanoid elevator only to find no external controls. They tried various radio frequencies to trip a hidden device to no avail. Finally, a minor psionic with object read was able to successfully read the elevator's history and operation. Behind the wall was a simple switch normally activated by telekinesis. Unfortunately, the players had nobody with telekinesis and had to fight off attacking Runners while a G.V.P.M. character carefully cut away the wall panel with a fusion torch and flicked the switch by hand. A simple function such as flicking a switch suddenly became a life and death conflict lasting several minutes.

Communications

Mechanoids use radio and laser communication techniques as well as psionics to communicate between themselves. The preferred method is psionics, but limited range makes alternative long range communications a necessity. Mechanoids generally utilize conventional radio communications and artifical synthesized voices when communicating with humanoids. Psionics are not for lesser creatures.

Mechanoid Base

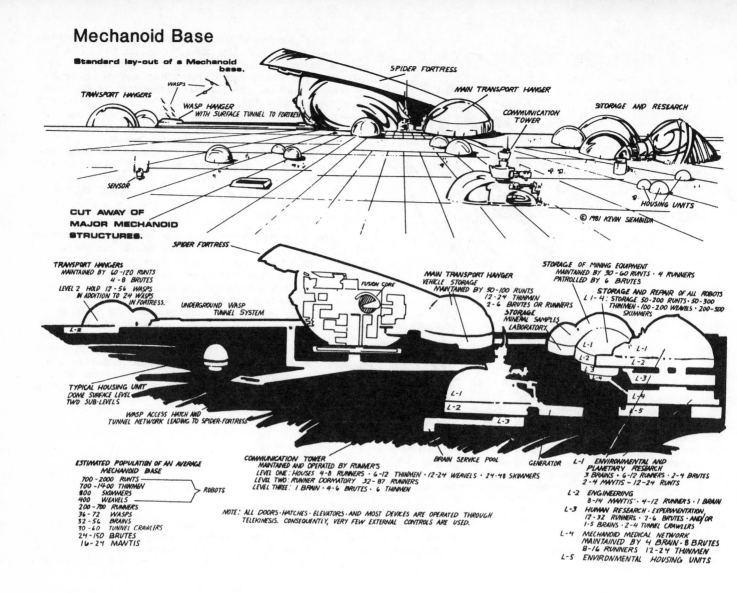

Standard lay-out of a Mechanoid base.

TRANSPORT HANGERS

WASPS

WASP HANGER
WITH SURFACE TUNNEL TO FORTRESS

SPIDER FORTRESS

MAIN TRANSPORT HANGER

COMMUNICATION TOWER

STORAGE AND RESEARCH

SENSOR

HOUSING UNITS

© 1981 KEVIN SIEMBIEDA

CUT AWAY OF MAJOR MECHANOID STRUCTURES.

SPIDER FORTRESS

TRANSPORT HANGERS
MAINTAINED BY 60-120 RUNTS
4-8 BRUTES
LEVEL 2 HOLD 12-56 WASPS
IN ADDITION TO 24 WASPS
IN FORTRESS.

UNDERGROUND WASP
TUNNEL SYSTEM

FUSION CORE

MAIN TRANSPORT HANGER
VEHICLE STORAGE
MAINTAINED BY 50-100 RUNTS
12-24 THINMEN
2-6 BRUTES OR RUNNERS
STORAGE
MINERAL SAMPLES
LABORATORY

STORAGE OF MINING EQUIPMENT
MAINTAINED BY 30-60 RUNTS · 4 RUNNERS
PATROLLED BY 6 BRUTES

STORAGE AND REPAIR OF ALL ROBOTS
L1-4: STORAGE 50-200 RUNTS · 50-300
THINMEN · 100-200 WEAVELS · 200-500
SKIMMERS

TYPICAL HOUSING UNIT
DOME SURFACE LEVEL
TWO SUB-LEVELS

WASP ACCESS HATCH AND
TUNNEL NETWORK LEADING TO SPIDER-FORTRESS

ESTIMATED POPULATION OF AN AVERAGE MECHANOID BASE

700 - 2000 RUNTS	
700 - 1400 THINMEN	
800 SKIMMERS	ROBOTS
400 WEAVELS	
200 - 700 RUNNERS	
36 - 72 WASPS	
32 - 56 BRAINS	
30 - 60 TUNNEL CRAWLERS	
24 - 150 BRUTES	
16 - 24 MANTIS	

COMMUNICATION TOWER
MAINTAINED AND OPERATED BY RUNNER'S
LEVEL ONE: HOUSES 4-8 RUNNERS · 6-12 THINMEN · 12-24 WEAVELS · 24-48 SKIMMERS
LEVEL TWO: RUNNER DORMATORY 32-87 RUNNERS
LEVEL THREE: 1 BRAIN · 4-6 BRUTES · 6 THINMEN

NOTE: ALL DOORS · HATCHES · ELEVATORS · AND MOST DEVICES ARE OPERATED THROUGH
TELEKINESIS. CONSEQUENTLY, VERY FEW EXTERNAL CONTROLS ARE USED.

BRAIN SERVICE POOL

GENERATOR

L-1 ENVIRONMENTAL AND
PLANETARY RESEARCH
3 BRAINS · 6-12 RUNNERS · 2-4 BRUTES
2-4 MANTIS - 12-24 RUNTS

L-2 ENGINEERING
8-14 MANTIS · 4-12 RUNNERS · 1 BRAIN

L-3 HUMAN RESEARCH · EXPERIMENTATION
12-32 RUNNERS · 2-6 BRUTES AND/OR
1-5 BRAINS · 2-4 TUNNEL CRAWLERS

L-4 MECHANOID MEDICAL NETWORK
MAINTAINED BY 4 BRAIN · 8 BRUTES
8-16 RUNNERS · 12-24 THINMEN

L-5 ENVIRONMENTAL HOUSING UNITS

MECHANOID FOOTNOTES:

1. Mechanoids tend to believe themselves **superior** to all other races, especially humanoids (often underestimating humanoid foes).

2. Most Mechanoids have an **unreasoning hatred** for any humanoid life. Only the Haulers and Diggers are indifferent toward humanoids; and only an Oracle will ever aid or befriend a human. (There is a 42% likelihood of an Oracle befriending/aiding a human). But only a 5% chance of any human ever encountering one on the surface of Gideon-E.

3. Surprisingly, Mechanoids can be quite friendly to other **Non-Human** races (unless that race harbors any positive feelings about humanoids).

4. **Most equipment,** elevators, teleporter, and controls are operated through telepathy and telekinesis. Consequently, there are few external controls, knobs, buttons, screens, etc.

5. **Storage bins** designated as food are vast tanks of concentrated liquid nutrients. Most Mechanoids contain a food supply built right into their mechanical exo-skeletons (usually enough for 2 weeks).

6. **All Mechanoids** are encased in an environmental body armor (exo-skeleton) containing life support systems, independent energy source, independent oxygen and purification system, radiation and heat shielding, communications, and extraordinary scanning facilities.

7. **Mechanoids communicate** through radio and laser techniques and psionics.

8. **The Mechanoid organisms,** themselves are carbon based creatures of soft, fleshy tissue and intricate nervous system. They are completely integrated with their machine bodies.

9. **Mechanoid endurance/hit points:** Because of the Mechanoid organism's very special genetic construction and cybornetic integrations, they are extremely vulnerable when exposed from their metallic body armor. They're all very anemic and must breath "pure" oxygen to live. Consequently, if the environmental armor is penetrated (cracked, punctured, etc.), they will die from exposure in a matter of minutes (They lose approximately 10 hit points per melee from exposure alone. The organism's Armor Rating is 2).

S.D.C. Notes

Generally the structural damage capacity (S.D.C.) of an exterior metallic wall such as those found at a mechanoid base is 100 S.D.C. per two meter (8ft) area; A.R. 14. Interior wall panels and doors are S.D.C. 50 per two meters; A.R. 9.

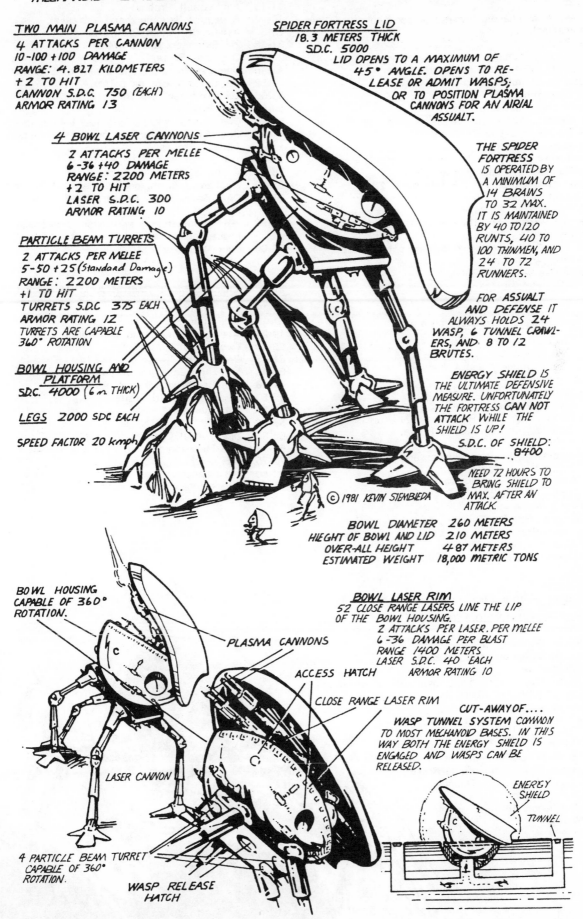

MECHANOID SPIDER FORTRESS: ONE IS PRESENT AT ALL MAJOR MECHANOID BASES.

TWO MAIN PLASMA CANNONS
4 ATTACKS PER CANNON
10-100 +100 DAMAGE
RANGE: 4.827 KILOMETERS
+2 TO HIT
CANNON S.D.C. 750 (EACH)
ARMOR RATING 13

SPIDER FORTRESS LID
18.3 METERS THICK
S.D.C. 5000
LID OPENS TO A MAXIMUM OF
45° ANGLE. OPENS TO RE-
LEASE OR ADMIT WASPS;
OR TO POSITION PLASMA
CANNONS FOR AN AIRIAL
ASSUALT.

4 BOWL LASER CANNONS
2 ATTACKS PER MELEE
6-36 +40 DAMAGE
RANGE: 2200 METERS
+2 TO HIT
LASER S.D.C. 300
ARMOR RATING 10

THE SPIDER
FORTRESS
IS OPERATED BY
A MINIMUM OF
14 BRAINS
TO 32 MAX.
IT IS MAINTAINED
BY 40 TO 120
RUNTS, 40 TO
100 THINMEN, AND
24 TO 72
RUNNERS.

PARTICLE BEAM TURRETS
2 ATTACKS PER MELEE
5-50 +25 (Standard Damage)
RANGE: 2200 METERS
+1 TO HIT
TURRETS S.D.C 375 EACH
ARMOR RATING 12
TURRETS ARE CAPABLE
360° ROTATION

FOR ASSUALT
AND DEFENSE IT
ALWAYS HOLDS 24
WASP, 6 TUNNEL CRAWL-
ERS, AND 8 TO 12
BRUTES.

ENERGY SHIELD IS
THE ULTIMATE DEFENSIVE
MEASURE. UNFORTUNATELY
THE FORTRESS CAN NOT
ATTACK WHILE THE
SHIELD IS UP!

BOWL HOUSING AND PLATFORM
S.D.C. 4000 (6 m. THICK)

LEGS 2000 SDC EACH

SPEED FACTOR 20 kmph

S.D.C. OF SHIELD:
8400

NEED 72 HOURS TO
BRING SHIELD TO
MAX. AFTER AN
ATTACK.

© 1981 KEVIN SIEMBIEDA

BOWL DIAMETER   260 METERS
HIEGHT OF BOWL AND LID   210 METERS
OVER-ALL HEIGHT   487 METERS
ESTIMATED WEIGHT   18,000 METRIC TONS

BOWL HOUSING
CAPABLE OF 360°
ROTATION.

PLASMA CANNONS

BOWL LASER RIM
52 CLOSE RANGE LASERS LINE THE LIP
OF THE BOWL HOUSING.
2 ATTACKS PER LASER. PER MELEE
6-36 DAMAGE PER BLAST
RANGE 1400 METERS
LASER S.D.C. 40 EACH
ARMOR RATING 10

ACCESS HATCH

CLOSE RANGE LASER RIM

LASER CANNON

CUT-AWAY OF....
WASP TUNNEL SYSTEM COMMON
TO MOST MECHANOID BASES. IN THIS
WAY BOTH THE ENERGY SHIELD IS
ENGAGED AND WASPS CAN BE
RELEASED.

ENERGY SHIELD

TUNNEL

4 PARTICLE BEAM TURRET
CAPABLE OF 360°
ROTATION.

WASP RELEASE
HATCH

MECHANOID ENCOUNTER TABLES

Remote Areas

1-5	A hostile Mechanoid genetic experiment (use your imagination).
6-10	One Brute
11-17	A pair of Skimmers
18-22	2-8 (2D4) Rovers common to the area.
23-27	A pair of Skimmers and a Weavel
28-31	One Exterminator
32-37	A pair of Tunnel Crawlers
38-44	An Assault Probe, two Weavels, and one Skimmer.
45-50	One Runner and two Thinmen.
51-54	One Wasp on patrol.
55-60	One Tunnel Crawler and a pair of Assault Probes.
61-65	One Runner; 1-4 Thinmen; 2-8 Runts.
66-75	A pair of Weavels and 2-8 Skimmers (2D4).
76-80	A pair of Wasps.
81-85	Two Brutes, 1-6 Runts.
86-88	One Multi-Brain, 1-6 Thinmen and a Brute.
89-90	One Mantis
91-98	Four Wasps on a seek and destroy patrol.
99	One Brain in a Hover Pod.
00	One Oracle with 2-8 Runts.

In The Ancient Tunnels or Ancient Dwellings

1-10	1-4 Tunnel Crawlers .
11-16	One lone Brute.
17-22	A pair of Skimmers and a Weavel.
23-26	A pair of Wasps.
27-34	One Brute and 1-4 Thinmen.
35-40	1-4 Assault Probes.
41-46	One Runner with 2-8 Runts.
47-53	1-4 Skimmers and an Assault Probe.
54-59	One Exterminator.
60-65	One Mechanoid Brain, a Runner and 1-4 Thinmen.
66-70	One Brute and a Runner
71-75	2-8 Assault Probes and a Weavel.
76-80	1-4 Tunnel Crawlers.
81-85	One lone Runner.
86-89	1-4 Brutes with 1-4 Thinmen.
90-95	One Multi-Brain.
96-99	One Oracle with 1-4 Thinmen.
00	2-8 Thinmen and One Mechanoid Brain.

Near Mining Base (within 19km/12 miles)

1-8	A Brute with 2-12 (2D6) Thinmen.
9-16	1-4 Tunnel Crawlers.
17-23	A pair of Wasps on patrol.
24-30	A pair of Skimmers and a Weavel.
31-36	One Runner with 1-6 Runts.
37-42	1-4 Skimmers, one Tunnel Crawler and a Weavel.
43-50	One Brute with 1-6 Runts, 1-4 Thinmen.
51-56	A pair of Assault Probes.
57-60	A pair of Wasps on patrol.
61-66	One lone Brute.
67-75	1-4 Skimmers.
76-79	2-8 (2D4) Rovers common to the area.
80-84	2-8 Runts, 1-4 Thinmen, one Brute.
85-90	3-12 (3D4) Runts, 1-4 Thinmen.
91-95	One Exterminator.
96-98	One Mechanoid Brain.
99-00	1-6 Wasps.

Near A Mechanoid Base (within 32km/20 miles)

1-10	A pair of Wasps
11-15	1-6 Assault Probes
16-22	A pair of Skimmers and a Weavel.
23-30	A pair of Tunnel Crawlers.
31-36	2-8 Skimmers and a Weavel.
37-40	One lone Brute.
41-46	One Exterminator and a pair of Skimmers.
47-52	A pair of Wasps on patrol.
53-58	Two Thinmen, 1-6 Runts.
59-64	Two Brutes.
65-70	One Runner with 2-8 Runts, 1-4 Thinmen.
71-76	One Exterminator, a pair of Skimmers and two Assault Probes.
77-82	1-4 Brutes with 2-12 Runts.
83-87	A pair of Wasps on patrol.
88-90	Mechanoid Brain, one Runner, 1-4 Thinmen.
91-92	One Brute, one Runner, 3-12 (3D4) Thinmen and Runts.
93-95	2-8 Skimmers, 1-4 Tunnel Crawlers, 1-4 Assault Probes and a Weavel.
96-00	Four Wasps on patrol.

In A Mechanoid Base's Central Area/Research Labs

1-10	Two Thinmen.
11-18	One Runner.
19-24	Mechanoid Brain and 1-4 Runts.
25-30	Two Assault Probes.
31-35	One Brute.
36-40	1-4 Thinmen and 1-6 Runts.
41-46	One Brute with 1-4 Runts
47-50	Mechanoid Multi-Brain(1)
51-57	1-4 Runners.
58-62	2-8 Runts.
63-65	One Tunnel Crawler.
66-70	One Mechanoid Brain with 1-6 Thinmen.
71-75	One Wasp.
76-80	2-8 Runners.
81-85	One Mechanoid in a hover pod with 2-12 Thinmen.

Bridge Fort

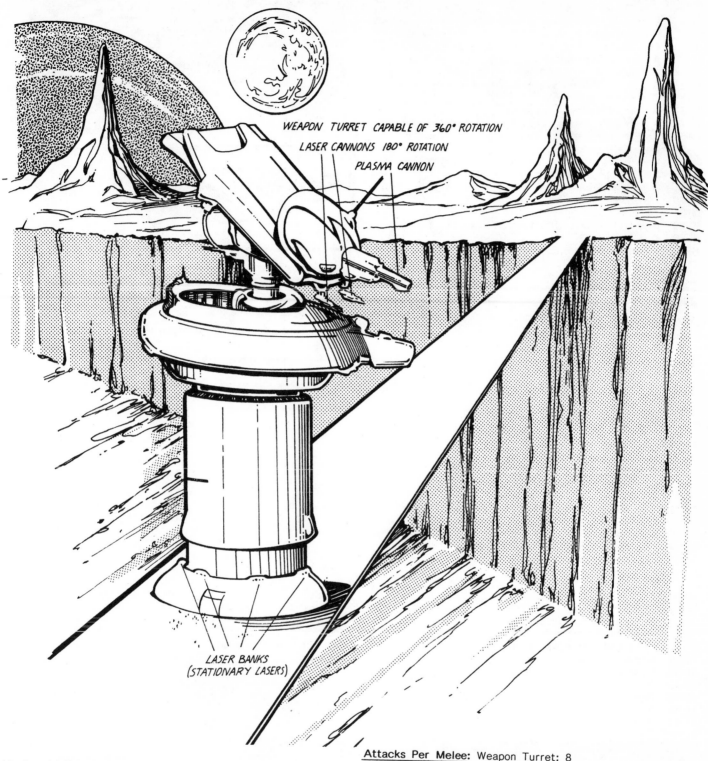

WEAPON TURRET CAPABLE OF 360° ROTATION

LASER CANNONS 180° ROTATION

PLASMA CANNON

LASER BANKS
(STATIONARY LASERS)

Mechanoid Bridge Forts

The Mechanoids, in their dissection of the planet, establish what humans call a bridge fort approximately every 1800km (5900ft). The bridge itself spans the 1km wide trench and is about 800 meters (2600ft) wide. In the center of the bridge is the bridge fort. ALL bridge forts are identical in size and capabilities, and apparently serve as outpost and power centers for the Mechanoids. A typical bridge fort will be staffed by 3-18 Brutes; 10-60 Thinmen; 10-60 Runts, 10-60 Skimmers; 10-60 Weavels; 1-6 Runners; 1-6 Wasps.

Attacks Per Melee: Weapon Turret: 8

Laser Banks: 4 each

Weapons: Weapon Turret: Plasma Cannon; 2 blasts per melee; 8-80+50 damage each. Laser Cannons: 3 blasts each per melee; 6-36+20 damage each blast. Lower Rim Laser Banks: 4 blasts per melee; 3-18 damage each blast.

Range: Plasma Cannon: 3000 Meters

Laser Cannon: 2200 meters (7500ft)

Lower Rim Laser Banks: 1600 meters

Armor Rating: All Parts 11

S.D.C.: Weapon Turret: 800

Plasma Cannon: 250 each

Laser Cannons: 250 each

Laser Banks: 150 each

Fort Body: 1100

93

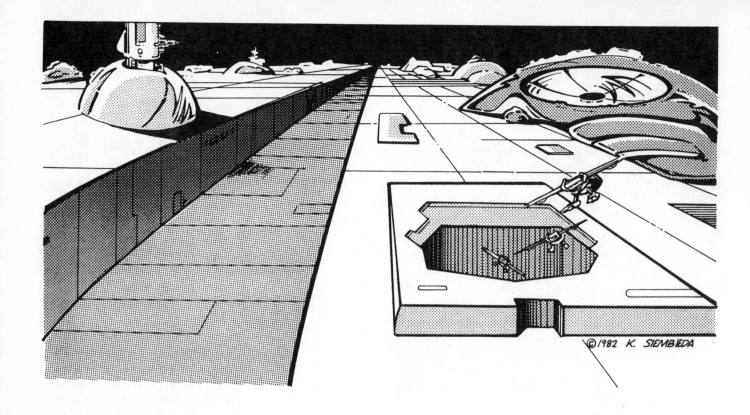

©1982 K. SIEMBIEDA

INSIDE THE MOTHERSHIP

Mechanoid Computers

The Brain Pools: S.D.C.: 50; A.R. 7; Hit Points 25. Aboard ship there averages one brain pool for every 1000 square kilometers, with many times that in engineering, navigation, research and power networks. Brain pools can only be used by Runners, Brains, Oracles and Overlords. No other Mechanoid has the physical or mental capacity to tap into these living psionic computer units. Only a master or major psionic (humanoid) can link with the brain pool.

The psionic humanoid must enter the unit (usually measuring 4m X 4m; although some are 8 times that size) making physical contact, flesh touching flesh, with the warm fluids and soft lumpy, fleshy membranes which line the entire interior of the brain pool. The psionic must then hear his thoughts via meditation and open his mind telepathically to the computer. The participant experiences a very pleasant euphoria, followed by a floating sensation. At this point he/she is oblivious of "any" external input/activity, and only a telepathic or empathic message will reach him/her. The brain pool then psionically probes and extracts ALL information, thoughts and knowledge of that person. This process is quite painless and takes only about 6 minutes. Remember, the brain pools are designed to be an information retrieval/exchange device; and does so automatically. EVERYTHING that person knows will be absorbed, recorded and filed for later analysis. When the brain pool has completed its probe, it then opens itself for information extraction.

The psionic person should direct his/her inquiries as simply and directly as possible via telepathy. These inquiries should be used to gather "small" blocks of information, because he/she is not likely to survive a massive psionic bombardment of information. Example: If the layout of the mothership is requested, the brain pool will respond with the entire ship schematics. Every nook and cranny is instantly provided. Unfortunately, the human (and Rover) brain cannot assimilate that much input at such a speed, and may result in loss of memory and even

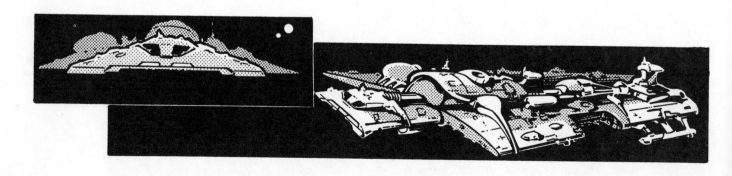

death. Rather, requesting the layout of a small specific area (such as "transport factory: Level 3") is very safe and painless. A person may ask as many questions as he/she desires, once contact with the computer is established.

The Master Computer

The computer brain pools are actual Mechanoid organisms linked to the Master Computer Brain. This Master computer is also a living creature of flesh, circuits and psionics. A sentient entity with a will and personality of its own, it serves the mechanoid society as an awesome living computer complex. The organism itself is over 4000km long, 10km tall 2600km wide. If this incredible entity were destroyed, it would radically impair the mothership, forcing secondary computer banks and brain pools to be used in its stead. This would cut efficiency levels by at least 40%, for in many ways the master computer complex "is" is the mothership.

For that reason only the Brute, Runner, Brain, Oracle and Overlord are allowed on the same level; and ONLY the Overlords are allowed to enter the master computer chamber.

As a precautionary measure, a false (though functioning) computer network, 3 times larger than the true master complex, has been erected as a decoy and back-up system. Only the Brains, Oracles and Overlords know that it is not the true master computer.

The Brutes and Runners are the main service technicians and defense, although Wasps and other Mechanoids can be summoned during an emergency. (Note: Robots of any kind are never allowed on this level).

Average number of Mechanoids on Level 5:
12,000 Brutes   3,000 Runners   250 Brains   6 Oracles
1 Overlord (63% likelihood of being in decoy section).

Internal Teleportation System

The typical Mechanoid (with the exception of free thinkers, Octopus, Wasp and Tunnel Crawler), seldom, if ever, leaves its assigned area. However, even a small processing network may span as much as 6000km. For that reason, teleportation chambers are scattered throughout the ship, approximately every 500km (often located within 100km of a brain pool). Three times that number are located in major areas of activity such as transport terminals, navigation, research labs, etc. The average size of these chambers is 90 meters tall by 120 meters wide, while the largest, located at transport/freighter terminals, hauler bays and storage areas, measures 40km tall by 150km long.

The teleporters are limited to the ship: level to level, section to section or the ship's surface. Example: If you were in a transport terminal teleport chamber on Level One and wanted to go to the navigation section on Level Four, it would teleport you to another chamber in navigation; Level Four.

The device automatically teleports everything in the chamber wherever it is directed to send it (acting instantly on first request). The teleportation chamber, like many Mechanoid devices, is activated through a telepathic command. Obviously, only creatures endowed with psionics (or any other form of telepathy; i.e.: magic) can activate the teleport chamber. It should be noted that there are "NO" external controls, screens or devices in the chamber. It simply appears to be a large empty room.

Total Mechanoid Population on a Typical Mothership*				
Type	Population	Intelligence	Relations to Humans	Degree of Hostility Toward Humans
Overlord	13	Free Thinker/ Brilliant	Hates	Very
Oracle	100,000	Free Thinker/ Super Genius	Dislikes (?)	Neutral
Brain	12 Million	Free Thinker/ Brilliant	Hates	Very
Runner	37 Million	Free Thinker/ Brilliant	Insane Hate	Extreme
Mantis	900,000	Very	Hates	Very
Octopus	12 Million	Very	Hates	Low
Battle Cruiser	600	Very	Extreme Hate	Extreme
Wasp	600 Million	Very	Extreme Hate	Extreme
Brute	40 Million	Fair	Extreme hate	Very
Black Widow	2 Million	Very	Extreme Hate	Extreme
Tunnel Crawler	11 Million	Fair	Extreme Hate	Extreme
Exterminator	12 Million	Fair	Insane Hate	Extreme
Seeker Pod	15 Million	Low	Insane Hate	Extreme
Digger	30,000	Low	Dislikes	Low
Haulers	40 Million	Very Low	Neutral	None
Robots	Est. 432 Million			
Thinmen	85 Million	Fair	Hates	Very
Runts	290 Million	Fair	Hates	Very
Others	57 Million	Varies	Varies	Varies

*This information is not known by the humans. Their estimates are about one third their true numbers.

The Mechanoids

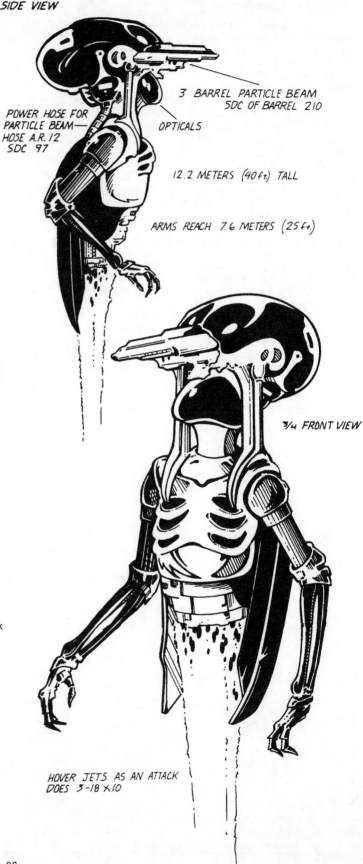

SIDE VIEW

3 BARREL PARTICLE BEAM
SDC OF BARREL 210

POWER HOSE FOR
PARTICLE BEAM—
HOSE A.R. 12
SDC 97

OPTICALS

12.2 METERS (40 ft.) TALL

ARMS REACH 7.6 METERS (25 ft.)

3/4 FRONT VIEW

HOVER JETS AS AN ATTACK
DOES 3-18 ×10

FREE-THINKERS/COMMANDERS

Overlord

Function: Mechanoid free thinker; prime mover, strategist, leader.

Weapons: Particle Beam
    Range: 2200 meters (7260ft)
    Attacks Per Melee: Two
    Damage: 6-60 (6D10) for a grazing blast and 6-60+40 damage from a direct hit (see PBR-10 particle beam rifle for details)
    Bonuses: +2 to strike

    Hand to Hand
    Range: 7.6 meters (25ft) reach
    Attacks Per Melee: Three
    Damage: 4-40+6 (4D10+6) from a striking blow or 6-36 (6D6) to crush.
    Bonuses: +1 to strike, +3 to parry.

Psionics: Master; I.S.P.: 2900; 15th level proficiency.
Abilities: All level one, two and three abilities, +3 to save vs. psionic attacks.
Alignment: Aberrant
Hit Points: 90
A.R.: 12
S.D.C.: 410 body, 97 for the P-beam energy hose.
Speed: Hover or up to 160kmph (100mph). Hover jets do 3-18 × 10 damage if used as an attack/weapon. One attack per melee.
NOTES: The overlord is the ultimate high command in the Mechanoid hierarchy. They seldom leave the mothership unless the situation demands it. If all thirteen overlords should be killed the brains will assume the overlords' responsibilities.

Oracle

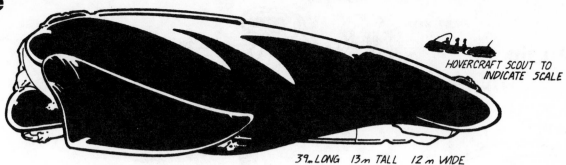

HOVERCRAFT SCOUT TO INDICATE SCALE

39m LONG   13m TALL   12m WIDE

HOVERS 0.3m - 2.4m OFF THE SURFACE

ATTACKS PER MELEE: 1 PSIONICAL
PSIONICS: ALL KNOWN PSIONIC ABILITIES.

SPEED FACTOR: 0 - 1200 kmph
BONUSES: +3 VS PSIONIC ATTACK

Function: Mechanoid free thinker; systems analysis.
Weapons: None, other than psionics.
Psionics: Master; I.S.P.: 4200; 13th level proficiency.
Abilities: ALL known psionic powers.
Alignment: Anarchist, but can be any; often good.
Hit Points: 90
A.R.: 12
S.D.C.: 600
Speed: Hover or up to 1200kmph (750mph)
Weight: 60 metric tons.

Size: 39 meters (130ft) long, 13 meters (45ft) tall and 12 meters (40ft) wide at its thickest point.
Equipment: Standard, see the brute.
NOTES: The oracle is the most mysterious of the Mechanoids. Until contact is actually made with one, the humans will believe it to be some type of uncommon transportation vehicle. The oracle is usually of a selfish or even good alignment, but may also be evil. Likewise, while most are secretly sympathetic toward humans, some are as hate filled as all the other Mechanoids. Very uncommon.

Brain

Function: Mechanoid free thinker; coordinator, 2nd in command.
Weapons: Laser, used as a tool and weapon.
> Range: 900 meters
> Attacks Per Melee: Two
> Damage: 1-6 (1D6) or 3-18 (3D6)
> Bonuses: +1 to strike
>
> Hand to Hand
> Range: 1.8 meters (6ft)
> Attacks Per Melee: Three (takes the place of any laser attack)
> Damage: 2-12+2
> Bonuses: +1 to strike, +2 to parry or dodge.

Psionics: Master; I.S.P.: 2000; 13th level proficiency.
Abilities: ALL level one and two, plus extended telepathy, extended telekinesis, see the invisible, and bio-manipulation Two psionic attacks per melee are possible, but takes the place of any physical attacks. +3 to save vs. psionic attacks.
Alignment: Aberrant (or any evil)
Hit Points: 35
A.R.: 10
S.D.C.: 90
Speed: Hover or up to 50kmph (32mph); Also see multi-brain housing and hover pod.
Weight: 720kg (1600lbs)
Size: 3 meters (10ft) tall.
Equipment: Standard sensory; see brute.
NOTES: The Mechanoid brain is not unlike a general in an army, wielding great power and nearly absolute control over those he commands. As far as the humans know the brains are the leaders of the Mechanoids, which is not entirely incorrect, because they generally have a free hand in their activities. The brain's genetic code and mental conditioning, as with all Mechanoids prevents it from wavering too far from its instinctive purpose. However, the brain has two superiors, the enigmatic oracle and the true Mechanoid overseer, the overlord. It is because the overlords rarely concern themselves with such trivial matters as routine extermination of humanoids and mining that one seldom leaves the mothership. Consequently, the

brains are perceived by the humans to be the absolute leaders.

The brain's functions are widely varied from coordination of almost every function of Mechanoid activity, to biological experimentation, navigation and data analysis. They are one of the few Mechanoids that are able to link into a Mechanoid computer (brain pool). The runner is a brain's right hand man with the brute not far behind, though not nearly the equal to a runner.

BRAIN (common)

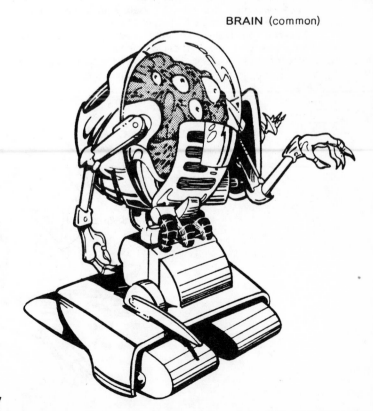

Multi-Brain

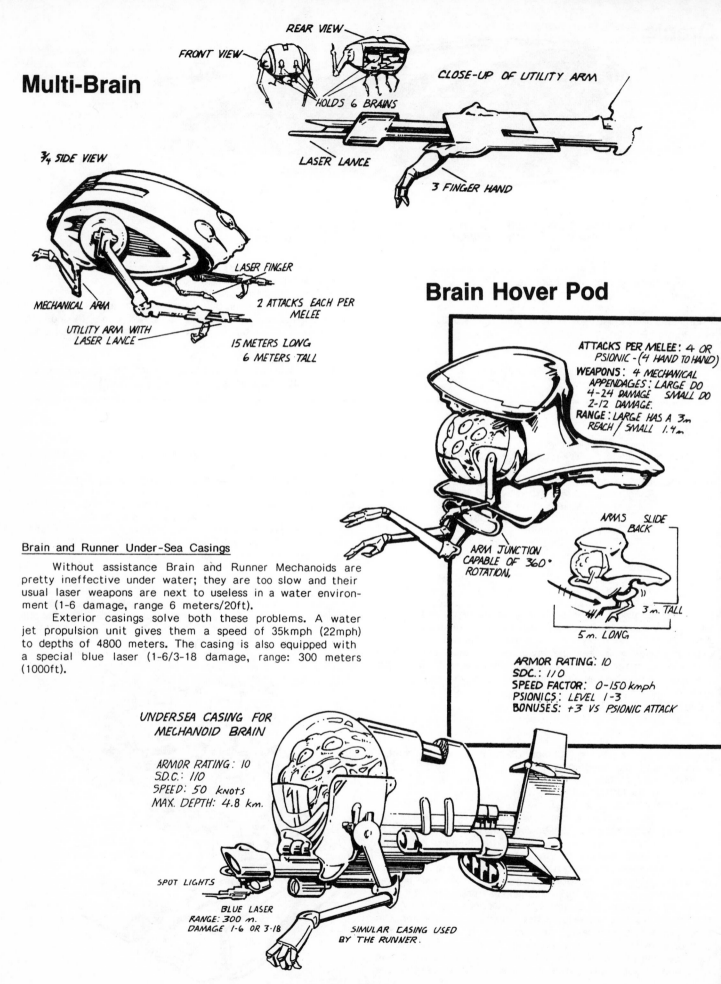

FRONT VIEW

REAR VIEW

HOLDS 6 BRAINS

CLOSE-UP OF UTILITY ARM

LASER LANCE

3 FINGER HAND

¾ SIDE VIEW

MECHANICAL ARM

UTILITY ARM WITH LASER LANCE

LASER FINGER

2 ATTACKS EACH PER MELEE

15 METERS LONG
6 METERS TALL

Brain Hover Pod

ATTACKS PER MELEE: 4 OR
PSIONIC - (4 HAND TO HAND)
WEAPONS: 4 MECHANICAL
APPENDAGES: LARGE DO
4-24 DAMAGE SMALL DO
2-12 DAMAGE.
RANGE: LARGE HAS A 3m
REACH / SMALL 1.4m

ARM JUNCTION
CAPABLE OF 360°
ROTATION.

ARMS SLIDE BACK

3m. TALL

5m. LONG

ARMOR RATING: 10
SDC.: 110
SPEED FACTOR: 0-150 kmph
PSIONICS: LEVEL 1-3
BONUSES: +3 VS PSIONIC ATTACK

Brain and Runner Under-Sea Casings

Without assistance Brain and Runner Mechanoids are pretty ineffective under water; they are too slow and their usual laser weapons are next to useless in a water environment (1-6 damage, range 6 meters/20ft).

Exterior casings solve both these problems. A water jet propulsion unit gives them a speed of 35kmph (22mph) to depths of 4800 meters. The casing is also equipped with a special blue laser (1-6/3-18 damage, range: 300 meters (1000ft).

UNDERSEA CASING FOR MECHANOID BRAIN

ARMOR RATING: 10
S.D.C.: 110
SPEED: 50 knots
MAX. DEPTH: 4.8 km.

SPOT LIGHTS

BLUE LASER
RANGE: 300 m.
DAMAGE 1-6 OR 3-18

SIMULAR CASING USED BY THE RUNNER.

The Mechanoid Brain has several types of body housings, each of which provides greater mobility under different conditions or circumstances. The following list are those body casings. Unless otherwise noted, all abilities remain the same as the "common" brain previously discussed. Remember, this is the same organism in a different body, hit points and psionics NEVER change.

Multi-Brain
Hover Pod
Underwater

THE MULTI-BRAIN
Weapons: Laser Lance
    Range: 1600 meters (5280ft)
    Attacks Per Melee: Four (2 from each main arm)
    Damage: 2-12, 4-24 or 6-36 (roll D6)
    Bonuses: +2 to strike

    Laser Finger (Mini-arm)
    Range: 90 meters (300ft)
    Attacks Per Melee: One
    Damage: 1-6 or 2-12
    Bonuses: +2 to strike

    Utility Arm (hand to hand)
    Range: 15 meters (50ft) reach
    Attacks Per Melee: Four (2 each), but takes the place of four laser attacks.
    Damage: 6-36+10 (6D6+10) from a striking blow or 6-36 to crush.
    Bonuses: +1 to strike, +2 to parry and dodge.

    Rear Mechanical Arm
    Range: 6 meters (20ft) reach
    Attacks Per Melee: One
    Damage: 3-18 (3D6)
    Bonuses: None

    NOTES: Total number of energy attacks are FIVE including the laser finger. Total number of hand to hand attacks are FOUR, plus the ONE laser finger attack or FOUR plus the One REAR mechanical arm attack.

A.R.: 12
S.D.C.: 210 on body housing, 100 per each arm, 30 for laser finger.
Speed: Hover or up to 250kmph (150mph)
Weight: 20 metric tons.
Size: 15 meters (50ft) long and 6 meters (20ft) tall. Holds a total of six brains.
NOTES: The multi-brain is basically a giant exo-skeleton operated by six brains. It's primarily used for heavy repairs (especially on the mothership), transportation and exploration. At least three brains are required to fully operate the multi-unit at maximum efficiency. The brains themselves are still in their complete "common" body housing.

HOVER POD
Weapons: Large Arms (or via psionics)
    Hand to Hand Only
    Range: 2.4 meters (8ft) reach
    Attacks Per Melee: Three
    Damage: 4-24 (4D6)
    Bonuses: +1 to strike, +2 to parry, +4 to dodge.

    Small Arms
    Range: 1.5 meters (5ft)
    Attacks Per Melee: Two
    Damage: 1-8 (1D8)
    Bonuses: +2 to parry, +4 to dodge.

A.R.: 10
S.D.C.: 110
Speed: Hover or up to 160kmph (100mph); maximum height attainable 240 meters (800ft). Bonus for high mobility, +4 to dodge (hand to hand dodge is not added to this number)
Weight: 810kg (1800lbs)
Size: 5 meters (17ft) long, 3 meters (10ft) tall.
NOTES: The hover pod simply allows much greater speed and mobility.

Runner

Function: Mechanoid free thinker; physics, genetics, biology, robotics and communications engineer.
Weapons: Laser (left hand)
    Range: 1600 meters (5280ft)
    Attacks Per Melee: Two
    Damage: 1-6 or 3-18 or 5-30 (roll D6); three settings possible.
    Bonuses: +2 to strike.

    Hand to Hand
    Range: 1.8 meters (6ft)
    Attacks Per Melee: Two, but takes the place of the laser attacks.
    Damage: 3-18+4 (3D6+4)
    Bonuses: +2 to strike, +2 to parry and dodge.
Psionics: Major; I.S.P. 690; 10th level proficiency
Abilities: All level one and two, plus extended telepathy and telemechanics.
Alignment: Miscreant or any evil alignment
Hit Points: 44
A.R.: 12
S.D.C.: 120
Speed: 25kmph (16mph) running
Weight: 1305kg (2900lbs)
Size: 4.6 meters (15ft) tall, 3 meters (10ft) long, 1.5 meters (5ft) wide.
Equipment: Standard sensory (see brute), plus magnification 1200 times, with a maximum range of 2.4 meters (8ft), targeting sight.
NOTES: The runner is the right hand assistant to the brain and often the head of research and other scientific pursuits. Runners are the master genetic engineers and responsible for much of the human experimentation/torture. They are usually found in the company of other Mechanoids or directing robots.

    Like the Mechanoid brain, the runner has more than one body housing. The following is a hover platform which the runner literally steps into for greater speed and mobility. ALL stats remain the same unless otherwise noted.

RUNNER HOVER POD

Function: Transportation
Weapons: None
A.R.: 10
S.D.C.: 100 (plus the runner's personal S.D.C.)
Speed: Hover or up to 160kmph (100mph); maximum altitude is 90 meters (300ft); +3 to dodge.
Weight: 540kg (1200lbs) for the hover pod combined total weight is 1845kg (4100lbs).
NOTES: This hover pod is specifically designed for use ONLY by the runner. It cannot be piloted by any other Mechanoid or human.

Runner

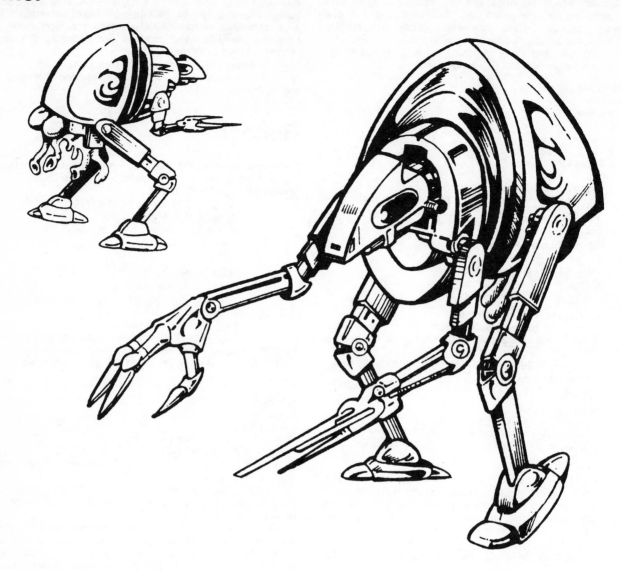

Runner Hover Pod

HOVER PLATFORM

DRAWN TO SCALE WITH
AVERAGE SIZE HUMANS

LASER

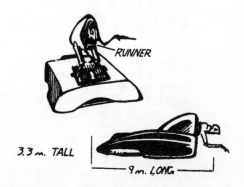

RUNNER

3.3 m. TALL

9 m. LONG

PREDATORS

Brute

ferocity in battle, cruelty, savageness and raw brute strength. Like most of its kind, the brute enjoys the torturing and destruction of humans. They are quite intelligent, fair tacticians, cruel and cunning.

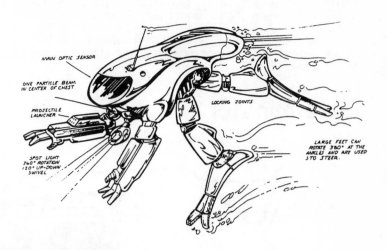

MAIN OPTIC SENSOR

ONE PARTICLE BEAM
IN CENTER OF CHEST

PROJECTILE
LAUNCHER

LOCKING JOINTS

SPOT LIGHT
360° ROTATION
120° UP-DOWN
SWIVEL

LARGE FEET CAN
ROTATE 360° AT THE
ANKLES AND ARE USED
TO STEER.

Undersea Brute
Attacks Per Melee: Two
Weapons: Particle Beam (2-20+15 damage) Standard on land.
Range: 35 meters (115ft) Standard on land.
Bonuses: +2 to damage; +2 vs. psionics
Function: Assault
Operation: Mechanoid
Size: 3.8 meters tall (12ft)
Armor Rating: 10
S.D.C.: 190
Speed Factor: 35kmph
Maximum Depth: Unlimited

Projectile Launcher
Range: 70 meters (230ft)
Damage: 4-24+4

Function: Mechanoid predator; orientation in robotics, mechanics, offense and defense.
Weapons: Particle Beam
Range: 1400 meters (4620ft)
Attacks Per Melee: Two
Damage: Standard (see PBR-10)
Bonuses: +1 to strike

Hand to Hand
Range: 2.1 meters (7ft) reach
Attacks Per Melee: Two in place of energy attack.
Damage: 4-24+4 (4D6+4)
Bonuses: +1 to strike, +2 to parry and dodge.
Psionics: Major, I.S.P.: 150, 8th level proficiency.
Abilities: All first level psi-powers plus extended telepathy, levitation, mind block, limited telekinesis, bioregeneration, telemechanics; +2 to save vs. psionic attacks.
Alignment: Aberrant
Hit Points: 45
A.R.: 12
S.D.C.: 180
Speed: 35kmph (22mph) on foot, 50kmph (32mph) via hover jets.
Weight: 990kg (2600lbs)
Size: 3.8 meters (12½ft tall), 1.8 meters (6ft) long, 1.6 meters (5½ft) wide.
Equipment: Standard full sensory: Optic, ultra-violet, infra red, night-sight, thermo-imager, scanners, radar/sonar with a 24km (15 mile) range, wide band directional radio with a 64km (40 mile) range and signal scrambler.
Special Equipment includes telescopic optics, range 360 meters (120ft) with a field of vision of 7.6 meters (25ft), targeting sight which provides the bonuses to strike.
NOTE: Strength factor of a brute enables it to lift up to four metric tons, carry up to two metric tons and throw up to half a ton up to 10 meters (33ft) away.
The human's label of "brute" reflects this Mechanoid's

Exterminator

EXTERMINATOR and SEEKER POD

Function: Mechanoid predators; assault, hunt, liquidation of humanoid life.
Weapons: Tri-Particle Beam
Range: 1400 meters (4620ft)
Attacks Per Melee: Two
Damage: Standard (see PBR-10)
Bonuses: +2 to strike

Ion Blasters (2 in front)
Range: 900 meter (3000ft)
Attacks Per Melee: Two
Damage: 2-12 (2D6)
Bonuses: +1 to strike
Plasma Ejector
Range: 1600 meters (5280ft)
Attacks Per Melee: One every second melee
Damage: 4-40 (4D10)
Bonuses: +2 to strike

Stomp with Foot (used in place of an energy attack)
Range: 3 meters (10ft)
Attacks Per Melee: up to Three
Damage: 4-24+8
Bonuses: None
Psionics: Major; I.S.P.: 120
Abilities: All level one abilities plus empathy, limited telekinesis, mind block, levitate, nightvision and extended telepathy.
Alignment: Diabolic
Hit Points: 50
A.R.: 10

S.D.C.: 180
Speed: 60kmph (38mph)
Weight: 1440kg (3200lbs)
Size: 4.6 meters (15ft) tall
Equipment: Standard (see brute)
NOTES: The exterminator is a cruel vindictive hunter whose sole purpose is to search out and destroy humanoids.

The **Seeker Pod** is generally considered to be part of the exterminator. If one is sighted the other can not be far away.

Exterminator

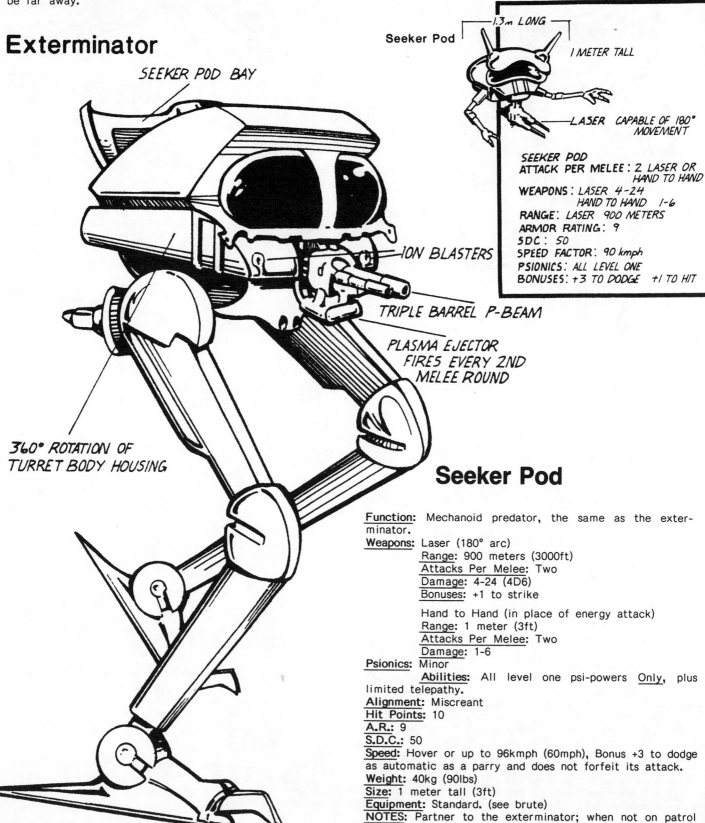

SEEKER POD BAY

ION BLASTERS

TRIPLE BARREL P-BEAM

PLASMA EJECTOR
FIRES EVERY 2ND
MELEE ROUND

360° ROTATION OF
TURRET BODY HOUSING

Seeker Pod

1.3m LONG

1 METER TALL

LASER CAPABLE OF 180°
MOVEMENT

SEEKER POD
ATTACK PER MELEE : 2 LASER OR
HAND TO HAND
WEAPONS : LASER 4-24
HAND TO HAND 1-6
RANGE : LASER 900 METERS
ARMOR RATING : 9
SDC : 50
SPEED FACTOR : 90 kmph
PSIONICS : ALL LEVEL ONE
BONUSES : +3 TO DODGE   +1 TO HIT

Seeker Pod

Function: Mechanoid predator, the same as the exterminator.
Weapons: Laser (180° arc)
Range: 900 meters (3000ft)
Attacks Per Melee: Two
Damage: 4-24 (4D6)
Bonuses: +1 to strike

Hand to Hand (in place of energy attack)
Range: 1 meter (3ft)
Attacks Per Melee: Two
Damage: 1-6
Psionics: Minor
Abilities: All level one psi-powers Only, plus limited telepathy.
Alignment: Miscreant
Hit Points: 10
A.R.: 9
S.D.C.: 50
Speed: Hover or up to 96kmph (60mph), Bonus +3 to dodge as automatic as a parry and does not forfeit its attack.
Weight: 40kg (90lbs)
Size: 1 meter tall (3ft)
Equipment: Standard. (see brute)
NOTES: Partner to the exterminator; when not on patrol it will rest in a special bay in the exterminator itself.

Wasp

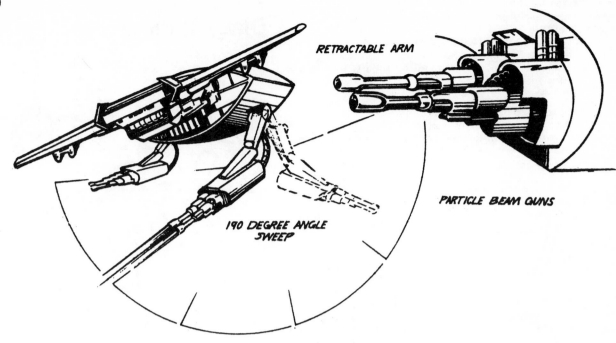

RETRACTABLE ARM

190 DEGREE ANGLE SWEEP

PARTICLE BEAM GUNS

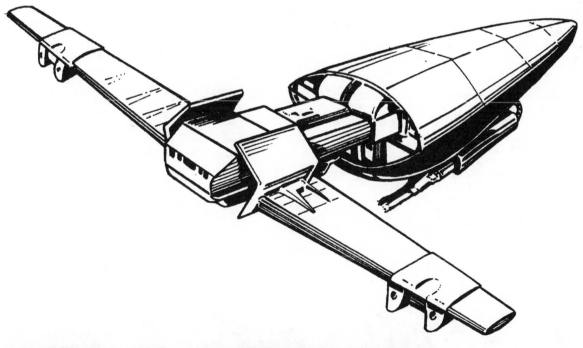

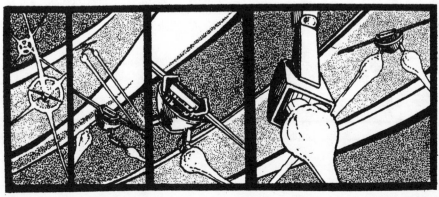

Wasp

Function: Mechanoid predator; assault and defense.
Weapons: Particle Beam
  Range: 1600 meters (5280ft)
  Attacks Per Melee: Four
  Damage: Standard (see PBR-10 particle beam rifle for details).
  Bonuses: +2 to strike

Hand to Hand
Although not really suited for hand to hand combat the wasp can use its wings or particle beam appendages as a bludgeon.
  Range: approximate reach 2.4 meters (8ft)
  Attacks Per Melee: Four, but takes the place of P-beam attacks.
  Damage: 4-24 from a striking blow at hover or slow speed. A high speed ram or charging attack does 4-24(4D6) x5 and reduces the number of attacks to ONE.
  NOTES: A wasp cannot ram at more than 321kmph (200mph) without doing equal damage to itself, such a suicide run at maximum speed does 4-24 X 100 damage. However, a FAVORITE PLOY when playing with humanoids is to scoop up humans fly up into the air and drop them or play catch, seeing how close to the ground the person can fall before the wasp misses and similar type games. Such aerial catches usually inflict the normal amount of hand to hand damage, 4-24 (4D6).
Psionics: Major; I.S.P.: 313; Tenth level proficiency
Abilities: ALL level one and two plus extended telepathy; +2 to save vs. psionic attacks.
Alignment: Miscreant or any evil
Hit Points: 56
A.R.: 12
S.D.C.: 225
Speed: Hover to dead stop to 1500kmph (950mph)+
Weight: 1620kg (3600lbs)
Size: 2.1 meters (7ft) long, total wing span from tip to tip is 4.6 meters (15ft)
Equipment: Standard sensory; plus targeting sight telescopic optics (3.2km/2 mile range).
NOTES: The wasp is bred exclusively for war which it excels at. It is a superior strategist, clever and fast thinking. When dealing with humans on a small scale they are often clearly sarcastic and playfully cruel in a sort of cat and mouse way. They are always devastating and never take combat as a lark.

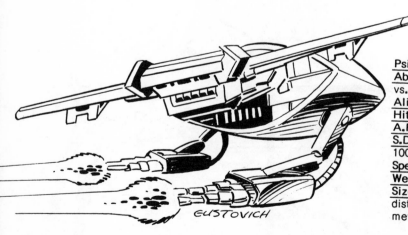

EUSTOVICH

Black Widow

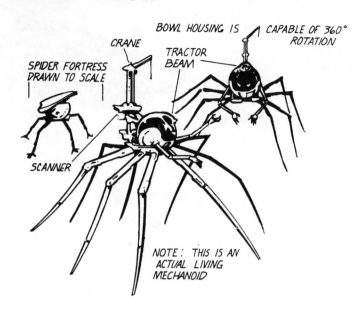

SPIDER FORTRESS DRAWN TO SCALE

SCANNER

CRANE

BOWL HOUSING IS CAPABLE OF 360° ROTATION

TRACTOR BEAM

NOTE: THIS IS AN ACTUAL LIVING MECHANOID

Function: Mechanoid drone; coordinator of storage, slavage vehicles and transportation.
Weapons: None per se, but the following can be used as such:

Tractor Beam
  Range: 9km (5½ miles) affects a ½km diameter area.
  Attacks Per Melee: One
  Damage: None object is drawn to the black widow.
  Bonuses: None
  NOTE: May be used continually for up to seven hours before needing to recharge (another 7 hours). Can pull/hold 40,000 tons.

Hand to Hand
  Range: 600 meters
  Attacks Per Melee: One
  Damage: 2-12 X 100 to crush (2D6 X 100)
        3-18 X 100 in a swatting blow
  Bonuses: None

Stomp By Foot
  Range: 1000 meters (3300ft)
  Attacks Per Melee: Two
  Damage: 2-12 X 1000 to crush/stomp
  NOTE: -2 to strike, because of its size and weight it is somewhat clumsy in combat.
Psionics: Major; I.S.P.: 500; 8th level proficiency
Abilities: All first and second level psionics; +2 to save vs. psionic attacks.
Alignment: Anarchist
Hit Points: 218
A.R.; 12
S.D.C.: Bowl housing 9000, legs (8) 2000 each, arms (2) 1000 each, crane 1200, tractor beam 1000.
Speed: 980kmph (600mph)
Weight: Estimated 56,000 metric tons
Size: Diameter of the bowl housing 660 meters (2178ft), distance from front feet to the back approximately 3960 meters (13,068ft).

104

Tunnel Crawler

Function: Mechanoid predator; assault, hunt and liquidation of humanoid life.

Weapons: Ion Blasters

    Range: 400 meters (1320ft)

    Attacks Per Melee: Two (can release gas simultaneously)

Damage: 2-12 (2D6)

    Bonuses: +1 to strike

    Nerve Gas

    Range: immediate area of 4.6 meters (15ft)

    Duration: Two hours

    Attacks Per Melee: Once every other melee.

    Damage: 4-24 (4D6) per each melee that the gas is breathed. Acidic quality causes an additional 1D6 damage to exposed flesh. NOTE: Does NO damage to E.B.A., L.B.A. with face mask and oxygen supply, gas mask and protective radiation suit, or space suit. Does half damage if an "air filter" is worn.

    Hand to Hand

    Range: 1 meter (3½ft)

    Attacks Per Melee: Three but takes the place of the ion attack.

    Damage: 2-12+4 (2D6+4)

    Bonuses: +1 to strike, +3 to parry and dodge.

Psionics: Minor; I.S.P.: 120, sixth level proficiency.

Abilities: Presence sense, see aura, detect psionics, mind block, limited telekinesis, and extended telepathy. +1 to save vs. psionic attacks.

Alignment: Miscreant or any evil

Hit Points: 43

A.R.: 14

S.D.C.: 137

Speed: 15kmph (10mph) walking, 64kmph (40mph) using hover jets. Excellent climber 89%; +2 to dodge.

Weight: 1170kg (2600lbs)

Size: 2.1 meters long (7ft), 1.5 meters tall (5ft), 1.4 meters wide (4ft)

Equipment: Standard sensory (see brute)

NOTES: The tunnel crawler is an independent agent of destruction permitted to wander where it will. They are often found with a pair of skimmers, assault probes or fellow tunnel crawlers. They are rarely found among their fellows, but found in the ancient alien tunnels, wilderness and tunnels and air shafts of the mothership.

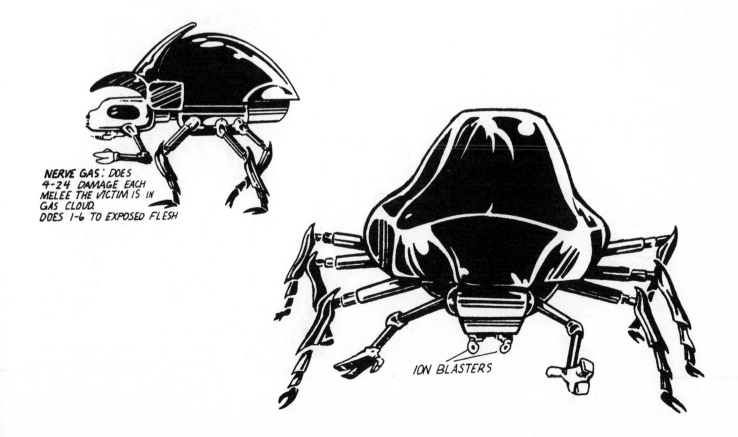

NERVE GAS: DOES 4-24 DAMAGE EACH MELEE THE VICTIM IS IN GAS CLOUD. DOES 1-6 TO EXPOSED FLESH

ION BLASTERS

Mantis

Function: Mechanoid Drone; engineering and mining.

Weapons: Electro Primer (left arm)
> **Range:** 12 meters (40ft)
> **Attacks Per Melee:** Two
> **Damage:** 6-36+8 (6D6+8)
> **Bonuses:** +1 to strike

> Hand to Hand (claw)
> **Range:** 9 meter (30ft) reach
> **Attacks Per Melee:** Two, but takes the place of the electro primer.
> **Damage:** 4-24+10 from a striking blow
> **Bonuses:** None

Psionics: Minor; I.S.P.: 570; 10th level proficiency

Abilities: Object read, presence sense, see aura, resist fatigue, extended telekinesis, extended telepathy. +2 to save vs. psionic attacks.

Alignment: Aberrant or anarchist

Hit Points: 90

A.R.: 13

S.D.C.: 350

Speed: Hover or up to 160kmph (100mph)

Weight: 22 metric tons

Size: 9 meters (30ft) tall, 18.3 meters (60ft) long, 7.6 meters (25ft) wide.

NOTES: Although usually absorbed in its work the mantis is far from stupid and as aggressive toward humanoids as any predatory Mechanoid. Extremely intelligent, the mantis is listed as a drone because it is almost exclusively oriented to its work.

The rear section houses a powerful fusion energy source. If the mantis is destroyed, the nuclear reactor will explode with devastating affect.

Blast Damage . . .

4-24 (4D6) X 200 at the blast core of 30 meters (100ft) and 4D6 X 50 for an additional 90 meters beyond the blast core.

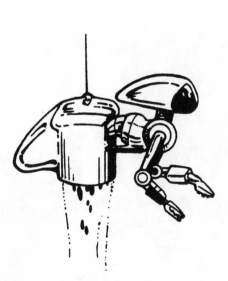

Octopus

Function: Mechanoid Drone; electronic and mechanical construction, maintenance and repair.

Weapons: Fusion Torch
Range: 900 meters (3000ft)
Attacks Per Melee: Three
Damage: 3 settings, 4-24+6, 6-36+6 or 5-50+50
Bonuses: +1 to strike

Laser Finger or Detachable Laser Tool
Range: 1200 meters (4000ft)
Attacks Per Melee: Three, but takes the place of the fusion torch.
Damage: 2 settings, 3-18 (3D6) or 5-30 (5D6)
Bonuses: +2 to strike

Hand to Hand
Range: generally a 5 meter (17ft) reach
Attacks Per Melee: Five, but takes the place of all energy attacks.
Damage: 4-40+10 (4D10+10) damage from a striking blow; 6-36 (6D6) damage to crush.
Bonuses: +2 to strike, +6 to parry, +3 to dodge. Always has the initiative.

NOTE: The body undercarriage with three arms and laser tool can rotate a full 360° in the blink of an eye. Its multiple sensors make it impossible to sneak up on.

Psionics: Major; I.S.P.: 1000; 10th level proficiency.
Abilities: All levels one and two, plus telemechanics; +2 to save vs. psionic attacks.
Hit Points: 130
A.R.: 12
S.D.C.: Main body 2000, fusion torch arm 520, additional arms 350 each, laser finger 160.
Speed: Hover or up to 800kmph (500mph). Maximum altitude is 120 meters (400ft).
Weight: 23 metric tons.
Size: 18.3 meters (60ft) tall, 13.7 meters (45ft) wide.
NOTES: Usually absorbed in its work. Primarily found on the mothership and large Mechanoid bases.

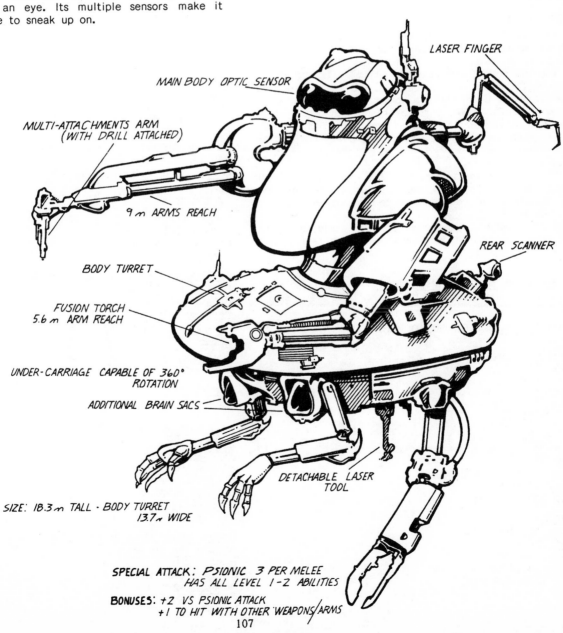

MAIN BODY OPTIC SENSOR

LASER FINGER

MULTI-ATTACHMENTS ARM
(WITH DRILL ATTACHED)

9 m ARMS REACH

REAR SCANNER

BODY TURRET

FUSION TORCH
5.6 m ARM REACH

UNDER-CARRIAGE CAPABLE OF 360°
ROTATION

ADDITIONAL BRAIN SACS

DETACHABLE LASER TOOL

SIZE: 18.3 m TALL · BODY TURRET
13.7 m WIDE

SPECIAL ATTACK: PSIONIC 3 PER MELEE
HAS ALL LEVEL 1-2 ABILITIES

BONUSES: +2 VS PSIONIC ATTACK
+1 TO HIT WITH OTHER WEAPONS/ARMS

Battle Cruiser

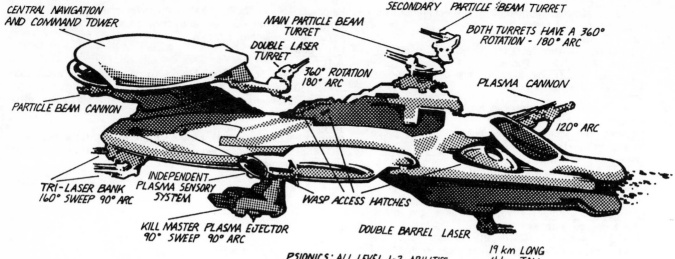

CENTRAL NAVIGATION AND COMMAND TOWER

MAIN PARTICLE BEAM TURRET

SECONDARY PARTICLE BEAM TURRET

DOUBLE LASER TURRET

BOTH TURRETS HAVE A 360° ROTATION - 180° ARC

360° ROTATION 180° ARC

PLASMA CANNON

PARTICLE BEAM CANNON

120° ARC

TRI-LASER BANK 160° SWEEP 90° ARC

INDEPENDENT PLASMA SENSORY SYSTEM

WASP ACCESS HATCHES

KILL MASTER PLASMA EJECTOR 90° SWEEP 90° ARC

DOUBLE BARREL LASER

19 km LONG
4 km TALL
4.5 km WIDE

PSIONICS: ALL LEVEL 1-2 ABILITIES +2 VS PSIONIC ATTACKS

The Mechanoid Battle Cruiser

Critical Points

The Battle Cruiser has two critical or weak points which can destroy or immoblize it; the controlling organism/forward section and the power core/mid-section.

The controlling Mechanoid organism is housed in the Navigation/Command Tower located at the forward section. If the Tower is penetrated, the protective computer banks destroyed (S.D.C.: 2000), and the organism slain the entire vessel will be rendered completely immobile. ALL weapons hatches, communication, life support and power distribution ceases. (The remaining crew may take independent action however).

The power core is located in the mid-section. If this is destroyed (S.D.C.: 2000) then the entire ship explodes doing 90,000 points of damage to everything within a 100km radius.

NOTE: The Battle Cruiser has not been deployed against the human colonists. It is usually saved for real threats against the mothership.

The Mechanoid Battle Cruiser: A.R. 14; Speed factor 0-light speed. Battle speed 0-1200kmph. I.Q.: 12; Psionics Level 1-2.

Forward Section: S.D.C.: 20,000; A.R.: 14
Weapons:
Particle Beam Cannon
Attacks Per Melee: 2
Range: 160km
Damage: 5-50X5 damage
Bonuses: +1 to hit
S.D.C.: 1600; A.R.: 14

Tri-Laser Bank
Attacks Per Melee: 6 (per each laser bank)
Range: 321km
Damage: 6-36+100 (6D6+100)
Bonuses: +2 to hit
S.D.C.: 3000; A.R.: 14

Double Laser Turret
Attacks Per Melee: 4
Range: 321km
Damage: 6-36+50
Bonuses: +1 to hit
S.D.C.: 1200; A.R.: 14

Navigation/Command Tower
S.D.C.: 40,000; A.R.: 16

Mechanoid Organism and Computer Banks
S.D.C.: 20,000; A.R.: 10
Hit Points: 390

Mid-Section: S.D.C.: 40,000; **A.R.:** 14
Weapons:
Main Particle Beam Turret
Attacks Per Melee: 2
Range: 321km
Damage: 5-50X10
Bonuses: +2 to hit
S.D.C.: 3500; A.R.: 14

Secondary P-Beam Turret
Attacks Per Melee: 2
Range: 321km
Damage: 5-50X5
Bonuses: +2 to hit
S.D.C.: 2100; A.R.: 14

Kill Master Plasma Ejector (right & left side)
Attacks Per Melee: 2
Range: 482km
Damage: 6-36X20
Bonuses: +1 to hit
S.D.C.: 5000; A.R.: 14

Plasma Ejector Sensory System
S.D.C.: 8000; A.R.: 14

Power Core
S.D.C.: 2000; A.R.: 12

Rear Section: S.D.C.: 20,000; A.R.: 14
Weapons:
Plasma Cannon
Attacks Per Melee: 2
Range: 321km
Damage: 6-36X10
Bonuses: +2 to hit
S.D.C.: 3200; A.R.: 14

Double Barrel Laser (right and left sides)
Attacks Per Melee: 4
Range: 321km
Damage: 6-36+30
Bonuses: +2 to hit
S.D.C.: 1200; A.R.: 14

NOTE: ALL Wasp <u>Access Hatches</u> are <u>S.D.C.</u>: 2200; <u>A.R.</u> 12.

<u>Crew and Strike Force</u>

Wasps	100,000
Brutes	500
Thinmen	50,000
Runts	10,000
Skimmers	10,000
Runners	10-60
Brains	2-12
Mantis	2-12
Octopus	2-12
Hauler Type II	2
Spider Fortress	2

BATTLE CRUISER

Hauler Type I

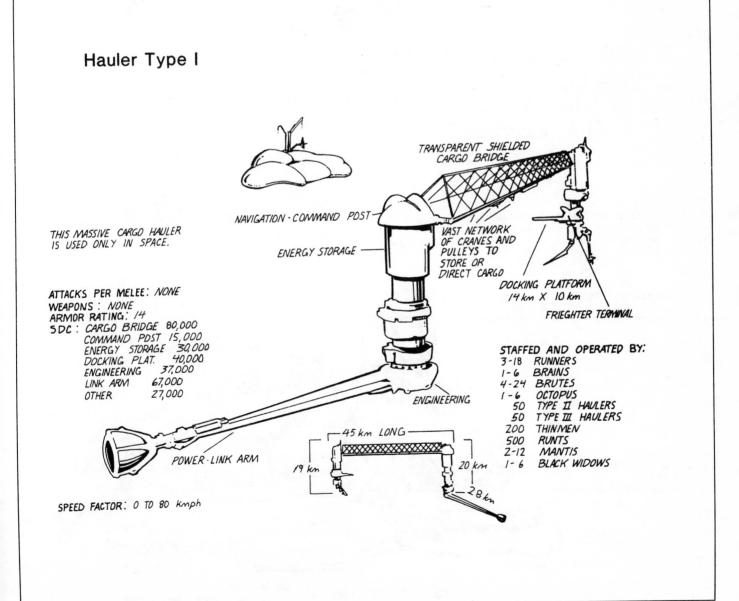

THIS MASSIVE CARGO HAULER IS USED ONLY IN SPACE.

ATTACKS PER MELEE: NONE
WEAPONS: NONE
ARMOR RATING: 14
SDC: CARGO BRIDGE 80,000
      COMMAND POST 15,000
      ENERGY STORAGE 30,000
      DOCKING PLAT. 40,000
      ENGINEERING 37,000
      LINK ARM 67,000
      OTHER 27,000

SPEED FACTOR: 0 TO 80 kmph

NAVIGATION·COMMAND POST
TRANSPARENT SHIELDED CARGO BRIDGE
ENERGY STORAGE
VAST NETWORK OF CRANES AND PULLEYS TO STORE OR DIRECT CARGO
DOCKING PLATFORM 14 km X 10 km
FRIEGHTER TERMINAL
ENGINEERING
POWER·LINK ARM
45 km LONG
19 km
20 km
28 km

STAFFED AND OPERATED BY:
3-18   RUNNERS
1-6   BRAINS
4-24   BRUTES
1-6   OCTOPUS
50   TYPE II HAULERS
50   TYPE III HAULERS
200   THINMEN
500   RUNTS
2-12   MANTIS
1-6   BLACK WIDOWS

Hauler Type II

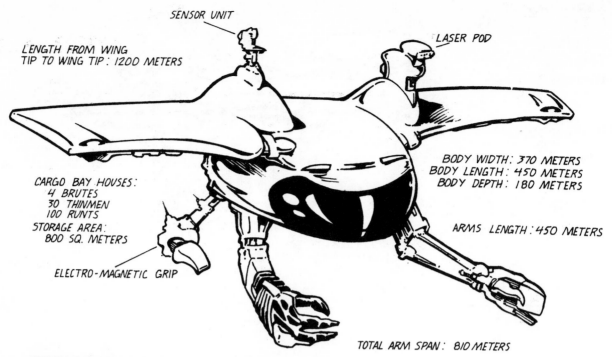

SENSOR UNIT

LASER POD

LENGTH FROM WING
TIP TO WING TIP: 1200 METERS

BODY WIDTH: 370 METERS
BODY LENGTH: 450 METERS
BODY DEPTH: 180 METERS

CARGO BAY HOUSES:
4 BRUTES
30 THINMEN
100 RUNTS
STORAGE AREA:
800 SQ. METERS

ARMS LENGTH: 450 METERS

ELECTRO-MAGNETIC GRIP

TOTAL ARM SPAN: 810 METERS

ATTACK PER MELEE: 2 LASER·OR HAND TO HAND
WEAPONS: LASER POD: 5-30+20   HAND TO HAND: 5-50+60
RANGE: LASER POD 2 km
ARMOR RATING: 12
SDC: WINGS 600 EACH · BODY 920 · ARMS 880 EACH · LASER POD 250
SPEED FACTOR: 0-1200 kmph
BONUSES: +3 TO HIT · +1 VS PSIONICS
PSIONICS: ALL LEVEL ONE ABILITIES

Hauler Type III

ATTACKS PER MELEE: 6 HAND TO HAND
WEAPONS: 4-40+40 DAMAGE EACH
ARMOR RATING: 12
SDC: TOP MID-SECTION BODY 600
     FORWARD SECTION   400
     REAR SECTION   400
     TRACTOR BEAM   310
SPEED FACTOR: 0-1200 kmph
PSIONICS: ALL LEVEL ONE ABILITY
BONUSES: +2 HIT   +1 VS PSIONICS

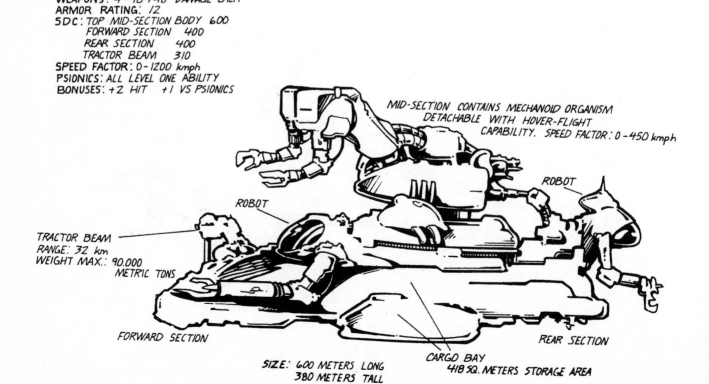

MID-SECTION CONTAINS MECHANOID ORGANISM
DETACHABLE WITH HOVER-FLIGHT
CAPABILITY. SPEED FACTOR: 0-450 kmph

ROBOT

ROBOT

TRACTOR BEAM
RANGE: 32 km
WEIGHT MAX.: 90.000
METRIC TONS

FORWARD SECTION

CARGO BAY
418 SQ. METERS STORAGE AREA

REAR SECTION

SIZE: 600 METERS LONG
380 METERS TALL

ROBOTS

Assault Probe

Function: Robot; search out and terminate humanoids.
Weapons: Ion Blaster
  Range: 400 meters (1320ft)
  Attacks Per Melee: Two
  Damage: 3-18 (3D6)
  Bonuses: None
Psionics: None, non-living
Alignment: Considered miscreant
A.R.: 10
S.D.C.: 40
Speed: 30kmph (20mph), bonus of +3 to dodge which is automatic just like a parry and does not lose any attacks.
Weight: 106kg (255lbs)
Size: 1.5 meters (5ft), 1 meter wide and tall
Equipment: Standard sensory, see brute; plus targeting sight.
NOTES: This unit is usually found at Mechanoid bases, the mothership and the ancient tunnels that honeycomb Gideon-E.

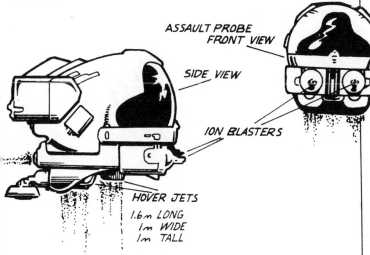

ASSAULT PROBE
FRONT VIEW

SIDE VIEW

ION BLASTERS

HOVER JETS
1.6m LONG
1m WIDE
1m TALL

Runt

Function: Robot; maintenance droid, also used in reconnaissance.
Weapons: Hand to Hand Only
  Range: Arms' length (about 2ft)
  Attacks Per Melee: Two
  Damage: 1-8+2 (1D8+2)
  Bonuses: +1 to strike, +1 to parry and dodge.
Psionics: None, non-living
Alignment: Considered miscreant
A.R.: 12
S.D.C.: 60
Speed: 10kmph running (6½mph)
Weight: 225kg (500lbs)
Size: 1.4 meters tall (4½ft tall)
NOTES: The runt's primary purpose is to maintain, repair and assist in repairs of Mechanoid machines, vehicles and other robots. Their secondary function is to perform other physical tasks such as loading and unloading, construction and so on. A single runt can lift and carry up to 540kg (1200lbs). They are found in abundance wherever Mechanoids are found. They are often in the company of Thinmen robots, brutes and runners.

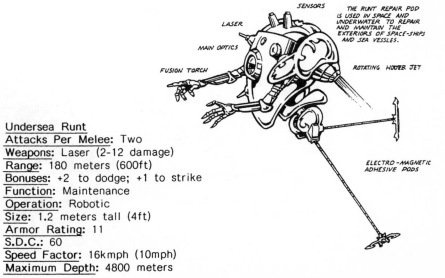

SENSORS

THE RUNT REPAIR POD IS USED IN SPACE AND UNDERWATER TO REPAIR AND MAINTAIN THE EXTERIORS OF SPACE-SHIPS AND SEA VESSLES.

LASER

MAIN OPTICS

FUSION TORCH

ROTATING HOVER JET

ELECTRO-MAGNETIC ADHESIVE PODS

Undersea Runt
Attacks Per Melee: Two
Weapons: Laser (2-12 damage)
Range: 180 meters (600ft)
Bonuses: +2 to dodge; +1 to strike
Function: Maintenance
Operation: Robotic
Size: 1.2 meters tall (4ft)
Armor Rating: 11
S.D.C.: 60
Speed Factor: 16kmph (10mph)
Maximum Depth: 4800 meters

Skimmer

Function: Robot; reconnaissance and defense
Weapons: Ion Blaster (front)
      Range: 900 meters (3000ft)
      Attacks Per Melee: Two
      Damage: 3-18
      Bonuses: None
Psionics: None, non-living
Alignment: Considered anarchist
A.R.: 11
S.D.C.: 40
Speed: 50kmph (32mph), bonus of +2 to dodge is automatic like a parry and does not forfeit any attacks.
Weight: 540kg (1200lbs)
Size: 2 meters (7ft) long, 1.3 meters (4½ft tall)
Equipment: Camera, sound recorder and transmitter.
Scanners: infra-red, ultra-violet, motion, vibration.
NOTES: The skimmer is designed to be an extremely mobile field unit to protect the Mechanoid base's perimeter.. It is also designed to hunt down and terminate humanoid life forms. Its third and final purpose is to act as a reconnaissance unit usually in conjunction with a Weavel. The protruding appendage at the top and center of the body is a video sound camera which can transmit everything the skimmer "sees" directly to a Weavel reconnaissance droid. It is the Weavel which records the data and transmits the information to a Mechanoid base. The transmission range of a skimmer is 64km (40 miles).

Undersea Skimmer
Attacks Per Melee: Two
Weapons: Blue/green laser (4-24 damage)
Range: 300 meters (1000ft)
Bonuses: +2 to dodge
Function: Reconnaissance
Operation: Robotic
Size: 2.2 meters long (7½ft)
Armor Rating: 11
S.D.C.: 60
Speed Factor: 40kmph (25mph)
Maximum Depth: 4800 meters

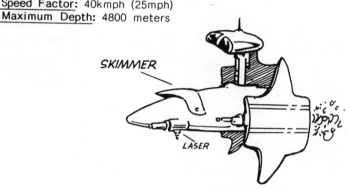

SKIMMER

LASER

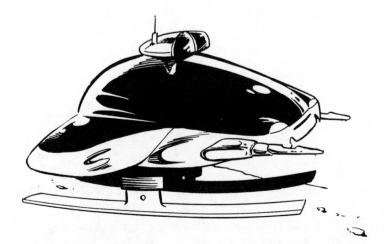

Thinman

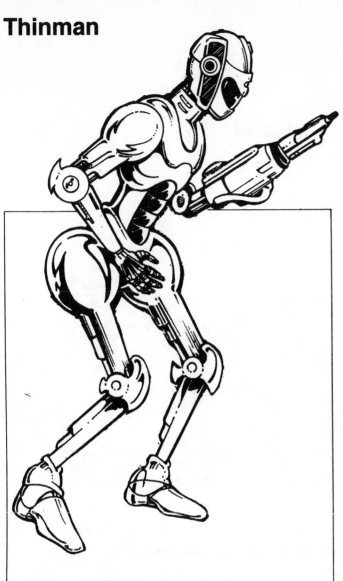

Function: Robot; maintenance and defense.
Weapons: Laser (left arm)
Range: 900 meters (3000ft)
Attacks Per Melee: Two
Damage: 1-6 (1D6) or 3-18 (3D6)
Bonuses: +1 to strike

Hand to Hand
Range: 1.4 meters (4½ft)
Attacks Per Melee: Three (takes the place of any laser attacks)
Damage: 2-12+4 (2D6+4)
Bonuses: +1 to strike, +2 to parry and dodge

Psionics: None, non-living
Alignment: Considered miscreant
A.R.: 10
S.D.C.: 90
Speed: 24kmph (15mph)
Weight: 720kg (1600lbs)
Size: 2.7 meters (9ft)
Equipment: Standard sensory, see brute; plus microscopic magnification 800 times up to 1.8 meters (6ft) away; nightsight, infra-red, ultra-violet and thermo-imager (all with a range of 360 meters (1200ft)).
NOTES: The thinman's primary function is to maintain, repair and assist in repair of robots, vehicles, machines and electronics. Their secondary function is in the area of defense. They, along with the runt, are the mainstay of the Mechanoid work force and found almost everywhere within that civilization. They are often in the company of brutes, runners and brains.

Weavel

Function: Robot; reconnaissance, defensive monitor
Weapons: None
Psionics: None, non-living
Alignment: Considered anarchist
A.R.: 10
S.D.C.: 60
Speed: 35kmph (22mph)
Weight: 810kg (1800lbs)
Size: 2 meters (7ft) long, 1.2 meters (4ft) in diameter.
NOTES: the weavel is a reconnaissance droid which usually is used to monitor the defensive perimeter of a Mechanoid base or sent out to survey an area. This can be done individually or in conjunction with two to eight skimmers. If linked with skimmers the weavel will receive video transmissions from them and record all "appropriate" data. Alone, it has a retractable nose that houses a number of sensory instruments which include radar/sonar (48km/30 miles), heat, radio, radiation, motion (180 meters/600ft), and even seismic. When threatened, it will retract the sensor stem, close its nose, signal its skimmer protectors and roll away.

Another retractable sensor head is housed in the body and has audio/visual recording capabilities. The recorded data can be transmitted up to 321km (200 miles) away or stored within for retrieval later. This Mechanoid robot travels by actually rolling over the ground.

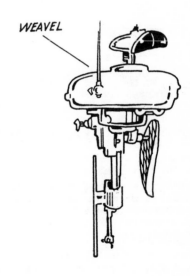

WEAVEL

Undersea Weavel
Weapons: None
Bonuses: None
Function: Reconnaissance
Operation: Robotic
Size: 2.4 meters tall (8ft)
Armor Rating: 10
S.D.C.: 60
Speed Factor: 30kmph (19mph)
Maximum Depth: 1800 meters

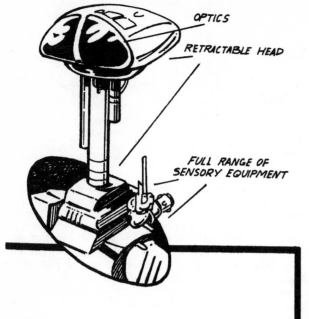

OPTICS

RETRACTABLE HEAD

FULL RANGE OF
SENSORY EQUIPMENT

Weavel

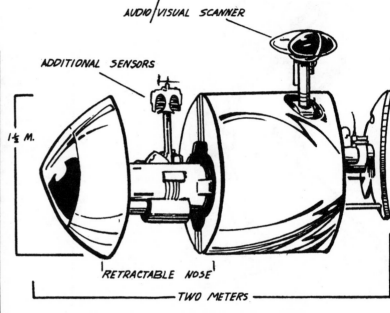

AUDIO/VISUAL SCANNER

ADDITIONAL SENSORS

1½ M.

RETRACTABLE NOSE

TWO METERS

Mechanoid Transport Vehicle

Like most Mechanoid machines the transport vehicle is inoperable until a Mechanoid brain, runner, oracle or overlord integrates itself with the vehicle.

A.R.: 12
S.D.C.: Small 450, large 1000
Speed: Hover or up to 3800kmph
Weapons: Particle Beam; all standard stats.

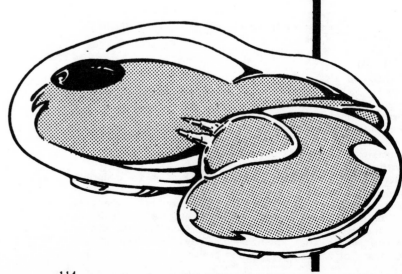

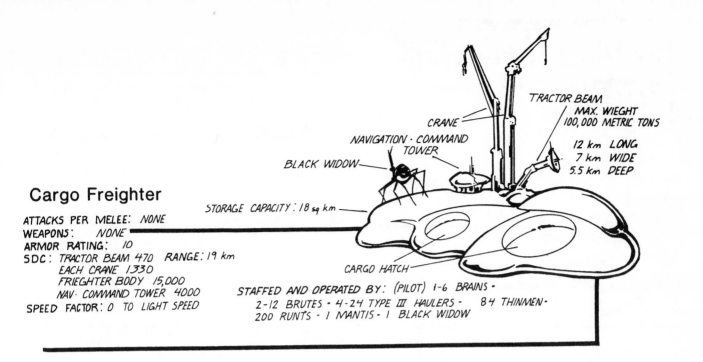

Cargo Freighter

ATTACKS PER MELEE: NONE
WEAPONS: NONE
ARMOR RATING: 10
SDC: TRACTOR BEAM 470   RANGE: 19 km
    EACH CRANE 1330
    FRIEGHTER BODY 15,000
    NAV· COMMAND TOWER 4000
SPEED FACTOR: 0 TO LIGHT SPEED

CRANE
NAVIGATION · COMMAND TOWER
BLACK WIDOW
TRACTOR BEAM
    MAX. WIEGHT
    100,000 METRIC TONS
    12 km LONG
    7 km WIDE
    5.5 km DEEP
STORAGE CAPACITY: 18 sq km
CARGO HATCH

STAFFED AND OPERATED BY: (PILOT) 1-6 BRAINS ·
2-12 BRUTES · 4-24 TYPE III HAULERS ·   84 THINMEN·
200 RUNTS · 1 MANTIS · 1 BLACK WIDOW

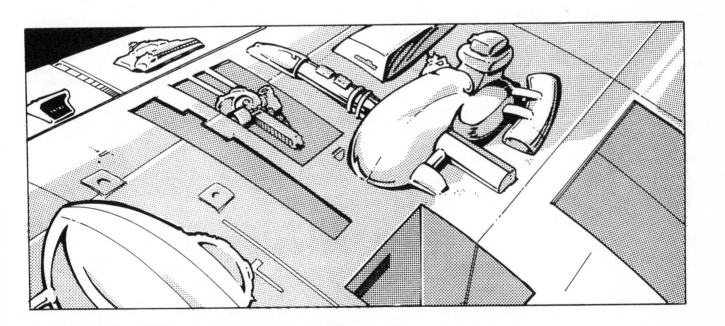

GAME MASTER SECTION

A NOTE ABOUT METRICS

Generally the equivalent in feet, miles or pounds is an "approximate" equivalent and not 100 percent accurate.

Combat System

First and foremost the Mechanoid combat system is designed to be <u>FAST</u> and <u>EASY</u>. A game that seems complicated or ponderous is not being handled properly. The whole point of the game is to give the players an enjoyable experience. In my opinion; that means keeping the hacks and slashes down to the bare minimum, and action to a maximum.

Simply put, it would be a cop-out to include more realism if it meant more boredom. Fun is more important than accuracy.

<u>Step 1: Hit</u> - Any attack starts with a roll to "strike" or hit. This is rolled on a twenty-sided die. To be successful the roll must be <u>over</u> the opponent's A.R. A roll of Natural Twenty is a strike that does double damage. NOTE: Humans always attack **first** unless they've been ambushed or surprised.

<u>Step 2: Dodge</u> - The victim of a strike usually has the option of dodging. Anyone choosing to dodge automatically sacrifices their next possible strike/attack. To be successful the dodge must equal or better the opponent's roll to strike you.

A character who dodges successfully takes NO damage. Failing the dodge roll means the same thing as not dodging at all; the character is hit and takes FULL damage.

The player must announce an intention to dodge immediately after the attempt to strike has been announced. A player may not dodge after the damage roll has been made.

<u>Step 3: Damage</u> - If a strike is successful and the victim fails to dodge or parry in hand to hand combat, then the attacker rolls for damage. Damage is **first applied** to S.D.C. When all the S.D.C. is depleted then the remaining damage points are taken from the victim's **Hit Points.**

<u>Exceptions:</u> Of course, none of these rules apply all the time. If an enemy is incapacitated (unconscious, dazed, or trapped) then the strike should be automatic. Just try to use a little common sense.

<u>Speed:</u> One more thing, it's important to keep the game moving. Therefore it's silly to slow things up trying to figure out complicated things like exact ranges in mid-combat. Make your judgments QUICK and as reasonably accurate as possible. If you get any grief, just remember the game master's motto, "Because I'm the game master that's why!" Even the feet to meters ratios in this book are approximations and rarely exact conversions.

TERMS

<u>Armor Rating (A.R.):</u> This indicates the protection provided against attack. In order to successfully attack anyone, the roll must be above the victim's A.R.

For example, someone with an A.R. of 15 can only be hurt by a hit of 16 or better. We must assume that a lower roll may have struck, but the battle tough armor and special alloy construction have held, thus NO damage occurs. However, if the roll to strike is higher than the A.R. then full damage is taken. First subtract from Armor S.D.C., when all S.D.C. points are gone then subtract from hit points.

<u>Attacks Per Melee:</u> The number of times a character can attack in a single 15 second melee round. For weapon fire this is determined by the weapon's energy capacity. In hand to hand combat the number of attacks per melee depend on the player's skill. Only one kind of attack either hand to hand or by energy weapon, is allowed per melee.

For Example, a combat-trained character with 3 attacks per melee can attack 3 times per melee in hand to hand combat (fists, knives, etc.). Using a PE-6 plasma ejector that character can attack only once per melee. The same character gets to fire (attack) seven blasts per melee with a SB-14, simple blaster or only twice per melee if firing a LP-10, laser pistol.

<u>Charges:</u> The total amount of shots that a weapon or a weapon's clip can hold.

<u>Damage:</u> This is the amount of physical damage done by an attack. The attacker rolls dice depending on the weapon. The victim must subtract the damage from his armor's S.D.C., and when that's reached zero, from his own hit points.

<u>Hand to Hand:</u> Using fists, feet, clubs (or empty weapons) and other hand held items. Trained fighters, anyone with any **skill** in hand to hand, can automatically <u>parry</u> hand to hand attacks. This differs from dodging in that the defender does not lose his next attack. An energy attack/blast CANNOT be parried, but may be dodged.

<u>Hit Points (H.P.):</u> This is the number of points of damage a character can take before dying. A character's base hit points is his P.E. plus 1D6. An additional 1D6 is added <u>everytime</u> the character gains a level of experience. Lost hit points represent physical wounds that require medical attention. Proper medical treatment and rest restore hit points.

<u>Natural Twenty:</u> An unmodified roll of 20 on a twenty-sided die. A natural twenty does double damage. <u>Note:</u> With bonuses a character may get a result of 20 or greater without actually rolling a 20. Only by rolling 20 on the dice does the character do double damage. A natural twenty can be dodged or parried but only by another "natural" twenty. Double damage should be handled by doubling the usual damage roll.

<u>Parry:</u> Useful <u>only</u> against hand to hand attacks. A skilled hand to hand fighter can parry instead of dodge and will not lose an attack.

<u>Range:</u> This is the maximum distance that a weapon can be fired.

<u>Structural Damage Capacity (S.D.C.):</u> This represents the amount of punishment that an object can take before breaking completely. When it comes to armor, this number is the maximum amount of damage taken before penetration.

<u>Weapon Proficiency (W.P.):</u> This is a character's skill level with a particular type of weapon. Bonuses to strike are accumulative.

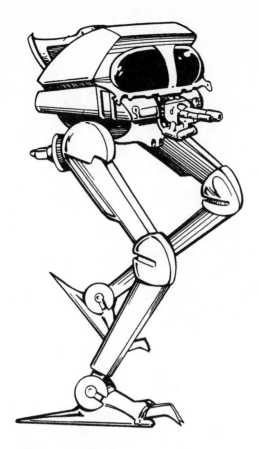

Mechanoid Combat Example

Here's an easy-to-follow example of a combat situation:

This scenario involves two player characters fighting it out with a single Exterminator. The two players, Rick and Sarah, are camouflaged and waiting to ambush the Mechanoid. Rick, a 2nd level E.B.A. is in E.B.A. AND IS ARMED WITH A PE-M8/Multiple Plasma Ejector and an IB-10/Ion Blaster. Sarah, a 3rd level L.B.A., has a M.A.A. Multi-Arm Antagonizer with P.E.W.S./Personal Energy Weapon Shield and L.B.A.

G.M.: You spot an Exterminator striding toward you. It's seeker pod flashes overhead.

Sarah: We'll stay hidden until he passes.

Rick: And I've got my plasma ejector ready to go.

G.M.: Okay. You wait nervously as the exterminator plants his multiple-ton footplate mere centimeters from your hiding place. Now he's directly between the two of you.

Rick: I want to wait until I've got a clear shot at his back.

Sarah: Also, we don't want to catch each other in our crossfire.

G.M.: Good thinking! The exterminator is now three paces away, about 15 meters.

Rick: Perfect! I'll open fire with a massive half load burst.

G.M.: Roll twenty-sided.

Rick: A . . . Arrgggh! A crummy 2!

G.M.: With your +1 that makes it a 3. Against the exterminator's A.R. that's a feeble miss.

Sarah: Well, I'm letting loose with my continual plasma generator (from a M.A.A.)

G.M.: Roll!

Sarah: Hah! 16. Plus my +2 for M.A.A., plus another +2, that makes it 20! Double damage!

G.M.: NO! You only get double damage on NATURAL twenties. But that's a solid hit. The exterminator was surprised so it didn't dodge. Roll damage.

Sarah: I do 4-40+4 damage . . . so I roll 4 ten-sided dice . . . 30! Plus 4, makes it 34 points of damage.

G.M.: Well, that's a good-sized hit, but the exterminator seems relatively undamaged. It's starting to turn around.

Sarah: We've both got 2 attacks per melee. Don't Rick and I get to hit it again?

G.M.: Nope. Since your weapons only do one attack per melee, that's all you can do for now. The exterminator opens fire on you. Let's see, it's got 5 attacks, 6 if it uses the plasma ejector. I'll shoot the two ion blasters and plasma at Rick. The triple barreled particle beam fires at Sarah . . . a 5 . . . a 14, and . . . another 14, it has a +2 to hit so that makes it a 7 and two 16s. Any hits on you Sarah?

Sarah: No; it needs a 19 to penetrate the P.E.W.S.

G.M.: Sarah takes no damage. I'll roll for the attacks on Rick . . . a 17 . . . a 12, and for the plasma . . . a 6. With bonuses that makes it a hit with 19, two misses. Damage is . . . poof! Just 4 points.

Rick: Off my E.B.A.'s S.D.C. of 150 that's hardly a scratch.

G.M.: Rick, what are you going to do?

Rick: Well, I've only got 4 charges left on the PE-M8, I don't know if I should blow 'em all on another simultaneous blast . . .

Sarah: What the heck, go for it, you're not going to miss again.

Rick: Okay. I roll . . . a 17! Plus 1, that makes it an 18!

G.M.: Good job. The exterminator is not going to dodge so roll damage.

Rick: This is good, 16-160+200 damage. I roll 16 ten-sided dice . . . (long wait) . . . 103 . . . plus 200 makes it 303

G.M.: And one exterminator bites the Gideon dust.

Rick/Sarah: Hooray!

G.M.: Now the seeker pod flashes towards the two of you with it's lasers glowing . . .

Rick: Oops.

Sarah: I take aim at it.

G.M.: It fires at Rick . . . first hit is an 8, then . . . a natural 20! Rick, do you want to dodge?

Rick: Uh . . . It would mean giving up my next attack. And I'd have to roll a natural 20. Right?

G.M.: Right on both counts.

Rick: I guess I'll take the damage.

G.M.: Fine . . . I'll roll 4 ten-sided dice for the seeker pod . . . 14, doubled, that makes it 28 points.

Rick: That puts my E.B.A. down to an S.D.C. of 118.

Sarah: Can I hit it now?

G.M.: Yeah, both of you can fire.

Sarah: Sheesh! Only a 5. Even with my bonuses that only makes it an 8.

G.M.: Sarah, you miss altogether.

Rick: My PE-M8 is empty, so I'll fire my Ion Blaster . . . I rolled an 18 . . . but I've got a +2 in that W.P. so that makes it a 20. Double damage?

G.M.: Rick, how often do I gotta' tell you guys, no double damage unless it's a NATURAL 20. Anyway, you've still got 3 more shots with an ion blaster if you want to use them.

Rick: But I only get 2 attacks per melee.

G.M.: That's only for hand to hand combat. Weapon combat depends on the number of shots that the weapon can fire per melee. With the IB-10 that's four blasts.

Rick: A . . . a 16 . . . a 15, and . . . a 3.

G.M.: With bonuses that makes for 3 hits. Roll your damage.

Rick: I'll just roll nine dice . . . for . . . 27 points.

G.M.: That's enough to make it realize that it's outnumbered. You see it go zipping off for help . . .

The Sea

OPTIONAL

The following material originally appeared as the Monthly Mechanoid, a supplement that saw publication in the trade magazine entitled the Game Merchant. Because so many people have inquired about these supplements I've included ALL the material that ever saw print in the pages of the Game Merchant. The underwater character classes (O.C.C.), skills, vehicles and devices are presented here rather than with the other O.C.C.'s because they are OPTIONAL!

OPTIONAL . . .

Occupation and Skills Pilot Vehicle Mechanic

UNDERWATER OCCUPATIONAL CHARACTER CLASSES

Human O.C.C. Requirements

W.P.V.M./Water Vehicle Pilot Mechanic: I.Q. 8, P.P. 8, P.E. 8

D.S.R.S./Deep Sea Research Specialist: I.Q. 13, M.E. 10

Commando O.C.C. (Underwater Specialist): I.Q. 10, P.S. 12, P.P. 12

Water Vehicle Pilot Mechanic (W.V.P.M.) O.C.C.

Water Vehicle Pilot Mechanics are trained in the operation and repair of the various ocean-going vessels of Gideon-E. There are three sub-specialties, surface craft, hydrofoil/hover craft and submersibles.

Attribute Requirements: I.Q. 7, P.P. 5, P.E. 8

Major Areas of Expertise:

P.F.V. (Pilot Flotation Vehicle)	+30%
F.V. Mechanics	+30%
S.V. Mechanics	+30%
Swimming: Basic	+15%
Underwater Sensory Equipment	+5% to operate; +10% to repair

Elective Skills

Audio/Visual Communications	
Air Vehicle Mechanics	
Computer Operation (+5% to repair ONLY)	
E-Clip Recharging	
Electronics	+10%
Hand to Hand: Basic	
Oxy-Filter Operation	+20%
Oxy-Filter Mechanics	+10%
P.F.V. (Pilot Flotation Vehicle)	
P.M.S. (Pilot Minnow Scout)	
P.S.V. (Pilot Submersible Vehicle)	
Swimming: S.C.U.B.A.	+10%
Swimming: Deep Sea	
W.P. Handgun	
W.P. Harpoon Gun	
W.P. Knife	
W.P. Laser Rifle	
W.P. Sonic Pulse	
W.P. Torpedo	

Combat and Weapons

Even though this is a non-combat occupation, hand to hand and many W.P. Skills are available as electives.

Attacks Per Melee: Two; plus possible hand to hand bonuses.

Use of Battle Armor: Web vest or L.B.A. are commonly used, especially in combat or potentially dangerous situations.

Standard Equipment
Hand held communicator
Mini tool pack
Laser lance
Flashlight
Utility belt
Diving knife
Gas mask or air filter

Authorized Clearance Upon Assignment: Handgun, laser rifle, S.C.U.B.A. Equipment or M.P.O.F., web vest or L.B.A. long range communicator, additional tools, water vehicle appropriate to mission.

Monthly Wages: 2700 credits at levels 1-4; 4000 credits for 5th level or higher. Roll 1D4 X 1000 to determine savings.

Scientist

Deep Sea Research Specialist (D.S.R.S.) O.C.C.

The Deep Sea Research Specialists are usually trained in oceanography, marine biology and basic underwater operations. Because they are virtually the only personnel on Gideon-E with this kind of training they've been drafted in the fight against the Mechanoids.

Attribute Requirements: I.Q. 13, M.E. 10

Major Areas of Expertise:

Computer Operation	+20%
Marine Biology	+30%
Swimming: Basic	+20%
Swimming: S.C.U.B.A.	+10%
Underwater Sensory Equipment	+20%

Elective Skills

Audio/Visual Communications	
Computer Programming	+20%
Electronics	
Medical: First Aid	
Medical: Paramedic	
Oxy-Filter Operation	+10%
P.A.V. (Pilot Air Vehicle)	
P.F.V. (Pilot Flotation Vehicle)	+10%
P.G.V. (Pilot Ground Vehicle)	
P.M.B. (Pilot Minnow Scout)	+5%
P.S.V. (Pilot Submersible Vehicle)	+5%
Swimming: Deep Sea	
W.P. Handgun	
W.P. Harpoon Gun	
W.P. Knife	
W.P. Sonic Pulse	
W.P. Torpedo	
W.P. Underwater Explosives	

Combat and Weapons

As with other scientists, there is relatively little training in combat skills. However, the rough-and-tumble of working the high seas and the physical demands of underwater work means most can pick elective hand to hand skills. Large and aggressive underwater life forms means that at least one weapon skill is mandatory.

Attacks Per Melee: Two; plus possible hand to hand bonuses.

Use of Battle Armor: Any

Standard Equipment:
Mini tool pack
Laser lance
Diving knife
Utility belt
Goggles
Gas mask or air filter
Hand held communicator
Portable laboratory
Portable personal computer
Monthly Wages: 3500 credits at levels 1-3; 4100 credits for 5th level or higher. Roll 1D8 X 1000 to determine savings.

Commando

Commando O.C.C. (Underwater Specialist)

This is not another Occupational Character Class, it is just a division of the standard Commando O.C.C. Players wishing to be part of DEEP SIX, the underwater speciality section, should apply the following changes. All other attributes remain unchanged.

Major Areas of Expertise:
Hand to Hand: Martial Arts
W.P. Handgun
W.P. Knife
W.P. Laser Rifle
Swimming: Basic
Swimming: S.C.U.B.A.
Swimming: Deep Sea

Elective Skills
Audio/Visual Communications	+10%
Oxy-Filter Operation	+10%
P.F.V. (Pilot Flotation Vehicle)	+10%
P.G.V. (Pilot Ground Vehicle)	
P.M.S. (Pilot Minnow Scout)	+10%
P.S.V. (Pilot Submersible Vehicle)	+5%
Surveillance Systems	+5%
Underwater Sensory Equipment	+5%
W.P. Heavy	
W.P. Harpoon Gun	+10%
W.P. Sonic Pulse	+10%
W.P. Torpedo	+10%
W.P. Explosives	
W.P. Underwater Explosives	+20%

Standard Equipment:
Choice of body armor
PW-11 Laser Pistol
LRW-21 Laser Rifle
Diving knife
Gun and utility belt
Wetsuit
Hand held communicator
Uniform
Gas mask or air filter
S.C.U.B.A. OR M.P.O.F. system

Skills

Skill Descriptions

Flotation (F.V.) Mechanics: Training in diagnosis and repair of surface-going vehicles, including conventional ships and boats, hydrofoils, and water-borne hovercrafts. There are two base skill percentages, the first for diagnosis of the problem(s) and the second for the actual repair. Base Skill is 20% diagnose/15% repair +5% (for both) per level.

Marine Biology: Knowledge of aquatic life forms in general and of Gideon's ocean life in particular. Base Skill is 40%+2% per level of experience.

Oxy-Filter Operation: Character will know how to use and adjust various oxy-filter devices. This is a requirement for the use of the Man-Portable-Oxy-Filter (M.P.O.F.) Base Skill is 25%+5% per level of experience.

Oxy-Filter Mechanics: Training in the diagnosis and repair of oxy-filter devices. There are two base skill percentages, the first for diagnosis of problems and the second for the actual repair. Base Skill is 30% diagnose/25% repair +10% (for both) per level of experience.

P.F.V. (Pilot Flotation Vehicle): Includes all surface craft, including conventional ships, hydrofoils and some hovercraft. Base Skill is 25%+5% per level of experience.

P.M.S. (Pilot Minnow Scout): Specific use of the Minnow Scout submersible. Base Skill is 40%+5% per level.

P.S.V. (Pilot Submersible Vehicle): Includes all submarine craft, except Minnow Scout. Base Skill is 15%+10% per level of experience.

Submersible Vehicle (S.V.) Mechanics: Training in the diagnosis and repair of submersible vehicles, including submarines and minnow scouts. There are two base skill percentages, the first for diagnosis of problem(s) and the second for actual repair. Base Skill is 20% diagnosis/15% repair +5% (for both) per level of experience.

Underwater Sensory Equipment: Skill involving underwater scanning and communications equipment. Also includes knowledge of the sounds emitted by various Gideon aquatic life. Base Skill is 25%+5% per level of experience.

W.P. Harpoon Gun: Weapon proficiency with the underwater harpoon gun. Although the harpoon gun can be used with a plain pointed end (2-12 damage), it is usually used with an explosive head (4-24+10 damage)

W.P. Sonic Pulse: Use of the sonic pulse generator.

W.P. Torpedo: Maintenance and use of the range of torpedos.

W.P. Underwater Explosives: Using explosives in an underwater environment requires a completely different kind of training. Base Skill is 35%+10% per level of experience.

Equipment

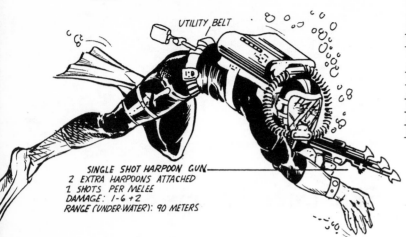

D.S.C. WITH 2 HOUR OXYGEN TANK

UTILITY BELT

SINGLE SHOT HARPOON GUN
2 EXTRA HARPOONS ATTACHED
1 SHOTS PER MELEE
DAMAGE: 1-6+2
RANGE (UNDER-WATER): 90 METERS

Human Underwater Breathing Equipment

S.C.U.B.A.

This is the standard equipment used for underwater operations. It consists of face mask, respirator, hoses, regulator, oxygen tank with backpack. BCD (Buoyancy Compensator Device), wet suit, fins, and weight belt. Oxygen tanks are good for about 2 hours of use. Maximum Depth: 75 meters (250ft).

Oxy-Filter

Oxy-Filters are used in underwater bases and vehicles to extract oxygen from the water. They are large, bulky machines that require constant monitoring from computers or technicians.

Man-Portable Oxy-Filter (M.P.O.F.)

This experimental device was being extensively tested throughout the underwater colony.

Bulk is one of the disadvantages of the M.P.O.F., Scuba gear is far lighter and easier to operate. M.P.O.F. backpack system's mass is 115kg (250lbs). On the other hand, since the device works by filtering the oxygen out of the water it can provide unlimited time underwater. The amount of water forced through the membranes can also be used for propulsion. This water-jet lets a character move at speeds of up to 35kmph (22mph). The M.P.O.F. operates for 12 hours per E-clip.

Maximum depth is 50m (165ft) for unprotected humans. An optional pressurized suit extends the maximum depth down to 240m (800ft).

Modified L.B.A. and E.B.A.

Standard armor is NOT suitable for underwater use. In fact, going in deep water with E.B.A. is a quick route to a watery death. However, aquatic versions of both modern armor suits are available. These suits come equipped with 2, 4 or 6 hour oxygen supplies.

Swimming is very awkward in armor. A hand held water jet is used to get around. Speed is a maximum of 25kmph (16mph). Maximum depth for L.B.A. is 60m (200ft), for E.B.A. it is 120m (400ft).

Human Water Vehicles

Converted Pleasure Craft

As on any colony, humans on Gideon enjoyed vacationing in sailboats and motorboats. These vehicles came in great variety, but only a few models could be outfitted with the breathing filtration equipment needed after the Mechanoid invasion. The following figures should be considered average.

Weapons: None
Function: Modified for exploration, transportation or research.
Operation: Human
Size: 4 to 20 meters
Armor Rating: 9-11
S.D.C.: 100 to 350
Speed: 45kmph (28mph)
Maximum Depth: Surface Only

PARTICLE BEAM CANNON

Hydro-Foil Scout

Weapons: None
Bonuses: +5 to Dodge
Function: Exploration and Research
Operation: Human
Size: 14 meters long (46ft)
Armor Rating: 9
S.D.C.: 135
Speed: 100kmph (approx. 115mph)
Maximum Depth: Surface Only

Hydro-Foil 110

Attacks Per Melee: Six; 2 main cannon; 4 rear cannon
Weapons: Particle Beam and Rear Laser Cannon 6-36+6
Range: 1800m/1600m (5940ft/5280ft)
Bonuses: +2 to Dodge
Function: Scouting and Transportation
Operation: Human
Size: 43 meters (140ft)
Armor Rating: 10
S.D.C.: 210
Speed Factor: 115kmph (72mph)
Maximum Depth: Surface Only

Research Hover Craft

Unlike most hover crafts this vehicle can raise itself less than a meter up into the air. It is primarily a water vehicle but can also be used on smooth sand, ice, mud, and grasslands. It has been designed to float in anything from ocean gales to artic storms.

Weapons: None
Bonuses: +2 to Dodge
Function: Exploration and Research
Operation: Human
Size: 85 meters (280ft)
Armor Rating: 12
S.D.C.: 410
Speed Factor: 95kmph (60mph)
Maximum Depth: Surface Only

Mini-Sub
Attacks Per Melee: 1
Weapons: Mechanical Arm, 1-6 points damage
Range: 10 meter reach (33ft)
Bonuses: +1 to Dodge
Function: Exploration and Research
Operation: Human
Size: 8.3 meters (27ft)
Armor Rating: 10
S.D.C.: Body - 175, Arm - 80
Speed Factor: 32kmph (20mph)
Maximum Depth: 2500 meters

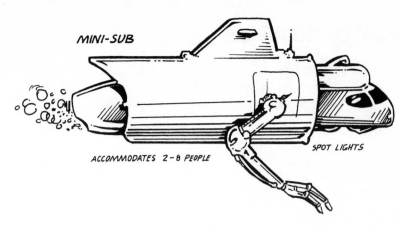

MINI-SUB

ACCOMMODATES 2-8 PEOPLE

SPOT LIGHTS

Transport Cruiser
Attacks Per Melee: None
Weapons: Ram Prow (normally used for ice-breaking operations) 6-36 X 10 damage.
Function: Transport and Research
Operation: Human
Size: 200 meters long, 60 meters wide and 42 meters tall (660ft X 200ft X 138ft).

Armor Rating: 12
S.D.C.: Stern - 280
      Mid-Section - 235
      Ram Prow - 620
Speed Factor: 70kmph (45mph)
Maximum Depth: Surface Only

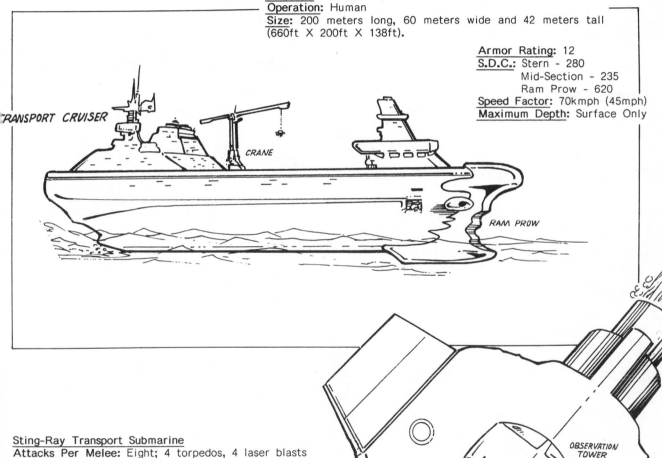

TRANSPORT CRUISER

CRANE

RAM PROW

Sting-Ray Transport Submarine
Attacks Per Melee: Eight; 4 torpedos, 4 laser blasts
Weapons: Torpedos (6-60+80 damage (6D10)); Laser (6-36+10 (6D6)))
Range: Torpedos - 1200m (4000ft); Lasers - 300m (1000ft)
Bonuses: +3 to hit with laser, +1 to hit with torpedo; +1 to dodge with torpedo
Function: Transport and Research
Operation: Human
Size: 80 meters long, 80 meters wide and 9.6 meters tall (265ft X 265ft X 36ft)
Armor Rating: 12
S.D.C.: Body - 310; Observation Deck - 130
Speed Factor: 55kmph (35mph)
Maximum Depth: 3600 meters (11,880ft)
Attacks/Weapons: The observation deck tower is fitted with a sonic pulse generator. This device fires amplified sound waves in devastating pulses ONCE every 8 melees.
Damage: 3-18 X 10
Range: 550 meters (1820ft)

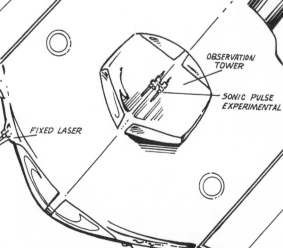

OBSERVATION TOWER

SONIC PULSE EXPERIMENTAL

FIXED LASER

TORPEEDO TUBE

360° ROTATING LASER

121

MINNOW SCOUT

HARPOON GUNS

SPOT-LIGHTS

Minnow Scout Submarine
Attacks Per Melee: 2 or 6
Weapons: Harpoon 3-18 damage
(optional explosive head does 4-40+20)
Range: 170 meters
Bonuses: +3 to dodge; +1 to hit
Function: Scout
Operation: Human
Size: 4 meters long, 1.8 meters wide (13ft X 6ft)
Armor Rating: 9
S.D.C.: 112
Speed Factor: 50kmph (32mph)
Maximum Depth: 1500 meters

The Mechanoids

Underwater Conversion For Other Mechanoids

Wasp

Wasps can operate underwater to almost unlimited depths. On the other hand, Wasps HATE operating underwater. They don't even like getting WET. When on underwater missions they lose all their usual playfulness. All they want to do is kill their targets and get out as quickly as possible.

Part of the reason they don't want to be underwater is because their particle beams are severely limited. Range is cut down to a mere 35 meters. Damage is only 2-20+15. To top it all off, their speed is a crummy 600kmph (350 miles per hour).

Mantis

If any Mechanoid is more uncomfortable underwater than the Wasp it would have to be the Mantis. With their open fusion reactor they travel with their own area of boiling steam. In spite of this disadvantage they are often found around ocean mining operations at seemingly unlimited depths.

One advantage the Mantis has underwater is the increased range and effectiveness of their Electro-Primer. In water it has a range of 36 meters (120ft) and does 6-36+20. Additionally the electric shock can be used on multiple targets at the same time. Anyone within 3 meters (10ft) of the victim will take identical damage. Their speed through the water is only 25kmph (16mph).

Tunnel Crawler

Tunnel Crawlers are unaffected by underwater operations. The only differences are a reduction in weapon range (to 7 meters/22ft) and a reduction in speed (15kmph/10mph crawl, 20kmph/13mph hover). They are capable of descending to unlimited depths.

Brain and Runner Under-Sea Casings

Without assistance Brain and Runner Mechanoids are pretty ineffective under water; they are too slow and their usual laser weapons are next to useless in a water environment (1-6 damage, range 6 meters/20ft).

Exterior casings solve both these problems. A water jet propulsion unit gives them a speed of 35kmph (22mph) to depths of 4800 meters. The casing is also equipped with a special blue laser (1-6/3-18 damage, range: 300 meters (1000ft).

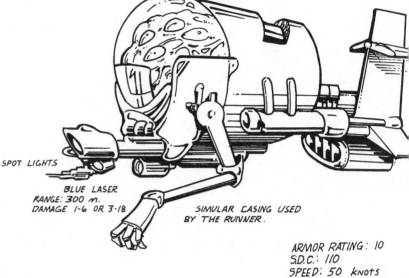

SPOT LIGHTS

BLUE LASER
RANGE: 300 m.
DAMAGE 1-6 OR 3-18

SIMULAR CASING USED
BY THE RUNNER.

ARMOR RATING: 10
S.D.C.: 110
SPEED: 50 knots
MAX. DEPTH: 4.8 km.

Specially Designed Undersea Mechanoids

Specially designed for underwater reconnaissance, the **undersea Mechanoids** are basically similar to their land-based counterparts.

Undersea Skimmer
Attacks Per Melee: Two
Weapons: Blue/green laser (4-24 damage)
Range: 300 meters (1000ft)
Bonuses: +2 to dodge
Function: Reconnaissance
Operation: Robotic
Size: 2.2 meters long (7½ft)
Armor Rating: 11
S.D.C.: 60
Speed Factor: 40kmph (25mph)
Maximum Depth: 4800 meters

SKIMMER

LASER

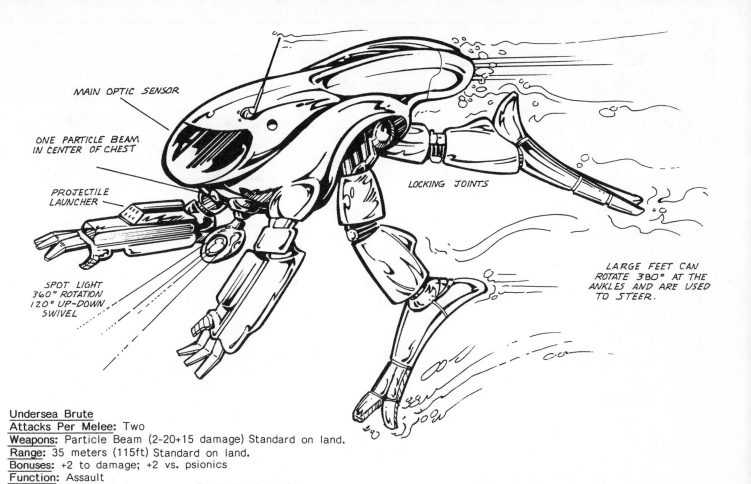

MAIN OPTIC SENSOR

ONE PARTICLE BEAM
IN CENTER OF CHEST

PROJECTILE
LAUNCHER

SPOT LIGHT
360° ROTATION
120° UP-DOWN
SWIVEL

LOCKING JOINTS

LARGE FEET CAN
ROTATE 380° AT THE
ANKLES AND ARE USED
TO STEER.

Undersea Brute
Attacks Per Melee: Two
Weapons: Particle Beam (2-20+15 damage) Standard on land.
Range: 35 meters (115ft) Standard on land.
Bonuses: +2 to damage; +2 vs. psionics
Function: Assault
Operation: Mechanoid
Size: 3.8 meters tall (12ft)
Armor Rating: 10
S.D.C.: 190
Speed Factor: 35kmph
Maximum Depth: Unlimited

Projectile Launcher
Range: 70 meters (230ft)
Damage: 4-24+4

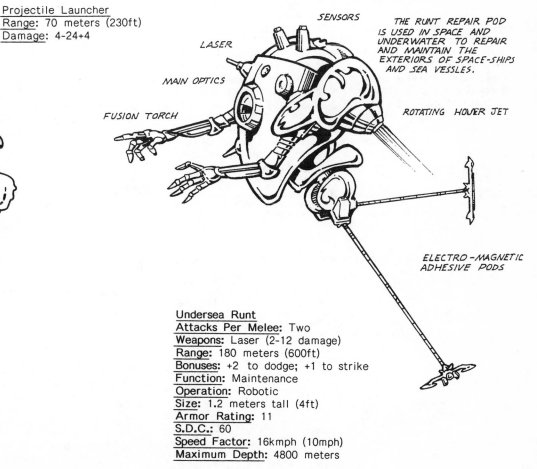

SENSORS

LASER

MAIN OPTICS

FUSION TORCH

THE RUNT REPAIR POD
IS USED IN SPACE AND
UNDERWATER TO REPAIR
AND MAINTAIN THE
EXTERIORS OF SPACE-SHIPS
AND SEA VESSLES.

ROTATING HOVER JET

ELECTRO-MAGNETIC
ADHESIVE PODS

WEAVEL

Undersea Weavel
Weapons: None
Bonuses: None
Function: Reconnaissance
Operation: Robotic
Size: 2.4 meters tall (8ft)
Armor Rating: 10
S.D.C.: 60
Speed Factor: 30kmph (19mph)
Maximum Depth: 1800 meters

Undersea Runt
Attacks Per Melee: Two
Weapons: Laser (2-12 damage)
Range: 180 meters (600ft)
Bonuses: +2 to dodge; +1 to strike
Function: Maintenance
Operation: Robotic
Size: 1.2 meters tall (4ft)
Armor Rating: 11
S.D.C.: 60
Speed Factor: 16kmph (10mph)
Maximum Depth: 4800 meters

Adventure

Survival

Note: While this is an Introductory level mission, it's also a very long mission that will take many hours of play. Suitable for campaigns with any type and number of player characters.

Mission Background: All the player characters should be informed by the GM that they have been assigned to take E.B.A. training. Any characters who already have E.B.A. are to serve as assistant instructors. For this scenario let us assume any characters of a different O.C.C. have been recruited to give a go as an E.B.A. Their normal O.C.C. skills still apply and characters can quit the E.B.A. Division as soon as they get back to base to pursue their chosen O.C.C. NO E.B.A. SKILLS are earned, because training is far from complete.

The camp is on the extreme southern shore of Lake Phe, due south of the Stelvenson colony. Transport is by regular aircraft to Stelvenson, then by hover craft across the lake.

After 11 days in the rustic camp they will have learned the basics of E.B.A. operation but will have very little actual experience. This is an exhausting program involving constant physical exercise alternating with highly technical courses where the potential dangers of E.B.A. are constantly discussed.

The adventure should begin with a pre-dawn summons. All trainees are to report to the **main cabin**. Bring full E.B.A. and be there in 5 minutes. Characters will be instructed to bring their standard issue equipment (E.B.A., IB-10, LR-20, NO E-clips for either weapon, flashlight, knife, uniform and utility belt.

Formal Mission Briefing: Captain Estarv, a senior officer in E.B.A. gives the following talk:

Good morning troopers!

Today promises to be ideal for your first field exercise. We are expecting heavy fog, cold rain, and hail. Perfect for testing your newly gained E.B.A. knowledge.

Each group will be assigned a sector. The mission is simple, clear out all the Mechanoids in your sector. Oh, you've got nothing to worry about. Most of the Mechanoids are just metal cut-outs.

Another important point. Any moving Mechanoids you see are holographic projections. These projectors are expensive so be sure you aim HIGH. You'll find the cut-off switches directly below the image.

Remember that you are using live ammunition. Be very, very careful not to shoot when another team member is in view.

Rules in this game are simple. The first team to wipe out the Mechanoids in their area will be rewarded. Missing targets in your area, using excessive shots, or damaging equipment will count as negative points. Stay inside your area. Anything you shoot outside the red ribbons will be credited to an opposing team.

Any questions?

[G.M. NOTE: Most questions regarding equipment operation will be answered briefly. Questions about the specific mission will be ignored. No heavy weapons will be issued. If anyone asks about the reward, read the following.]

Ho ho! I'm sure you'll find the prize worthwhile. The first group to finish clearing their sector will be awarded two extra hours of sleep tomorrow morning.

[G.M. NOTE: Finish off the briefing with the following:]

You should leave immediately after you've formed into groups of twos and threes. Each group will be given a heading. Start from the back door of this building. When you cross the red ribbon you'll be in your section. Hit all the Mechanoids inside the area roped off with red ribbons. Remember to conserve your ammunition.

Good Luck and Good Hunting!

Player Tips: Rumors about Captain Estarv are pretty common. They all say that he's a tough teacher who can be mean, but usually turns out top-notch E.B.A. specialists.

No information about the upcoming Mechanoid raid will be available to any player.

Game Master Background

Before assigning the players to their areas they will be given one (1) E-clip for each weapon, a hand-held metal detector (range 25 meters), a flask of fruit juice and a bag lunch.

Almost all of this adventure will take place in the huge, defoliated forest. The trees will still have leaves, but they'll be the dead leaves of late autumn.

Finding all 16 of the **fake** Mechanoids and the 2 holograms should be fairly easy if the characters remember to use their metal detectors. Since they've got to search 4 hours this also makes it easy for them to find the **real** Mechanoids.

The real fun of this adventure will start when the characters first shoot a REAL Mechanoid. Unlike the cardboard cut-outs, these guys will shoot back. Game masters should wait until the players seem bored with shooting cut-outs. Then, when they're off-guard let them spot a real Mechanoid which they must, at first, believe to be another cut out or holographic image.

Each group will encounter one of the following small groups of Mechanoids:

Group #1 - Weavel with two Thinmen escorts
Group #2 - Two Skimmers
Group #3 - A Brute with two Runt escorts

Group #4 - Four Thinmen
Group #5 - One Runner
Group #6 - One Wasp

Actual combat should not be terribly difficult for the players. As soon as they defeat their Mechanoid playmates they will notice the sounds of the E.B.A. camp being attacked.

No living thing and only a few usable objects will survive the devastation. Characters attempting to interfere will be attacked and pursued by Mechanoid Wasps. After nightfall it will be safe to enter the camp.

At this point the only possible option is for the characters to start walking back to Stelvenson. Aside from the vast distance involved (over 3000km) there are problems of food, energy, hostile Mechanoids, etc. . . .

How much ground is covered depends on how fast the characters want to move. Explain that their E.B.A. suits will have to be **recharged** every 8 days. A standard E-clip will fully recharge two E.B.A. suits. Water isn't a problem so long as they stay near the lake.

Well fed and rested characters are <u>healthy</u> and should be able to cover about 60km a day. Really pushing it, they can double that but the next day they'll be exhausted.

After a day without rest or food the characters will be <u>tired</u>. Tired characters in E.B.A. can only cover about 40km each day. Tired characters become healthy after a full days of rest with regular meals.

Characters going without food and rest, or without food for more than 3 days will be <u>exhausted</u>. Exhausted characters will be lucky to make 20km a day through the rough terrain. In order to recover to tired status the character will need two days rest and food.

Characters who go without sleep for 3 nights, or who have gone 4 days without food are said to be wrecked. Wrecked characters travel less than 10km per day. Recovering from wrecked to exhausted takes three days of rest and food. A character can stay wrecked for a number of days equal to the character's P.E.

For example, a character with a P.E. of 9 can travel wrecked for 9 days. Attempting to walk on the 10th day will probably kill the character. Provided adequate water is available, the character can rest for another 9 days before finally dying of starvation.

Fortunately for the players there are a variety of possible encounters between then and civilization. These range from old hunting lodges and vacation homes to an occasional rover(s). Mechanoid reconnaissance units and a few remaining samples of the local wild life.

Game masters are free to include other novelties like exotic terrain (swamps, quicksand, rivers, and cliffs), ancient artifacts and new Mechanoid encounters.

Phase 1 - Cut Out Mechanoids: The Adventure Begins

First step for each team will be finding a few fake Mechanoids. Each group will have an area containing 5 Runts, 2 Brutes, 1 Thinman, 1 Weavel (cleverly hidden in bushes), 2 Runners, 4 Wasps (high up in trees), 1 Wasp holographic projection (seen in a clearing about 6 meters off the ground), and 2 Tunnel Crawlers (hidden in bushes or small tunnels). Let the characters find and shoot at least half the available targets.

Phase 2 - Cut Outs That Shoot Back

The next thing to do is introduce a few **real** Mechanoids. Have them do the same kinds of things as their cut-outs. Each area should contain 2 runts, a brute and a runner. Around the time that all the characters realize they are fighting living Mechanoids they will hear explosions in the direction of the training camp.

Phase 3 - The Ruins of E.B.A. Camp

By the time they return to the area all humans will have been killed. Eight Wasps will be circling overhead and at least two dozen assorted Mechanoids will be seen searching through the wreckage. Smart characters will wait and watch. All these Mechanoids will leave at around nightfall.

After dark it will be safe to venture into the camp. Inside there isn't much other than debris, dead bodies and burning buildings. Salvage will yield 2 meal packs for each member of the party. In addition, a thorough search will uncover a cache of 24 energy clips. There is nothing else of value.

GUSTOVICH

Now the group will have to make their most important decision. Which way to go? The only possible destination is Stelvensen colony which is roughly 1200km straight across Lake Phe. There are no vehicles left in the camp and no communications equipment other than hand held communicators (range: 3km)

Walking around the lake to the east should be eliminated because it involves crossing two major rivers. Walking around to the west presents fewer problems.

Phase 4 - The Big Walk

Encounter #1 - At 200km distance the group will find the remnants of a vacation village. 18 abandoned cottages are scattered at kilometer intervals along the beach. All the houses have been ransacked by rovers and no food remains.

There are three broken power generators that were left behind. Fixing one will take a qualified mechanic about 8 hours. It can be used to recharge on E-clip every hour.

Encounter #2 - About 150km further along the coast the characters will be able to see some large object sunk in the water about 30 meters from shore. This is a wrecked HS-180/hovercraft scout. Inside it are the bodies of 6 humans. A medical kit and a compass are salvageable.

Encounter #3 - Another 100km along the coast a character may be able to spot a far-off oil derrick. About 50km southwest of the coast inland is an abandoned exploratory mining rig. No valuable items.

Encounter #4 - 350km from the sunken hovercraft is an abandoned hunting lodge. There is a small log cabin and a small dock. In the woods behind the cabin there is a tarp-covered small boat. This open, 8 meter boat has a gasoline motor.

Encounter #5 - Scattered along the coastline are the remains of a massive air battle between Mechanoids and human aircraft. Scavengers can find a few days worth of food and perhaps 3 E-clips.

Encounter #6 - 400km from the hunting lodge is a small store and refueling stop. There is a dock with three ruined boats. Inside the store has been trashed but enough canned goods are left to feed one person 40 days. Another broken power generator could be fixed and run for a few hours.

Encounter #7 - An old dirt road goes from the store westward. 130km from coast there is an old abandoned airfield with a few broken aircraft. A crashed hover jet fighter could be fixed after a couple of weeks work.

Encounter #8 - 545km further along the coast. This is an old emergency station set up for lost colonists. Inside are 24 food packs and 24 E-clips. There are also 6 hand held signal flares, 12 survival knives, 6 sleeping bags, 2 portable tents (with attached air filters), 12 air filters, 2 mini-tool packs and a medical kit.

Encounter #9 - Yet another 310km along, there is a Mechanoid area control base. This is designed to be a field base for Mechanoid reconnaissance operations. The following Mechanoids are stationed in a landed small Mechanoid transport vehicle:

- (1) Brain
- (5) Runners
- (10) Tunnel Crawlers
- (12) Wasps
- (24) Brutes
- (36) Thinmen
- (48) Runts
- (48) Weavels
- (24) Skimmers
- (4) Exterminators
- (12) Seeker Pods

Encounter #10 - 190km further along the coast. Old crashed hovercraft. Among the dead crew are a SB-14, a PBR-10, an M.A.A. and 14 E-clips.

Encounter #11 - 225km extreme outskirts of Stelvenson and the beginning of actual roads. Just 80km from downtown Stelvenson.

Encounter #12 - Stelvenson colony. By the time the group arrives they will find that the colony is 90% destroyed and totally abandoned. Fortunately for them, once a day a hovercraft scouts the area looking for survivors.

Encounter #13 - Just like #9, this is another Mechanoid area control base.

Encounter #14 - This major river spills into Lake Phe in a delta roughly 8km across.

Encounter #15 - This is a major river between Lake Phe and Gideon's great lakes. The water is 2km across and runs very quickly to the north. 35km upriver there is an enormous waterfall, at least 130 meters tall.

Non-Player Characters are all the various forces that will be involved in the conflict.

Important Note: Throughout this adventure the game master should involve the characters in action, encounters and thought provoking difficulties. Encounters with small bands of rovers, mechanoids and animal predators are likely. You may want to use the Mechanoids encounter tables located in the Mechanoid section of this book.

An Example of EBA Dialog for this Adventure

An illustration of a typical adventure with a game master (GM), and two players MaryBeth (MB) and Steve

(ST). There could be several teams, but we'll deal with just the one.

G.M.: A bored-looking officer hands each of you two weapon clips, a hand-held metal detector, a canteen, and a paper bag.

M.B.: What's in the paper bag?

G.M.: You're going to look?

M.B.: Yes. I look in the paper bag.

G.M.: You see two wrapped sandwiches, a container of cole slaw and a dessert bar.

S.T.: Great! We got lunch.

G.M.: Okay, now you're given your assignment. Your heading is 170°. Are you going to do anything before you move out?

M.B.: Do we have all our equipment?

G.M.: Yep.

S.T.: How about explosives?

G.M.: You weren't assigned any. Do you want to go ask for some?

S.T.: Yes.

G.M.: All right. You head back to where some of the other trainees are talking to the officers. You overhear Captain Estarv yelling at a trainee for requesting unnecessary equipment. What are you doing?

S.T.: Hey! Didn't I already tell you? MaryBeth and I are on our way on heading ... uhhh ...

M.B.: Heading 170.

G.M.: Okay. You're on your way.

[No serious encounters happen on the way. If the troops get trigger happy then throw in a few surviving squirrels. Remind them that they only have one E-clip for each weapon.]

G.M.: After travelling for about 7km through dense, defoliated woods you finally come to a red ribbon.

S.T.: Can we get by the ribbon?

G.M.: Sure, just step over it.

M.B.: Okay. I'll step inside. What do I see?

G.M.: More woods.

S.T.: I'll step over the red ribbon also.

M.B.: Do I pick up anything on this metal detector?

G.M.: Yes. You notice it is pointing south. IN that direction you see the outline of a Mechanoid Brute.

M.B.: I'll shoot with my IB-10.

G.M.: Roll.

M.B.: A ... 7, is that good enough?

G.M.: Fine, you blast a metal cut-out, it falls over.

[Once the players have "terminated" eight fake Mechanoids the following takes place.]

G.M.: Oh! Your metal detector is buzzing again.

S.T.: Big deal. MaryBeth it's your turn.

M.B.: Do I see a Mechanoid.

G.M.: Looking into a clearing you see a Mechanoid Thinman turning slowly in your direction.

S.T.: Must be the first hologram.

G.M.: What are you doing.

M.B.: I'm not going to waste another LR-20 shot so I'll shoot it with a ... 8 using the IB-10.

G.M.: You have a +2 to hit?

M.B.: Yes, why?

G.M.: Okay. You hit, roll damage.

M.B.: What? All right ... a 6.

G.M.: It returns fire . . .

M.B.: Pretty realistic hologram.

G.M.: The tree next to you bursts into fire as the "hologram's" beam strikes. You hear far-off explosions . . . (the destruction of the training camp base) . . .

127

A Journey to Stelvenson in E.B.A.

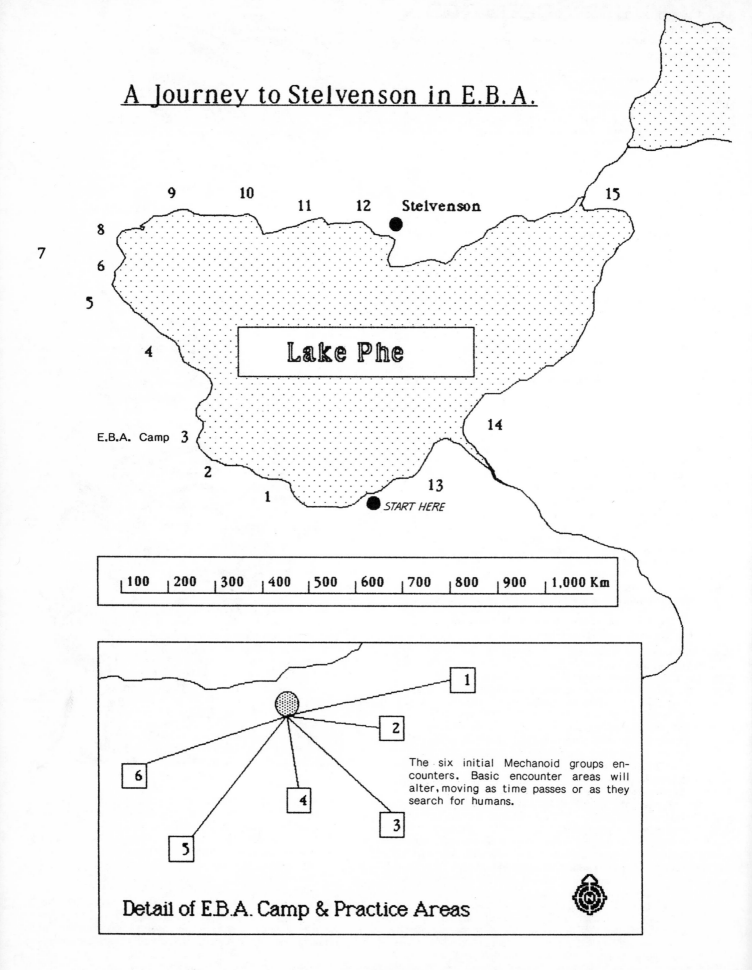

Lake Phe

E.B.A. Camp

Stelvenson

START HERE

100 200 300 400 500 600 700 800 900 1,000 Km

The six initial Mechanoid groups encounters. Basic encounter areas will
alter, moving as time passes or as they
search for humans.

Detail of E.B.A. Camp & Practice Areas

Adventure Scenarios

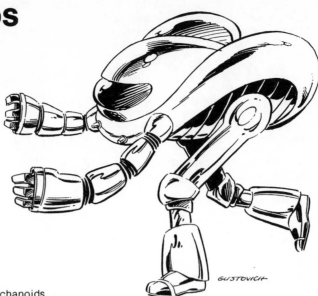
GUSTOVICH

LITTLE MECHANOID LOST

<u>Note:</u> An EASY (well, as easy as anything with Mechanoids can get) thinking mans mission suitable for any level and number of player characters.

<u>Formal Mission Briefing:</u> characters are told to report to **Commander Sheldon Schwab**, Chief of Experimental Weapons Testing. The briefing will take place in a large room outfitted with chairs and a large viewing screen. The numbers in parenthesis (1) indicate pictures that will be displayed during the presentation. When they report he will say the following:

If I can have your attention please. Thank you.

Many of you will recall the major battle of last month. That was one of the few times we have managed to defeat a Mechanoid detachment. At the conclusion of the battle . . . (1), before the Mechanoid follow-up invasion, we found something very unusual. A Mechanoid that was inactive but completely intact.

This Mechanoid Brute . . . (2) was undamaged but for some minor surface scratches. The unit was retrieved and returned to our laboratories here. After some initial difficulties we managed to open the Mechanoid's external casing . . . (3). Inside we found that the organic portions of the Mechanoid had been ruptured due to some tremendous shock . . . (4).

After a few weeks of research we determined that the best use of the hollowed out Mechanoid husk . . . (5). The Mechanoid Brute would be used to infiltrate a major Mechanoid base . . . (6).

We constructed a **major** thermonuclear device . . . (7), a hydrogen bomb. This was designed to be installed in the Mechanoid Brute . . . (8). Our next step was to animate the Mechanoid with an installed computer controller . . . (9). The Mechanoids would have no reason to suspect any treachery. Theoretically "our Brute" could walk right into a base without detection and detonate, wiping out the whole base.

It was shortly after this step that our research staff was killed . . . (10). How this can be remains a mystery. Speculation is that a preprogrammed Mechanoid computer unit in the Brute has seized control and is continuing to function on a very basic level. Another possibility is that there is a still living Brute brain casing which has seized control of our automated Brute. Basically we know so little about the Mechanoids and how they function it could be almost anything. The bottom line is that the Brute is missing and <u>must</u> be found. If this creature is not found and deactivated it could eventually trigger the bomb destroying half this base. Even if the thing doesn't trigger the nuclear device it will injure or kill dozens of people as it runs amok. One of its basic directives seems to be self preservation and destruction of human life. The presence of the bomb also complicates the thing's capture. Particle beam and plasma weapons can NOT be used without greatly risking the bomb's detonation. Even lasers and hand guns must be used with extreme caution. Ideally, I'd like to see this "thing" enticed out of the base where it can be properly terminated. Better yet, I'd like to see it perform its original mission of infiltrating a Mechanoid base. We believe that if it could be lead out of our complex it would automatically return to its own Mechanoid base.

<u>Presentation Illustrations</u>

1. Battle scene with Mechanoids and Plasma Tank.
2. Mechanoid Brute on a devastated battlefield.
3. Technician using a plasma torch on the Mechanoid's waist joint.
4. Damaged tissue.
5. Hollowed out Mechanoid Brute.
6. Long distance photograph of Mechanoid base.
7. Incredibly complicated machinery of the bomb.
8. Open Mechanoid body with bomb inside.
9. Open Mechanoid body filled with a maze of electronics.
10. Laboratory with mangled bodies of researchers.

Player Tips: Commander Schwab will answer any questions about the abilities of the Mechanoid Brute (same as the player information in this book). He will also stress that the Mechanoid and computer portions of the Brute's body may be struggling for control. IF player's ask about the computer's programming (a good idea!) tell them the following:

The computer has been programmed with several directives. Most important is that it is supposed to detonate the bomb if it is captured without any possibility of escape. Therefore, you should be cautious about over-whelming it or surrounding it in a hostile manner. Other conditions for detonation include severe damage to the unit or gaining access to the interior of a Mechanoid base.

The computer has been hooked up to the Mechanoid's sensory equipment. It should recognize humans, and was intended to obey only human commands. Unfortunately, the added complication of mechanoid interference makes this directive unreliable. However, it may be possible to get "our" computer to respond from time to time.

129

Few other humans or rovers at the base have witnessed anything of the escaped Mechanoid's movements. A thorough search of the surrounding area will reveal a few Brute footprints off to the east of the human base, the warehouse and automated factory district.

Game Master Background: Actually finding the Mechanoid is relatively easy. Its heavy footprints outdoors, an occasional over turned vehicle, smashed doors or holes in walls will clearly mark its passage. An occasional dead body will also confirm that it is near by.

Unfortunately, even in its lobotimized condition it is a sneaky and merciless predator. It will use the factory noise, machines and robots to cover its trail, hiding and striking out at humans whenever possible. Fortunately its condition makes it oddly stupid . . . a sort of psychopathic murdering child.

At the game master's option it can have fallen into the hands of a few rovers just outside the human's base (but still dangerously close). Getting it away from rovers should be expensive or dangerous if force is used.

The problem for the players is that the lost Mechanoid is very confused, but it is very clear on what it perceives to be its directives: 1) Avoid capture. 2) Avoid the enemy (but who's the enemy) 3) Kill humanoids (an old mechanoid directive) 4) Find a mechanoid base and self destruct (but where's a mechanoid base and what is a mechanoid). It just isn't sure what they mean. For example, the Mechanoid will ask if it is being captured . . . and if someone answers "yes" then it may detonate or go berserk. Everytime the Mechanoid is **confused** and everytime it's **told something new,** there is a 40% chance that it will go berserk. During this time it will only attack physically, not with particle beams as they are disconnected. If it is attacked with energy weapons there is a 48% chance that it will go berserk, attacking in a mad frenzy as it attempts to escape.

So the players need to keep the Mechanoid calm. Their first objective should be keeping it away from any human habitation. The only way they can truly "win" the scenario is by getting the Mechanoid to leave the human base, lead it to a Mechanoid base, have it enter and blow itself up. Of course, in the best outcome they'll also manage to avoid blowing themselves up with it.

The Brute's computers can communicate by radio on human and Mechanoid frequencies (the latter is not known by the humans). Attacks are only physical in nature and directed at humanoids. However, the brute's confusion can allow a clever human(s) to communicate, approach and perhaps even direct it, as long as conditions do not appear to be threatening. The brute's attitude should be considered to be paranoid and hostile, but also inquisitive as it attempts to fulfill its directives. For example: when calm it may ask a human to describe a Mechanoid and or reveal its location . . . "before I destroy you".

Generally the brute is prowling around the less inhabited areas of the human base as it attempts to fulfill its directives: avoid capture, kill humanoids, which seem to abound here (but with caution as to not jeopardize its other directives) locate a Mechanoid base and self destruct at the base or if captured (by anyone). NOTE: ANYTHING that could be construed as being captured will incite it to detonate but only after a berserker attempt to escape.

The thermonuclear device will destroy everything within 2.25km. Beyond that point everything will take 8-80+25 points of damage. Characters beyond 5km will take only 3-30+15 points of damage. Beyond 15km there will be only radiation damage and earth shocks.

Equipment for this assignment is up to the G.M.'s discretion, but the following is likely:
A.T.V. Walker and/or hover scout(s) or some other fairly conventional vehicle. L.B.A. (E.B.A. for the E.B.A. Division O.C.C.), laser rifles, handguns, glop projector, H.A.V.O.C. camouflage system (only two units), smoke grenades, and the usual field equipment.

Game Master Note: The specific encounters in escorting the Brute to a Mechanoid base is up to you. Both rover and Mechanoids are likely.

GUSTOVICH

Adventure

THE RESCUE OF DOCTOR DRUALL
(The Mockmen Menace)

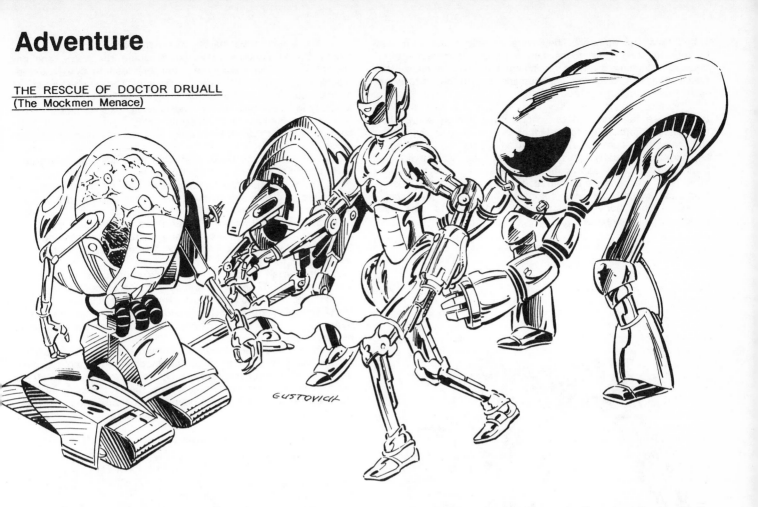

GUSTOVICH

Note: This is a Moderately difficult adventure suitable for any level or number of player characters.

Formal Mission Briefing: The information supplied by commanding officers at the Original Gideon Colony before the mission begins:

> We have just received an emergency signal from Coarley, a small base along the southern coast of the western region. Since we've had no communication from the time of the first Mechanoid invasion until yesterday we had assumed that Coarley was destroyed.
>
> The actual message was incoherent. A plea for help from Doctor Ralph W. Druall, former chief engineer of the base. We have positively matched the voice of Druall but have been unable to make any further contact due to Mechanoid radio interference.
>
> Your mission is to travel to Coarley, rescue the Doctor and any other survivors, scavenge the base for any useable materials, and return as quickly as possible.
>
> Vehicles for overland travel will be provided. You will also be issued whatever weapons and equipment you might need. Finally, Geneweg, a friendly Rover scout, is being assigned to act as your guide and interpreter.

Player Tips: P.A.V.M. Characters with good connections may be able to get information on the terrain and remaining road sections leading to Coarley. This information will cost the character. Experienced P.A.V.M. scouts expect a few bottles of alcohol or some other luxuries in exchange for accurate information.

Commando characters can easily find out rumors about active Mechanoid units to the south. They will estimate from 1,500 to 3,000 active Mechanoid ground units and from 20-40 Wasps regularly patrolling the area. Since all information will be outdated and unreliable, game masters are encouraged to give out all kinds of specific details, but not too misleading.

By talking to a lot of people the characters will discover that Coarley is well known. A major road went directly there. It's common knowledge that the base was designed as a center for oil and mineral exploration. The airport, hotel, administration building and several other structures were completed just before the invasion.

Characters with Rover contacts can find out quite a bit about the tribes in the area. As usual this information is never free. The Rovers will "trade" for as much as they can get. In order to drive the price up they may mention something about "a couple of hungry Arrow Head tribes in the area." NOTE: Geneweg himself will NOT provide any information unless the bribe is unreasonably large. Once they're paid they will tell the characters the following:

> Between four and five hundred **Arrow Head** rovers are in this area. **Ubar-Que** is the lawful chief of the southern Arrow Head. But an evil one has broken the tribe into two hate filled pieces. **Blood-Sand** calls himself a holy one and claims that the Mechanoid death comes because of the humans, he calls the colonists the "bringers of death." At the hands of his followers the hearts of humans are spice to their broth.
>
> There are also two handfuls of **Sand Pirates** with Rosenstein Land Buggies. They are making much profit of the splintered Arrow Head tribe by trading with both sides.

Game Master Background: This is a Mechanoid horror story. The characters are being deliberately lured to Coarley by the Mechanoids, so that their bodies and brains can be used for their twisted experiments and games.

Along the way the party may have problems with the rovers but will not be bothered by Mechanoids. Only mock resistance to the humans by weavels, skimmers and a thinman or two will bar their approach. Leaving on the other hand will be quite a different story.

The Mechanoids have started playing a new game. It's

called "playing human." They have created a new kind of Mechanoid, one that looks and acts like a human being. Because Mechanoids have a crazy hate for humans this means that all the Mechano-Humanoids will be **totally insane.**

It also means that they require human brains in order to simulate humanity. After capturing a human alive, they transplant his brain into a Mechano-Humanoid body, under the complete control of a permanent psionically linked Mechanoid. Basically, this means that the Mechanoid has psionically transferred its mind and essence into the human mind and Mechano-Humanoid body. The controlling Mechanoid now experiences everything the humanoid body experiences. If that body is destroyed the Mechanoid dies. The mind link is irreversible.

GUSTOVICH

There are five hatches (at the **dock**, in the basements of the **administrative building** and the **hotel**, and on the floors in the **garage** and **hanger**) leading down to the Mechanoid base built under Coarley. The single level is divided up into large chambers for manufacturing, storage, Mechanoid repairs, power generation, surveillance, and Mechano-Humanoid unit testing. This last chamber will contain units that look exactly like the members of the group.

The Mechanoid base is staffed by 1 Mechanoid Brain 8 Runners, 12 Brutes and 50 Runts.

These Pseudo-Mechanoids are far from invulnerable to detection. Among other weaknesses they are made mostly of metal and plastic, the organics count less than 20% of the total mass. Therefore, a Mechanoid appearing as a normal 6' human would have a mass of something like 250kg (550lbs) and would light up any radar system or metal detector.

Dr. Druall is the first successful example of a Mechano-Humanoid. The Mechanoids who are controlling the experiment want to see him interact with humans. Therefore, the Mechanoids will stay out of sight and leave the humans. If the humans attempt to leave Coarley they will be attacked.

This study period will last for at least a week. That is how long it will take for the Mechano-Humanoid bodies of each of the characters to be constructed. When all is ready the Mechanoids will capture the humans, transplant their brains and send the Mechano-Humanoid dopplegangers back to the human base to wreak havoc.

Journey Encounters: The Rovers

On the long journey south there will be several opportunities to meet with rovers. The Sand Pirates are easy to identify and fairly safe, just make sure you count your fingers after shaking hands with one.

Dealing with the Arrow Heads is more difficult. They will all claim to be followers of Ubar-Que. Even Blood-Sand himself will claim to be Ubar-Que. This is to lull the humans into being vulnerable to attack. Of course, the real Ubar-Que and the genuine Ubar-Que followers are quite friendly and could even be helpful . . . if only the characters could be sure who is who.

The party's guide, Geneweg, will try to get them to avoid all rover contacts. If they do end up in trouble he will switch sides immediately and claim to be a "loyal" rover.

An Occasional Mechanoid drone such as a weavel, skimmer or thinman may be spotted as they near Coarley. This would be normally expected from the Mechanoids.

Coarley Encounters

Outwardly this town appears to be a typical human colony. On the surface are the still fairly intact remains of an airport, an administrative center, a residence hotel, a large garage for exploration vehicles, a dock, a bar/restaurant, and several small homes. The place is deserted and save for a few bloodstains, there is no sign of the previous inhabitants.

The only inhabitant is the confused Dr. Druall. He acts strangely but knows things that only the real Druall could know. If the group attacks Druall the Mechanoids will respond by attacking the party and killing them on the spot if necessary. NOTE: There is absolutely no reason to suspect Dr. Druall of anything! Although the characters may believe him to be mentally unbalanced by his ordeal.

ROVER ENCOUNTERS

The Arrow Head Rover Tribe: Ubar-Que

The majority of the Arrow Head rover tribe have a long and friendly relationship with the humans. Their leader is **Ubar-Que** a 9th level mild mannered warrior. If Ubar-Que is encountered he will be escorted by at least three, 4th level warrior body guards at all times and will greet the humans with enthusiastic good will. SEE the "Rover Tribes" section for character details.

Likewise the members of Ubar-Que's tribe are also friendly toward humans. Of course, this doesn't mean that they won't steal from the group, but that they'll be pleasant and helpful as well.

Blood-Sand

The power hungry shaman, Blood-Sand, has broken away from the main tribe taking a small portion of loyal or fearful tribes men with him. Blood-Sand's followers number less than four hundred, but are completely loyal to him and many are warriors (3rd & 4th level). Blood-Sand is a cold-blooded fanatic who will lie, cheat, steal or kill to destroy humanity. He likes to disguise himself and invite humans into his camp. Rather than risk battle he prefers to capture humans alive and let them die slowly. Unlike Li-amba of the Black Fist tribe, he really believes that humans are evil and must be destroyed. Blood-Sand is quite insane. SEE the "Rover Tribes" section elsewhere for character and psionic power details. The group may encounter Blood-Sand and a handful of his men or a wandering group of his scouts (2-8 members). Both will attempt to capture or slay the group.

DOCTOR RALPH W. DRUALL

Communications Engineer: Seventh Level
Administrator of the Coarley Mini-Base
Alignment: Unprincipled
Attributes: I.Q. 15, M.E. 10, M.A. 13, P.S. 8, P.P. 7, P.E. 11, P.B. 9, Spd. 7
Age: 58 Male **Weight:** 90kg (200lbs)
Height: 1.7m (5ft 7in) **Hit Points:**75 (actually the robot's S.D.C.) A.R.: 8
Disposition: Known to be a good organizer, analytical, strong leader. Good natured, easy going. Dr. Druall's odd behavior will be considered a result of his traumatic experience at the hands of the Mechanoids. Seems to be scattered and disorganized from time to time. He will seem normal for a while but every 5 to 15 minutes he will momentarily lose track of what's going on.
Psionics: None
Skills: Audio/Visual Communication 98%, Computer Operation 98%, Sensory Equipment 98%, Surveillance Systems 98%, Linguistics 90%, Electronics 90/75%, Computer Programming 85%, P.G.V. 98%, G.V. Mechanics 70/64%, P.A.V. 85%, W.P. Handgun (at 2nd level proficiency)
Special Abilities as a Mechano-Humanoid: Hand to Hand does 3-18 points damage. +2 to parry & dodge, three attacks per melee.
Personal Profile: Administrator of Coarley and specialist in computers and electronics. Of course, this is not Doctor Druall, but a Mechanoid robot creation that looks and feels like a real human being. The plan is to send this Mechano-Humanoid, which is actually controlled by a Mechanoid Runner, amongst the humans to secretly subvert their plans from within. The humans should suspect nothing odd about the doctor and will do everything they can to rescue him by bringing the Doctor back to their main base. Once among the humans the doctor will cause whatever trouble and mayhem possible. At first his methods should be subtle and insidious, but as the weeks pass the controlling Mechanoid will become increasingly psychotic. The doctor will secretly attempt to sabotage special projects, assassinate key personnel and kill anyone who gets in his way. After two weeks in the humanoid body the controling Mechanoid is likely to go off the deep end (60% chance)

and will become increasingly savage, wreckless and obviously deranged. <u>Roll percentile dice</u> once for each additional weeks time in the body;
  1-60 Turned Psychopath
61-00 Still in Control

Why have the Mechanoids gone through all the trouble and expense of this ruse? Simply for the fun of it. This is just another game with which to torment the humans.
<u>NOTE:</u> Geneweg and/or the other player characters may secretly fall to the Mechanoids at Coarley and be transformed into Mechano-Humanoid monstrosities. If this occurs they will function in a similar way as Dr. Druall.

GENEWEG OF THE BLACK FIST TRIBE

Friendly Rover Scout for the Humans
Thief: Fourth Level
Alignment: Anarchist
Attributes: I.Q. 9, M.E. 14, M.A. 8, P.S. 12, P.P. 15, P.E. 9, P.B. 5, Spd. 11
Age: 29 Male **Weight:** 90kg (200lbs)
Height: 2m (7ft) **Hit Points:** 29
Disposition: Cold, quiet, observant; confident and cunning. He has established a reputation for helping humans while avoiding any injury himself. As trustworthy as a saint as long as you can see him and all is going well.
Psionics: Minor **I.S.P.:** 38
Psionic Abilities: Object Read, Detect Psionics, Hypnotic Suggestion, See Aura, Meditation.
Skills: Prowl, Climb 98%, Locksmith 65%, Electronics 65/50% P.A.V. 85%, Pick Pockets 70%, W.P. Knife, W.P. Laser Rifle, W.P. Handgun (both energy weapon W.P. skills are at second level).
Personal Profile: Although Geneweg has a solid reputation as being a "friendly" scout for the human colonists, his motives are completely self-serving. By working closely with the humans he can obtain weapons, equipment and information that he can trade to his fellow rovers for a great profit. Unlike his fellow Black Fist tribe members Geneweg harbors no hatred or resentment toward the humans. However, this does NOT mean that he is loyal. Geneweg will not volunteer any information, assistance or risk his life unless he is well paid. Even if he knows something crucial to the mission he's assigned to he will not make it known unless he is paid (usually in weapons, E-clips, battle armor or high-tech field equipment).

Geneweg has parlayed his services to make himself a rich man by rover standards. He personally owns one Rosenstein Land Buggy, two L.B.A. suits, a SB-14 Simple Blaster, laser lance, infra-red distancing binoculars, and his most coveted possession a PBR-10 particle beam rifle and a dozen E-clips for each weapon, along with a handful of miscellaneous items for trading.

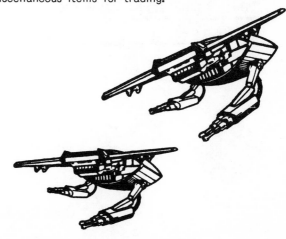

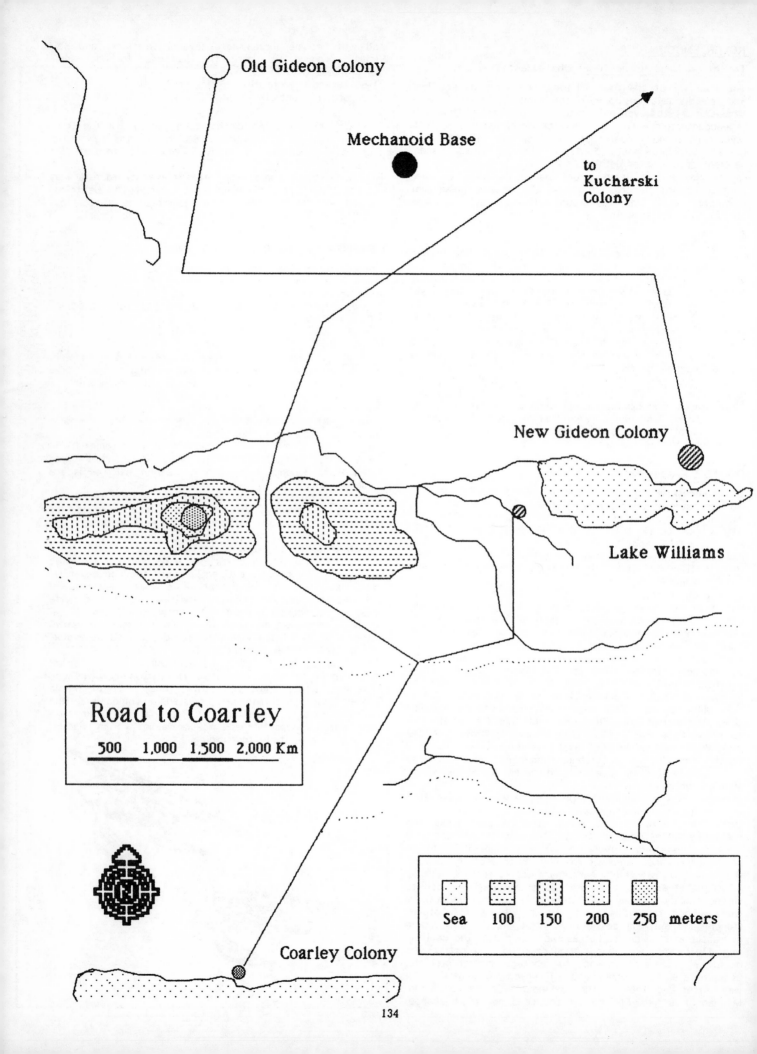

Old Gideon Colony

Mechanoid Base

to
Kucharski
Colony

New Gideon Colony

Lake Williams

Road to Coarley

500   1,000   1,500   2,000 Km

Sea   100   150   200   250   meters

Coarley Colony

Adventure

RUN TO RAMTAU

NOTE: This is a **Difficult** mission requiring at least five experienced characters. Smaller groups should be given a few non-player characters as back-ups. This mission begins only days before the Mechanoids completely level the Kucharski colony.

Formal Mission Briefing: Here is the information supplied by the commanding officers at the Kucharski Colony before the mission begins:

I'm going to start by telling you about the secret project that's been a major concern of the colony administrators. We're trying to build a space ship capable of evacuating the civilian population in case of extreme emergency.

Needless to say the situation is urgent. Seismographic studies indicate the Mechanoids may be in the process of destroying this moon. They did it to Thalos . . . and we may be next.

Project "Ramtau" has been concealed in the extensive caverns deep in the Ramtau Mountains. Although the project is well supplied with raw materials, they are short on food and a few crucial scientific instruments. It's up to you to get a Modified Land Rover through. There is also a backpack containing a **Critical Parts Package**. Losing the Land Rover would hurt, losing the Critical Parts Package would be a disaster.

An even more important shortage is technical talent. So you are to deliver two of our scientists, Dr. Martha Royton, P.A.V.M. and Casper Lenowitz, P.G.V.M. AS WELL. Let me repeat that - delivery of these two scientists is **second** only to the delivery of the Critical Parts Package.

You do have one other important asset. **Balrog 0591** has been assigned to assist you in this mission.

You will leave at dawn. Remember that the survival of all the women and children of Gideon may depend on your success. Good luck.

Player Tips: Players should be provided with a copy of the player map. Be sure to point out the nearby Mechanoid Bases.

There is no further valid information available. Sources may relate rumors, horror stories or anything else the game master wishes. None of the humans or rovers at Kucharski know any specific details about the mission or the planned route.

This adventure is supposed to take place before the humans have confirmed information about the Mechanoid trenches and bridge forts. Extreme measures and caution are recommended.

Game Master Background: The goal of this adventure is simple, to get the important stuff to the caves of Ramtau. Various Mechanoid and rover obstacles are included to make things interesting. On at least **three** occasions the characters will be forced into battles with Mechanoids. Even more dangerous is the encounter with the Black Fist rovers.

Clues and Encounters: No information, even rumors will be withheld from the members of this mission. No encounters will take place until the group gets past the original Gideon colony.

Encounter #1: The Weavel Patrol

Whoever is scouting farthest in front of the group (usually a Balrog hover droid) will notice one of the **two Mechanoid Skimmers** escorting a **Mechanoid Weavel**. If the character stays hidden he'll see that the three Mechanoids are headed towards the group. All three Mechanoids have standard attributes.

This is a perfect opportunity for the group to ambush the Mechanoids. This allows the group to "shake down" for further action. It's important that none of the Mechanoids escape. The two Skimmers will do anything to give the Weavel a chance to escape. If one of the Mechanoids escapes a pair of Wasps will be sent to investigate further.

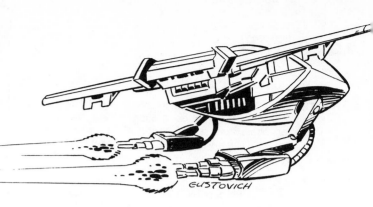

EUSTOVICH

Encounter #2: Sand Pirate Rovers

8 3rd level warriors, 4 4th level thief O.C.C. rovers of the Sand Pirate tribe can be encountered heading back towards Kucharski. Eight are in a HS-180 hover scout and there are two Rosenstein Land Buggies each carrying another pair. All the rovers are armed with laser lances. LP-10 pistols and LP-20 rifles. It's fairly easy to **avoid** them, because they're in a big hurry to get back.

They will stop to talk only if they're waved down by the group. They will **trade** information for any functional weapon or for a couple of energy-clips. Of course, they'll also attempt to steal whatever else is handy. If they're paid off they'll point off to the west and say the following:

The Mechanoid mother is eating this planet. We saw a bite in the earth that was wider than a good bowshot. It went into the sea in the north. We followed it south. There was a big bridge with many Mechanoids on it. We kept going south. Then we saw it. It was followed by its children, two handfuls of Wasps and many, many small Mechanoids. It is trying to eat the world. It is very big.

We were going to trade with the Black Fist of the western mountains. Instead we go back and come again when the Mechanoid mother is sleeping.

NOTE: The trench cannot be avoided and a bridge (and bridge fort) must be found for all to cross.

Encounter #3: The Bridge Fort

Neither the **Balrog** nor the Land Rover can get across the trench. The group really has only one option. They have to move 135km south and attack the nearest bridge fort. It's not easy but it's their best bet. (SEE Bridge Fort data in the Mechanoid section.)

This bridge fort has a major turret with two laser cannons (2 attacks per melee; 6-36+40 damage, 2200 meter range). Also mounted on the turret is the main plasma cannon (2 attacks per melee, 8-80+80 damage, 4800 meter range). The group needs to break through the east gate (A.R.: 14; S.D.C.: 1400) and then they have to break out the west gate (also A.R.: 14; S.D.C. 1400) in order to cross the bridge. From the moment they appear in range they will be attacked by the cannon and 4 Wasps. Inside they'll be attacked by 8 Brutes, 15 Thinmen, 43 Runts and 2 Runners.

Going **full** tilt they will be inside the fort for 6 melee rounds plus whatever extra time they need for breaking through the west gate. Note that the Balrog can easily plow through the runts although the tiny robots could do some damage if they climb atop it and vandalize it. The other Mechanoids are the main threat.

Encounter #4: Wasp Patrol

From this point on the mission becomes a dead run to the mountains. Wasp patrols will attack in ever increasing numbers. There should be a new attack every 1-6 hours. The first attack will be only 6 Wasps, the second will have 8, the third 10, and so on . . .

The sooner they can hide out in the Ramtau Mountains the sooner the Wasp attacks will stop.

Encounter #5: Black Fist Tribe

Once in the mountains there is only one passable route. It's fairly safe from Wasps because of the high walls and strange wind conditions. The problem comes 200km later. The Black Fist Rovers have carefully constructed an ambush site in a narrow pass.

Maneth-He, the leader, and Li-Amba, the shaman, charge a "toll" for anyone wanting to use the pass. Since there's no other way around the group will be stuck. 85 warriors (second level, A.R.: 6; S.D.C. 32) armed with crossbows and laser weapons are hidden in holes overlooking the pass.

300 meters to the north they have a force of 6 L.B.A equipped warriors (A.R.: 10; S.D.C.: 70). These rovers are armed with 4 PBR-10s and 2 PE-6s. They have also prepared a rockfall that will block the pass.

Finally, there are three major psionics standing by with two fusion blocks. If ordered to do so they will teleport the fusion blocks directly onto the Balrog.

This is the toughest encounter of the Ramtau mission. Fighting it out would be risky at best. These rovers are going to be very difficult to kill. Negotiation would be far more intelligent. Initially the Black Fist will demand **all** the group's vehicles, weapons and food. They would be happy to get the Land Rover with everything it contains. And if someone bargains especially well they might just settle for the food in the Land Rover and a dozen energy weapon clips.

Equipment Available to the Player Characters

Light Body Armor (L.B.A.) for all. Commando and E.B.A. Division O.C.C.'s can get E.B.A. instead.
Choice of Handgun and two extra E-clips.
Choice of One Rifle: LR-20 laser rifle (with one extra E-clip), E.M.B. bore rifle (with 4 sensory head and 6 explosive), glop projector, SLR spike launch rod (with 8 spikes and extra line). Commando and E.B.A. Division O.C.C.'s can elect to choose a PBR-10 particle beam rifle.
Standard Field Equipment
Portable Scan Dihilator if a communications engineer is one of the team members.

Special Equipment for the Over-all Mission (not individual)
Two Intelligent Long Range Missiles (I.L.R.M.)
One Tiger I.L.R.M.

Vehicles
Balrog Destroyer (reflecting the seriousness of this mission)
Two Flying Guns (can be stored on or in the MLR-20 or Balrog.
One Hover Scout
One MLR-120 Land Rover (to haul the equipment to Ramtau).
Two Rosenstein Land Buggies (more are available if they can be used). Each has an extra tank of fuel.

4 Sandwolf Torpedos
Concentrated Blasting Caps:
    40 Type One
    10 Type One
     5 Type Three
Shape Charges:
    60 Type One
    12 Type Two
    12 Type Three
Fusion Blocks:
    10 Type One
     1 Type Two
60 Survival Knives
24 I.R.D. Binoculars
40 150 meter lengths of nylon cord
24 Visors
52 L.B.A. Face Protectors
18 L.B.A.
 2 E.B.A.
64 Air Filters
24 Hand Held Communicators
50 Mini-Tool Packs
12 Fusion Torches
24 Medical Kits
1600 Ration Packs
144 Luxury Food Packs
156 Containers of purified water; 37 liters (10 gal. each)
1 Portable lab
1 KS-15 Computer
24 FGL Portable Power Packs

NON-PLAYER CHARACTERS

Air Vehicle Pilot - Doctor Martha Royton
Ground Vehicle Pilot - Casper Lenowitz
Balrog Destroyer #0591 (A player or two may opt to play the Balrog).

DOCTOR MARTHA ROYTON

P.AV.M.: Third Level   **Thief:** Third Level
Alignment: Anarchist
Age: 32 Female **Weight:** 58kg (140lbs)
Height: 1.7m (5ft 10in) **Hit Points:** 36
Attributes: I.Q. 14, M.E. 15, M.A. 11, P.S. 16, P.P. 12, P.E. 13, P.B. 14, Spd. 9
Disposition: Clever, observant, thinks on her feet; bold and confident. She is a feisty fighter who's got a grudge against the Mechanoids.
Psionics: None
Skills: P.A.V. 98%, A.V. Mechanics 65/60%, Sensory Equipment 55%, P.F.G. 84%, Audio/Visual Communications 55%, Medical: First Aid 84%, W.P. Handgun.
Thief Skills: Pick Pockets 45%, Locksmith 40%, Climbing 74%.
Equipment: Standard field equipment including: infra-red distancing binoculars, signal flares (4) and flare gun, fusion torch, laser lance, LP-10 laser pistol with two extra E-clips, medical kit and a mini-tool pack. L.B.A. has been issued.

NOTES: Martha Royton has extensive training in spacecraft engineering. Her skills are needed at Ramtau. In addition to her ingenuity, piloting and spacecraft skills she's a gutsy, impudent fighter who is very geared up for this expedition in hope of encountering and destroying Mechanoids. Her entire team of fellow researchers and friends died in the Mechanoids' initial assault. Among them her fiance. Martha's thieving abilities are from a rather wild youth. Although she craves vengeance against the Mechanoids she's far too smart to jeopardize the mission for personal revenge.

CASPER LENOWITZ

G.A.V.M.: Fifth Level
Alignment: Scrupulous
Age: 40 Male **Weight:** 72kg (160lbs)
Height: 1.8m (6ft) **Hit Points:** 29
Attributes: I.Q. 16, M.E. 12, M.A. 13, P.S. 13, P.P. 8, P.E. 9, P.B. 12, Spd. 11
Disposition: Honest, sincere, quiet, withdrawn, serious, loyal and brave. However he is not used to combat at all and a little jumpy.
Psionics: None
Skills: P.G.V. 98%, G.V. Mechanics 90/84%, Sensory Equipment 55%, E-clip Recharge 92%, Electronics 75/60%, Computer Operation 75% (85% to repair), Audio/Visual Communications 60%, P.P. Tank 70%, P.A.V. 70%.
Equipment: Standard field equipment including: infra-red distancing binoculars, signal flares (4) and flare gun, fusion torch, laser lance, SB-14 simple blasters with two extra E-clips, mini-tool pack and a L.B.A. suit.
NOTES: Casper Lenowitz is a specialist in fusion engines as well as modifying ground vehicles into armored war vehicles. He has no combat or weapon skills, but is not afraid to fight if he has too. Casper speaks fluent rover.

BALROG DESTROYER # 0591

The Balrog is a sentient, fully equipped, battle-ready war machine of incredible power. For specific details see the Balrog Destroyer under the Colony Vehicles Section.

The game master may wish to assign the balrog to one or two of his players as a special one time playing character. I encourage this as it can be a very fun playing experience. However, it's probably best if the player does NOT play both the balrog and his regular character, because of the number of aspects in playing the balrog. If it's assigned to two players each player should get one of the hover droids (Scitz or Fritz) control over either the front or rear section and share responsibility for the mid-section. REMEMBER, both players are playing "one" sentient machine and should work together as a team.
NOTES: The balrog is expendable but only if absolutely necessary. Preferably it will make it all the way to Ramtau in fairly whole condition where it will stay to protect the people there. Balrogs are totally loyal to humans.

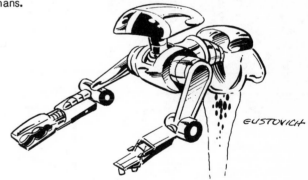

The Return Trip Home to "Old" Gideon Colony

Upon successfully reaching Ramtau the players will learn of the Kucharski colony's destruction (if they don't already know). The players can choose to stay on at Ramtau if they'd like or return to Old Gideon colony which is the coordinating headquarters for all human forces. If the players decide to return to Old Gideon, they will be provided with new L.B.A., laser weapons with one extra E-clip, field equipment and conventional ground or air vehicles of the following variety: Rosenstein Land Buggy, Modified Land-Rover, Hover-Scout, Flying Gun (un-armored) or A.T.V.-Walker. Only two vehicles and one or two flying guns will be provided. Ramtau's resources are extremely limited so characters should request as little as necessary.

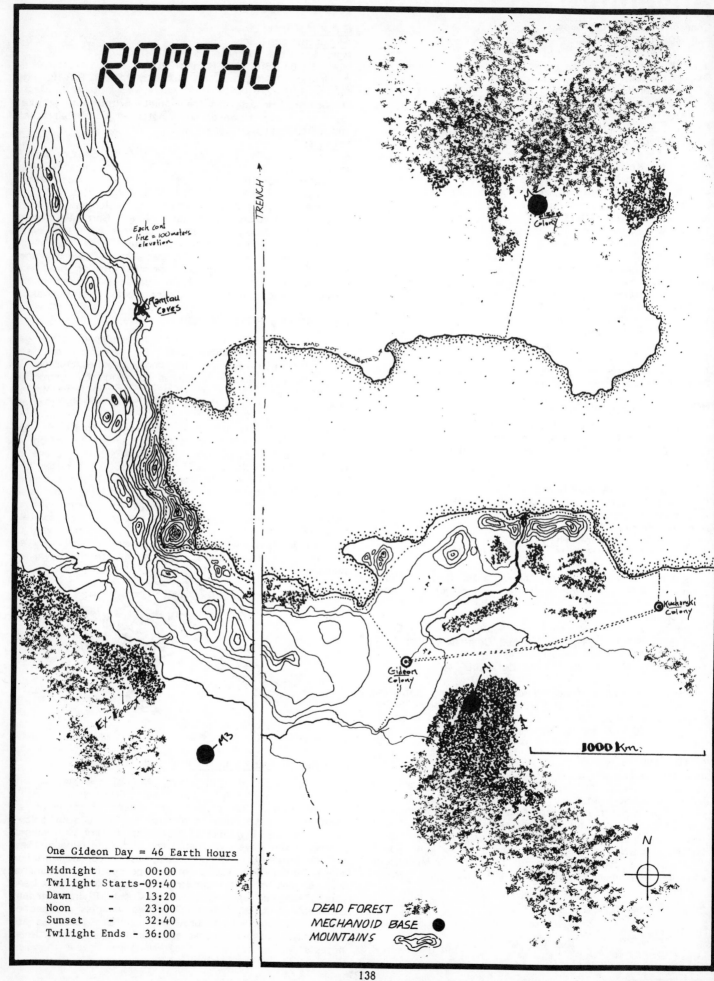

RAMTAU

Each cont line = 100 meters elevation

Ramtau Caves

TRENCH

ROAD NOT COMPLETED

Gideon Colony

Kucharski Colony

M1

EX-FOREST

M3

1000 Km.

N

One Gideon Day = 46 Earth Hours

Midnight   -   00:00
Twilight Starts-09:40
Dawn   -   13:20
Noon   -   23:00
Sunset   -   32:40
Twilight Ends -   36:00

DEAD FOREST
MECHANOID BASE
MOUNTAINS

Adventure

THE OCEAN'S OUTRAGE

Note: This is an <u>Intermediate</u> level mission suitable for any number and level of characters.

Formal Mission Briefing: After the characters are gathered in the briefing room read the following text supplied by the commanding officers before the mission begins.

As most of you already know, we have a tremendous problem coping with an ecosphere that's dangerously out of control. The Mechanoid poisons have affected relatively few of the aquatic life forms. But between the drop in small scale predators and the overall increase in dead vegetation we're experiencing massive growth in some organisms. In the long run it's a self-correcting problem. These giants just won't survive once the amount of decaying material starts to run out.

For the time being it's a real problem. I'm sure all of you have horror stories about Zoarm attacks. Getting swallowed by a Zoarm is unpleasant, and if you can't get out before your air supply runs out it's a nasty way to die.

There's nothing we can do about it. As long as the Zoarm keep eating the seagrass they're going to keep getting bigger. Right here we're seeing Zoarm up to 90 meters long. And we think that some Zoarm, especially those out in the really deep water, could be twice that size.

So, you're probably asking yourself, what do the Zoarm have to do with anything? We think that the deep water Zoarm may be large enough to be used. Used to attack the underwater Mechanoid base.

That's where you come in.

<u>Your assignment</u> is to locate at least six of the largest Zoarm you can possibly find. We expect that the optimum growth conditions are available in the spillway west of the Vega Channel. Roughly 1500km out to sea there's a huge region of tangled seagrass and normal seaweeds. This is where we expect to find the largest Zoarm. That's step one.

Step two calls for implanting bio-control devices into the Zoarm. You'll work in teams of two. One member will be swallowed by the Zoarm. The partner will remain outside with the sensory equipment. The interior worker will move through the creature guided by the exterior worker. Eventually it will be necessary to cut into the main nerve complex at the base of the brain. Extreme caution is required at this point since the creature will probably react violently to any touch in that region.

Step three is a little more difficult. Once you've got control of the Zoarm you'll want to use them against the Mechanoids. Herding a few Zoarms, even Zoarm with controls, across 2500kms of Mechanoid-controlled sea is going to be difficult.

After arrival at the Mechanoid underwater base your mission is straight forward; drive the Zoarm into the most vulnerable areas. As a cover for your own escape the Zoarm neutral control has been equipped with a "delimiter." This will cause the Zoarm to go into an extremely hostile phase, attacking anything approximating their own size.

Good luck!

Game Master Background

All characters must be outfitted with full underwater E.B.A. with attached M.P.O.G. units. In addition they will have enough E-clips and rations to last a couple of weeks. A sting-ray transport sub and two minnow scouts will be used as a mobile base. If necessary, non-player characters can be used for underwater vehicle pilots.

The Seagrass Meadows

Only the largest Zoarm have survived in this area. All the others have been eaten. The only other threat to the characters are occasional sharks.

Open Sea

Starting at a distance of 500km from their base, Mechanoid scouts can be found on routine patrol. This includes underwater skimmers and weavels. The Mechanoid scouts are a danger only if the humans are spotted. They will take no notice of Zoarm, however large.

If Mechanoid scouts come in contact with humans and then escape they will report back as quickly as possible. Within hours that area of the sea will be filled with small patrols of major Mechanoid underwater units.

The Mechanoid Underwater Base

This consists of a modified spider fortress surrounded by 8 large pressurized bubbles (150 meters in diameter, A.R.: 9, S.D.C.: 90). The base floats 30 meters underwater and is home to most of Gideon's underwater Mechanoids.

The entire base is anchored to the seabed (9300 meters down) by a drilling tube. **At its base** is a small pressurized dome staffed by 1 mantis, 8 runners, 8 tunnel crawlers, and 35 runts.

Mechanoid population includes 28 brains, 78 runners, 750 skimmers, 340 weavels, 1400 runts, 400 brutes, 12 wasps, 4 mantis, and 1 oracle. All Mechanoids are underwater versions or (where applicable) have undersea casings.

Gideon Sea Life

Seagrass: A general term for dozens of varieties of floating life forms. While seagrass is vegetation in that it uses chlorophyll to process sunlight, it is animal in the sense that the community of micro-organisms can move and 'feed' on decaying matter. With all the dead land plants and animals being washed into the ocean, the seagrass is growing out of hand.

The other problem is that most of the seagrass eaters were also wiped out. That meant more food and less population control. The Zoarm are the only predators left to feed on seagrass.

It's easy to swim through seagrass. The main problem is total lack of visibility. Sonar and other sensory devices are also ineffectual, creating confusing signals, false images and have a reduced effective range of about 300 meters. To the characters inside the seagrass it will seem like a murky green fog. Visibility is possible only with artificial lighting. Handheld flashlights will illuminate a beam of 3 meters. Strong searchlights (mini-subs, sting-ray and minnow) create 10 meters of visible area, but can be seen dimly up to 50 meters away.

Zoarm: Early researchers looking at the Zoarm had classified them as 17 different species of simple crustacean. Further study revealed that they were actually all the same creature with a physiology that varied according to size. The complex, highly evolved gene pattern was the clue. It was eventually proved that the Zoarm has a few genetic 'triggers' that allow the body to shift size without penalty. A nifty evolutionary advantage in areas where the food supply could vary radically.

After the microscopic egg cycle, Zoarm grow into tiny shrimp-like creatures. Common stages beyond that resemble types of cray-fish.

With the imbalance in the ocean's ecology some of the Zoarm have taken full advantage. Apparently there were two growth steps beyond even those studied by oceanographers. Before these were discovered, the largest stage shifted the creatures up to the 45-60 meter range (roughly the size of the largest Earth whales). At this point the creatures look like tentacled sperm whales.

After that the creatures started growing a massive spinal ridge, a rib cage and a thick, armored skin layer (A.R.: 7, S.D.C.: 70). The final known growth level brings the creatures into the 85-200 meter range. This stage is one of sexual immaturity, a fact that should be a hint to the characters that the worst is yet to come.

Unknown to Seabase scientists there is yet another growth level for the Zoarm. This puts the creatures up to 250-300 meters. At this stage the skin forms a series of armored bands (A.R.: 9, S.D.C.: 120) much like an armadillo. The spinal bone extends out of the body and forms a wicked spike on the forehead.

<u>Sharks:</u> No, they're not terrestrial sharks. However, they <u>look</u> like sharks, <u>act</u> like sharks, and <u>attack</u> like sharks, so everybody just calls 'em sharks. The sharks aren't upset with the overgrown Zoarm, there's just more to eat and they're taking full advantage.

Fortunately for humans the sharks don't have the Zoarm genetic defense for size. Sharks literally eat 'til they die of stomach bloat. That means there aren't a whole lot of them left. But the ones that are left are either big or very unpredictable (what can be more unstable than a shark who won't eat?).

Unlike the other sea creatures, the sharks are a real threat to man. Most species averaging 16 meters in length and have teeth and jaws to match. Even before the Mechanoids arrived there were rumors of sharks biting through the hulls of ships and swallowing men whole. <u>Attacks Per Melee:</u> Two. <u>Damage:</u> bite doe 2-12 if small, 4-24 if medium, 6-36 damage if large. <u>Bonuses:</u> +1 to strike, +3 to dodge (without losing an attack).

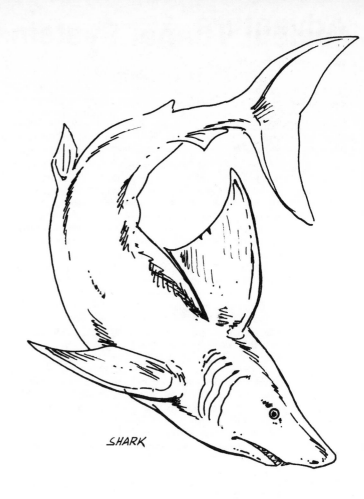

SHARK

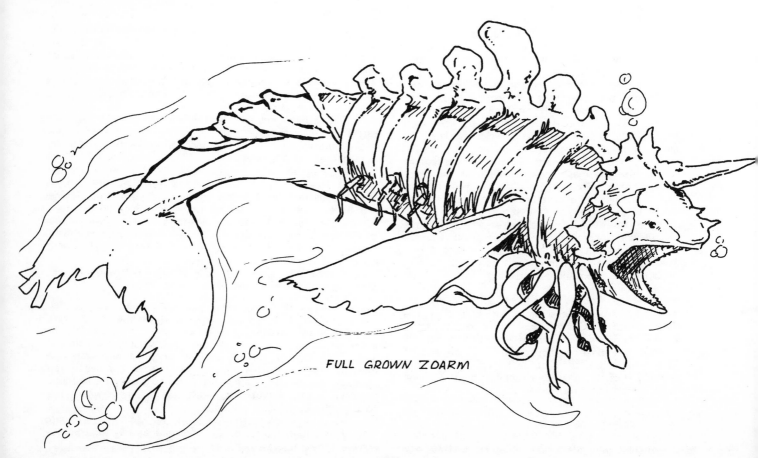

FULL GROWN ZOARM

140

Ancient Tunnel Systems

The Ancients Of Gideon-E

Archaeologists had only just begun their exploration of Gideon-E's fascinating history when the Mechanoid invasion interrupted their research. Up to that point their best guess was that the planet had been inhabited by a technologically advanced race called "The Ancients" by humans and "The Golden Ones" by rovers. Since various similar artifacts have been found on other worlds it is not known if the ancients originated on Gideon-E or if they were colonists like the humans and rovers.

Prior to the Mechanoid invasion human scientists were starting to discover just how advanced the ancients really were. For example, the tunnel vehicles have some kind of inertialess drive, a feat beyond human or Mechanoid technology. Also, since the tunnels were originally constructed there has been notable tectonic activity (earthquakes, volcanos, continental plate movement), why is there no breakage in the system? Add to that the complete mystery of the phase balls and you end up with a genuine enigma.

Ancient Transit Tunnels

The remnant of ancient cvilization is the planet-wide system of transit tunnels. This masterpiece of planetary transportation was constructed at least 4.2 million years ago and is still in perfect working condition.

Research into the tunnels has always been hampered by the native inhabitants. Presently, in the wake of the Mechanoid invasion, large numbers of Black Fist rovers, Sand Crawler larvae, and other unpleasant life forms make any exploration dangerous.

Judging by recent numbers of Mechanoids found in the tunnels they must also be intrigued by the ancients' technology. In spite of the danger, the mechanoids interest makes it even more urgent that humans discover the ancients' secrets.

There are only three possible ways into the tunnels. A few entry points have been reported near the site of recent earthquakes. Mechanoid destruction has added another couple dozen new entrances. The safest and most reliable form of entry is through the ancient junctions. Only ten have been found so far. Scientists speculate that many others remain to be found, and perhaps entirely new tunnel complexes have not yet been discovered.

Entry Ramps To The Ancient Tunnel Complex

On the ground, the entrances appear to be nothing more than large holes. Gradually sloping tunnels will lead down to the tunnel grid.

In the first section leading to the ancient tunnel complex are a small grid of tunnels. On the walls are large alien glyphs only visible with ultra-violet. Encounter with 2-8 rovers (15%) or with Sand Crawler larvae will occur in this area.

Two long curving ramps lead down. Each ramp ends at a boarding ledges. Each tunnel accomodates only the Transit Module that go in one direction. The right tunnel is west bound and the left is east bound.

Between the two tunnels there is a solid 3 meter rod of titanium jacketed with a meter of carbon. 6 meters directly above the titanium rod a crawl tunnel parallels the track. Roughly every 50 meters there is an access tube leading from the tunnels to the crawl tube.

The ancient transit modules are controlled by use of a phase ball in the hands of a psionic. Psionically ordering 'come' (or a similar command) will summon a module. The command must be broadcast while located on the platform of the transit tube. Vehicles arrive from one to six hours after they have been summoned. Then they zoom in at roughly 1200kmph, stopping without any

sign of slowing down. Ancient vehicles have only two move states; fast and stopped.

Vehicles admit passengers through a portal into their featureless spherical interiors. The vehicle will then wait for an order to continue. The vehicles stop at every complex along the way. Anything in the way of an ancient transit module will be completely destroyed, including a Mechanoid.

Magna Core Junction

The most common of the ancient's artifacts are their phase ball. Both these and the rods that serve as their 'fuel' are stored in quantity at every tunnel complex.

These artifacts aren't easy to get to. A circle of white-hot molten rock intimidates most casual intruders. A central platform can extend bridges in three directions. A phase ball in command mode can be used to order the bridges to appear.

One bridge will lead to the rod chamber. Rods for the shperes are stored in massive round columns. Nine of these large pillars extend from floor to ceiling. Each pillar has an inner and outer shell with an A.R. of 14 and an S.D.C. of 450. The shells, with a 2.4 meter gap, are not complete circles. These two shells can be ordered to rotate open with a phase ball in command mode. The two gaps alligned allow for access to the interior contents. All the exterior shells are marked by ancient (ultra violet) glyphs. Filled storage shells will have 1-100 element rods.

The contents of the storage shells are rods of pure elements. They are made of either **carbon, silver, titanium** or **zirconium**. Element rods are 4.32 centimeters in diameter and 61.41 centimeters long. Each can be inserted in any of the holes of a phase ball.

The third bridge across the magna leads to a 3 meter square passageway. After 100 meters visitors will be blocked by thick chromium-steel bars (each A.R. 17, S.D.C. 80) extending from floor to ceiling. Only one bar needs removal for a person to crawl through. Four separate sets of bars are spaced 7.3 meters down along the corridor.

Past the final set of bars the hallway opens into a smooth sphere some 30 meters in diameter. The bottom of this chamber is filled with a pool of mercury. Upon the mercury there are 1-100 phase balls floating high.

Phase Ball Operation

Phase Balls are .5 meter spheres of hard white porcelain material. Equally spaced are three round shafts drilled through the center of the ball. The shafts are on exact right angles from each other. They are 4.32cm in diameter and accommodate the element rods smoothly. Surprisingly, more than one rod can be inserted. They seem to pass right through each other in the center of the ball.

The ball is turned on with different combinations of element rods. Fabricating replacements for element rods is risky, only about 5% of human-made rods will work in a phase ball.

Phase balls 'use up' the element rods. After 47 minutes the element rods will simply vanish and the ball will stop working. Element rods will not come out of a working phase ball. The effects of the phase ball depends on the element rods inserted into it. The following are the possible combinations:

Silver-Titanium-Carbon: This combination causes the phase ball and whoever is holding it to go **"out of phase"** In this condition the holder becomes invisible to all observers. Vision will be limited to dim outlines of objects and an ability to see through solid objects. An "out of phase" person moves by 'swimming' through the atmosphere and can actually move through **any** kind of solid object. Setting down an 'out of phase' ball is potentially fatal. If the ball turns solid while the person is away from it then the character will simply stay in the 'out of phase' condition.

Silver-Zirconium-Carbon: The holder becomes invisible but remains solid. While in this state of 'half phase' the character can touch and be touched by physical objects but is invulnerable to any kind of energy attack. It works both ways, a 'half phase' person can't attack with energy weapons either. This 'half phase' has the same strange visual effects as the 'out of phase' person. Likewise a person separated from the ball can be trapped in this phase forever.

Titanium-Zirconium-Carbon: The 'command mode' used for mastering other ancient artifacts. Psionics are needed for communicating commands. The ball can be passed from person to person and if so the effect will be transferred with the phase ball. Commands should be kept as simple as possible to avoid simple-minded interpretation.

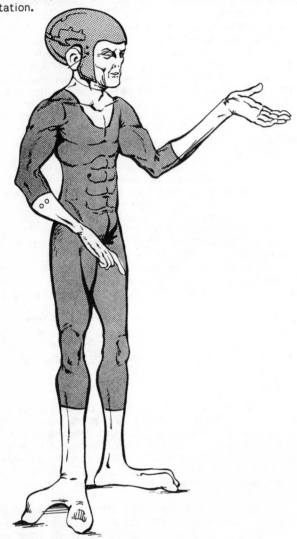

OPTIONAL . . .

THE APPEARANCE OF THE LAST ANCIENT AND HIS WEAPONS

The Alien, Salen-Dar

At the time close to the last Mechanoid battles, just before the final conflict on Gideon-E, the humans will be joined by a new ally. This is Salen-Dar, the last of the ancient aliens.

Already he will have destroyed the Mechanoids' undersea bases. Unfortunately, that effort required the use of most of his strange weapons.

Even now, the tide of battle may turn with the help of Salen-Dar, his knowledge, and his remaining weapons.

Attributes: I.Q. 30, M.E. 24, M.A. 20, P.S. 15, P.P. 19, P.E. 23, P.B. 12, Spd. 20
Bonuses: +2 to dodge, +1 to hit, +4 vs. psionics.
Hit Points: 57
Psionics: Has all psionics with I.S.P. 600 and 10th level proficiency.
NOTE: Salen-Dar communicates exclusively with telepathy and empathy, he never speaks.
Size: 3 meters.

Cybernetic Helm

Contains a force-field generator activated psionically or manually, this is Salen-Dar's primary personal defense. He will keep it until he dies. Force Field: A.R. 12, S.D.C.: 550. Recharges to full S.D.C. strength within 12 hours.

Body Suit

This is a custom tailored, skin-tight outfit with A.R.: 10, S.D.C.: 60.

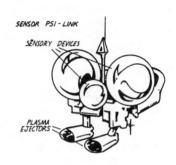

Sensory Psi-Link

This device follows Salen-Dar at all times using an unknown form of propulsion. It is mentally linked to Salen-Dar and continuously relays information to him within a range radius of 150km. It can be used as a weapon or as a scanning device.

Attacks Per Melee: Two
Weapons: Plasma Power Rod
    Range: 1200 meters
    Size: .6 meters long, .7 meters tall
    Damage: 5-50+5
A.R.: 11
S.D.C.: 84
Bonuses: +3 to dodge, +1 to hit, +4 vs. psionics
Psionics: All level one, I.S.P.: 100

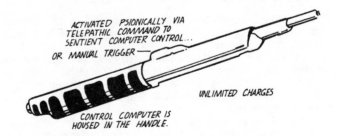

The Power Rod

Salen-Dar knows the location of 100 of these psionically activated weapons. A tiny sentient computer controls the device. There is also a small manual trigger. It is designed to absorb energy from its surroundings and has unlimited charges.

Attacks Per Melee: Two
Weapons: Plasma Bolts, 5-30+5 damage
Range: 1600 meters
Size: .9 meters, weight: 1.4kg
S.D.C.: 20
Bonuses: +1 to hit.

Behemoth

Salen-Dar can call up to 8 of these vehicles. Pilots require psionics to operate these devices. The interior is capable of holding a pilot, co-pilot and an additional 12 passengers. The cargo bay is a 6 meter cube.

Attacks Per Melee: Total of 6 - 4 laser and 2 photon

Weapons: Lasers, 6-36+10 damage
Photon, 5-50+50 damage

Range: Laser, 1800 meters
Photon, 2200 meters

Size: 20 meters tall, 16 meters wide

A.R.: 12

S.D.C.: Head 800, body 2000, turret 600, lasers 200 each, energy globe 2000.

Bonuses: +2 to hit.

Speed Factor: 1100kmph, maximum hover height to 60 meters (200ft).

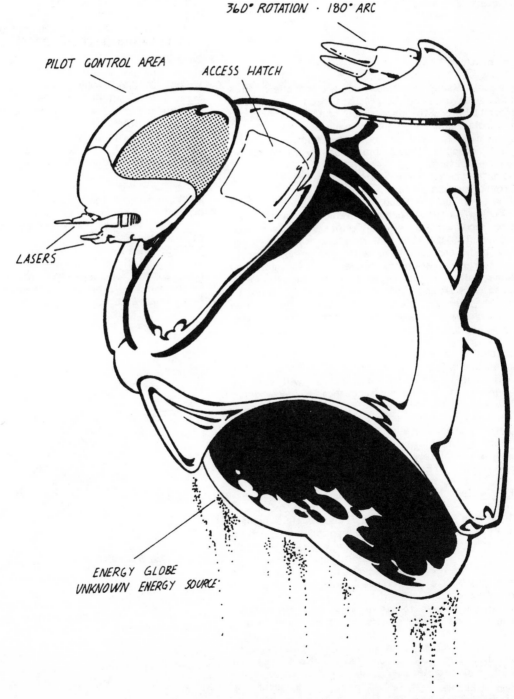

PHOTON BEAM ENERGY TURRET
360° ROTATION · 180° ARC

PILOT CONTROL AREA

ACCESS HATCH

LASERS

ENERGY GLOBE
UNKNOWN ENERGY SOURCE

143

PHASE CANNON
Classification: Alien; restricted

This ancient weapon resembles a large search light. When fired it projects a ring of energy one meter in diameter. The ring contracts until it is one centimeter in size at which point it explodes. The most amazing aspect of this weapon is that until the energy ring reaches the one centimeter size it will pass harmlessly through any solid matter living or not. This means a good operator can focus the device so that the ring explodes inside an object (such as a Mechanoid) by-passing any exterior armor/protection. Because it takes time to focus the phase cannon, it is always the last weapon to fire in a melee. The difficulty in focusing it means the cannon has NO bonus to strike.

Range: 1600 meters (5180ft)
Attacks Per Melee: One
Damage: 4-24 X 10 (4D6 X 10)
Weight: 96kg (215lbs)
Size: 1.5 meters (5ft) long

THE NEEDLE RACER

The Needle Racer is actually an ancient alien transport vehicle discovered by Col. A.E. Gideon and utilized by the colonists before the appearance of the last Ancient One. The Needle Racer is unique in many aspects:
1) It can travel up to 1200 kilometers per hour.
2) It has an incredible, though finite, energy supply of an undetermined nature.
3) An automatic energy barrier defense shield.
4) An energy disruption wave
5) Composed of an unknown superstrong metal alloy.

Considering its great speed the vehicle is fairly easy to maneuver and anyone with a "pilot ground vehicles" skill can drive it (but -15% skill penalty). Its super-tough metal alloy body enables it to withstand minor impacts and rugged terrain. The energy barrier defense shield engages automatically (cannot be overriden or by-passed) when a speed of 450kmph (250mph) or greater is attained. Presumably the energy shield is to protect the vehicle from obstructions which could normally destroy or seriously impair a ground vehicle traveling at such great speed. Because the energy shield is of a disruptor nature, it will actually shatter or disintegrate anything that it hits without damaging the vehicle or knocking it off course. The disruption field is limited and constant use will severely drain the needle racer of its non-rechargeable energy source.

Speed: 1200kmph (750mph)
Range: There are sixteen energy levels in a needle racer. A fully charged racer will start at level 16 and slowly decrease to zero as the energy is slowly consumed. At zero, the machine is completely inoperable. Travels 6000km per each energy level. NOTE: The use of the disruption shield drains power at a much increased pace.
Attacks Per Melee: None are intended, however the disruption shield has a unique response to energy bombardment such as ion, laser or plasma and particle beams. When struck by such energy the disruption energy field flares, discharging ripples or long narrow waves of energy. The waves always flow in a horizontal arc in a straight line left to right of the needle racer. The following applies to the determination of the ripples' size and amount of damage inflicted:
First: The attacker rolls to strike, if a successful strike roll for damage. The needle racer's disruption shield takes full damage.
Second: Disruption wave flares out, inflicting damage to ANYTHING, friend or foe, it touches in its wake. Length of the wave is one meter per each point of damage inflicted to it. Damage done by the wave is the amount of damage it received times ten (10). Duration: Is instant.

Example: A needle racer is blasted by a wasp. The wasp's particle beam inflicts 43 points of damage to the racer (only a nick). This creates a wave of disruption energy that's **43 meters long** (142ft) which does **430 points of damage** (43 X 10) to everything it strikes. **No Bonuses** to strike as the wave cannot be directed.

The needle racer, with disruption shield up, can also be used to ram Mechanoids, vehicles or objects. However, its use in this way uses up its energy source at an astounding rate. Since the consumption of energy is measured by the number of damage sustained by the energy shield (and kilometers traveled), the following chart indicates the amount of damage inflicted to the target by weight and S.D.C. damage sustained by the shield.

Target Object & Damage	Damage to Shield (S.D.C.)
Under 90kg (200lbs) 1D4 X 100	insignificant
91kg to 450kg (1000lbs) 1D6 X 100	20 S.D.C.
451 to 900kg (2000lbs) 2D6 X 100	40 S.D.C.
901 to 1800kg (4000lbs) 2D8 X 100	60 S.D.C.
1801 to 3200kg (8000lbs) 3D6 X 100	100 S.D.C.
3201 to 6400kg (16,000lbs) 3D6 X 100	180 S.D.C.

Bonuses: +2 to ram strike, +10% on special and evasive maneuvers (see P.G.V. skill)
Weight: 3240kg (7200lbs)
Size: 9 meters (30ft), can seat up to 8 comfortably, with a small 1.2 X 1.2 X 1.2 meter storage compartment (4ft)
A.R.: 18 (without shield)
S.D.C.: 600 (without shield)
Energy Shield: S.D.C. 200 per energy level.
Energy Consumption: One energy level per every 6000km of travel and/or one energy level per each 200 S.D.C. used up on a disruption shield. NOTE: The disruption energy shield engages automatically when going 450kmph (250mph) or faster and cannot be shut of unless speed is reduced to below 450kmph. The energy barrier can be activated at will at lower speeds.
NOTES: Because of their few numbers (39 needle racers in all), and potential danger within the colonies, they are reserved for special assignments ONLY. At this point no Mechanoid has ever seen a needle racer which can be a tactical advantage.

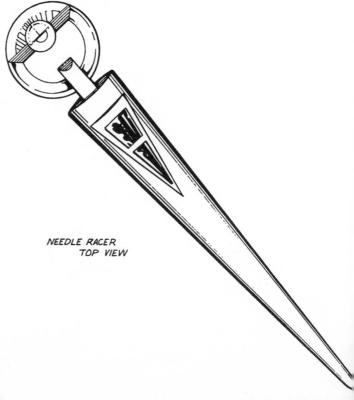

NEEDLE RACER
TOP VIEW

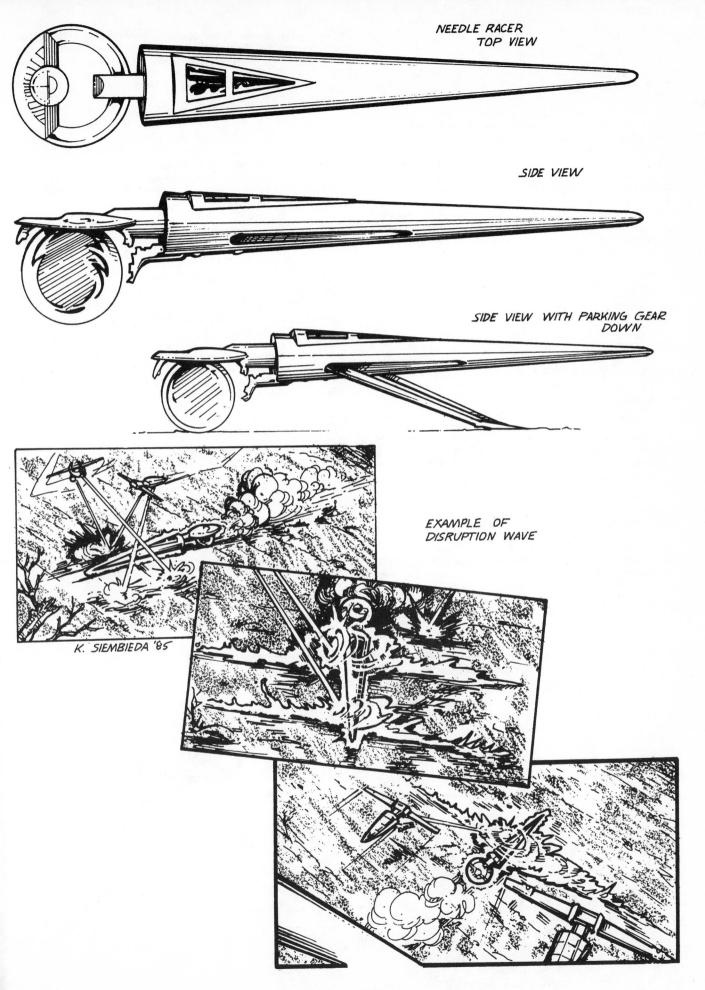

NEEDLE RACER
TOP VIEW

SIDE VIEW

SIDE VIEW WITH PARKING GEAR
DOWN

EXAMPLE OF
DISRUPTION WAVE

K. SIEMBIEDA '85

THE ARMAGGEDON DEVICE

Classification: Alien

The Armaggedon Device is a giant robot presumably used by the Ancient Ones to carve out their network of underground transit tunnels. Another possibility is that it was some sort of massive exploration/all terrain vehicle. At any rate, this gargantuan robot vehicle is powerful enough to engage in combat with a Mechanoid spider fortress and win.

It's major drawback lay in the fact that it was clearly NEVER intended to be a war machine. Consequently it has many weak spots. For example, it has only limited maneuverability, able to turn side to side in a 90° arc; has virtually no rear defenses/weapons (but is heavily armored). The laser pods are extremely vulnerable and the machine itself quite slow.

Weapons: Photon Arm (left)
Range: 2200 meters (7260ft)
Attacks Per Melee: Three
Damage: 5-50+50 (5D10+50)
Bonuses: +1 to strike
NOTE: Observation deck on arm holds 12 people.

Plasma Shield (right arm)
Range: 3200 meters (10,560ft)
Attacks Per Melee: One; this is in addition to photon arm.
Damage: 5-50 X 10 (5D10X10)
Bonuses: +2 to strike
NOTE: Can rotate up and down by 120°; can move side to side 90°. The huge shield like plasma ejector is a nearly solid protective shielding that helps protect the entire right side of the armaggedon device. The plasma generator is completely safe from harm.

Laser Pods (8 total)
Range: 1600 meters (5280ft)
Attacks Per Melee: Four (each)
Damage: 6-36 each
Bonuses: +2 to dodge, +1 to strike (W.P. heavy weapons and/or W.P. laser rifle skill bonuses are applicable).

NOTE: Each pod can be operated by one or two pilots (seats two) and moves independent of the main vehicle. The laser pods are not intended for combat and have a lowish S.D.C. of 200, A.R. is 14. The pods have a docking bay with an additional 100 S.D.C., but cannot fire or move while docked. Its mechanical arms are totally ineffectual in combat. Reach of 2 meters (7ft) does 2-12 points damage with two attacks per melee.

Particle Beam Cannon (human addition)
Range: 1600 meters (5180ft)
Attacks Per Melee: Two
Damage: Standard
Bonuses: +1 to strike
NOTE: This top mounted cannon is a human addition to help defend the two docking bays which house battle ready air vehicles. A.R. 10, S.D.C. 200.

The large docking bay is used to house additional weapons of destruction such as a dozen assault hover scouts or six hover fighter jets or 32 flying guns or 3 dreadnoughts or any combination of these.

The smaller docking bay usually holds a couple of HS-180 hover scouts and a battery of up to 24 I.L.R.M.s.

In both cases the air vehicles are generally deployed to help defend the Armaggedon Device's more vulnerable spots, such as joints, observation decks and the rear.

Observation Decks and Bubbles

The two main decks can easily house thirty-six people each, while the bubbles can hold about a dozen.
A.R.: 14 all parts
S.D.C.: Main observation decks 2000 each; observation bubbles 300 S.D.C., photon arm joints 400 S.D.C., leg joints 600 S.D.C. each, sensor tower (human addition) 200 S.D.C., laser pods 200 S.D.C. each, large spot lights 150 S.D.C.
Speed: is a ponderous 64kmph (40mph)
Size: 300 meters (approx. 980ft) tall; 260 meters (800ft) long.
Weight: 12,000 metric tons.

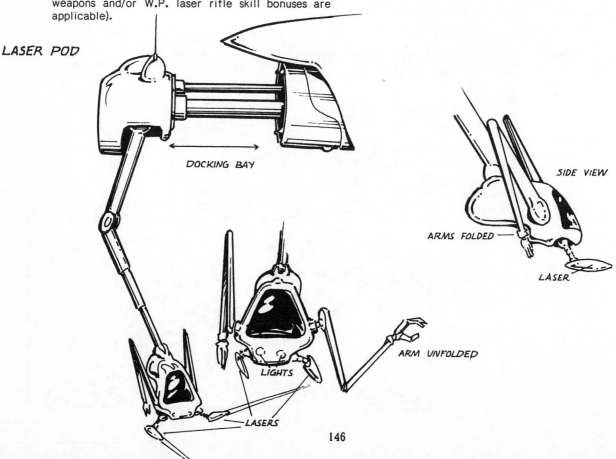

LASER POD

DOCKING BAY

LIGHTS

LASERS

SIDE VIEW

ARMS FOLDED

LASER

ARM UNFOLDED

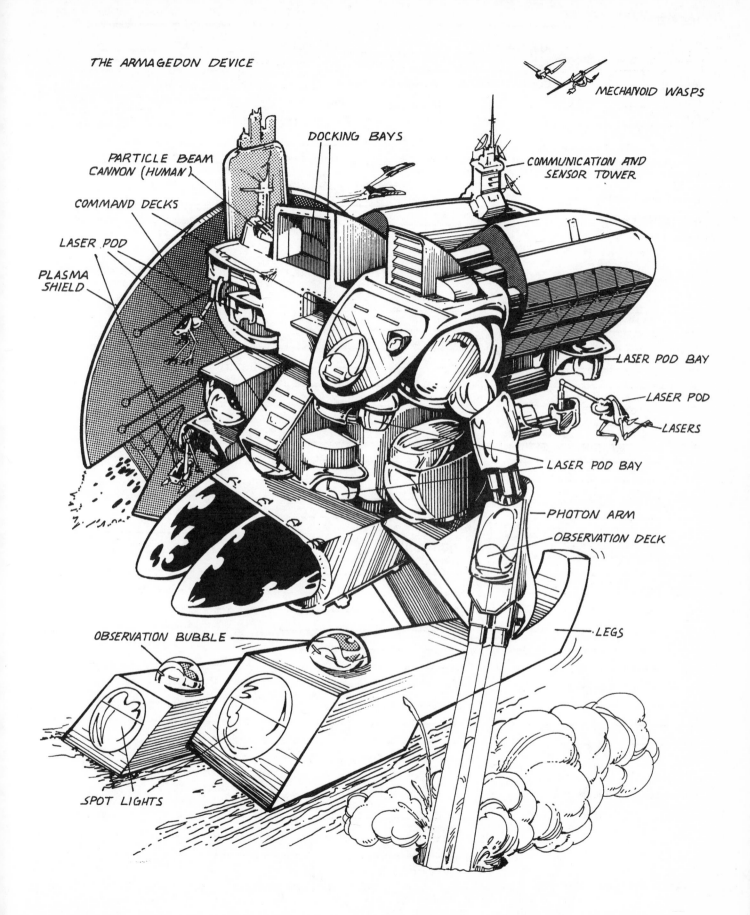

THE ARMAGEDON DEVICE

MECHANOID WASPS

PARTICLE BEAM CANNON (HUMAN)

DOCKING BAYS

COMMUNICATION AND SENSOR TOWER

COMMAND DECKS

LASER POD

PLASMA SHIELD

LASER POD BAY

LASER POD

LASERS

LASER POD BAY

PHOTON ARM

OBSERVATION DECK

LEGS

OBSERVATION BUBBLE

SPOT LIGHTS

IDENTITY _____   _____

IQ _____   ALIGNMENT _____ HIT POINTS _____ S. D.C. _____

ME _____   Age: _____ Sex: _____ Weight: _____ Height: _____ Disposition: _____

MA _____   COMBAT SKILLS: Attacks Per Melee: _____ Strike: _____ Parry: _____

PS _____   Dodge: _____ Dodge (only): _____

PP _____   Knock Out/Stun: _____ Damage: _____

PE _____   Critical Strike: _____ Deathblow: _____ Critical Strike from

PB _____   Behind: _____ Body Block: _____ Kick Attack: _____

SPD _____   Climb: _____ Prowl: _____

Experience Level: _____   Other: _____

Experience Points: _____   _____

SKILLS

WEAPON PROFICIENCIES (W.P.)

_____ _____ _____
_____ _____ _____
_____ _____ _____
_____ _____ _____
_____ _____ _____
_____ _____ _____
_____ _____ _____
_____ _____ _____
_____ _____ _____
_____ _____ _____

EQUIPMENT

_____ _____ _____
_____ _____ _____
_____ _____ _____
_____ _____ _____
_____ _____ _____
_____ _____ _____
_____ _____ _____
_____ _____ _____

PSIONICS:

Inner Strength Points (I.S.P.): _____   Abilities:

_____ _____ _____
_____ _____ _____
_____ _____ _____

OTHER INFORMATION:

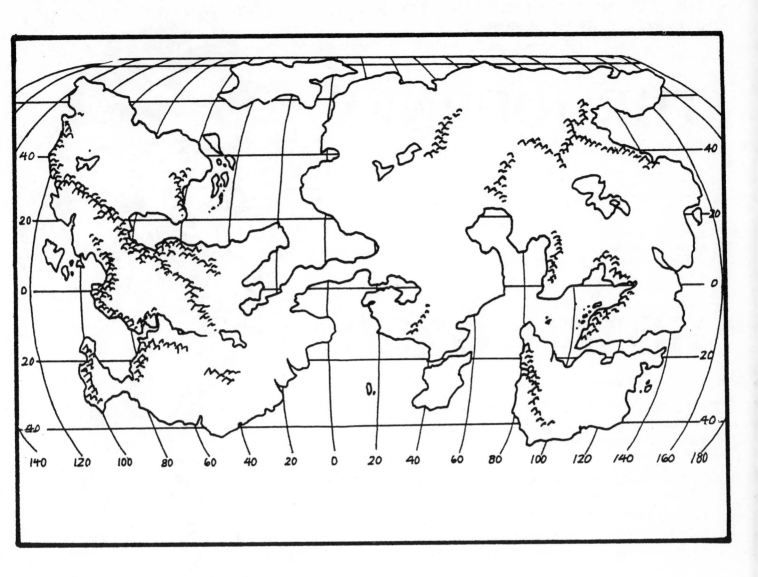

SPECIAL NOTE!

The Mechanoids is compatible with our other games <u>Heroes Unlimited</u>, <u>Teenage Mutant Ninja Turtles</u> and the <u>Palladium Role-Playing Game</u> (fantasy).

Although each game system has its variations and unique aspects, the basic game system is essentially the same and easily adaptable. <u>Heroes Unlimited</u> with its robotics, bionics and mutant rules may be particularly handy for extrapolation into an alien world(s) of the future.

Palladium Books products are available at fine hobby and game stores throughout the United States, Canada, Australia, New Zealand, Germany, Sweden and Norway. Or directly from **Palladium Books**. For more information send .50 cents for our annual catalog to:

> Palladium Books
> 5926 Lonyo
> Detroit, Michigan   48210

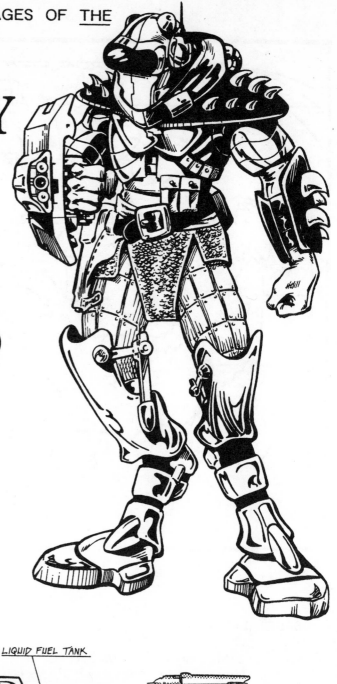

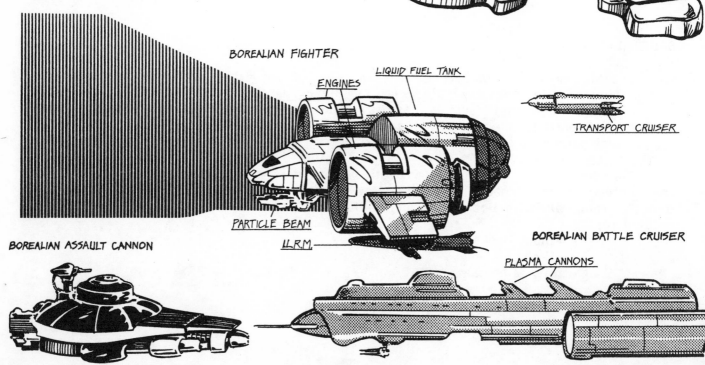

BOREALIAN FIGHTER

ENGINES

LIQUID FUEL TANK

TRANSPORT CRUISER

PARTICLE BEAM

I.L.R.M.

BOREALIAN ASSAULT CANNON

BOREALIAN BATTLE CRUISER

PLASMA CANNONS